Handbook to the Orders
LIVING MAMMALS

Timothy E. Lawlor

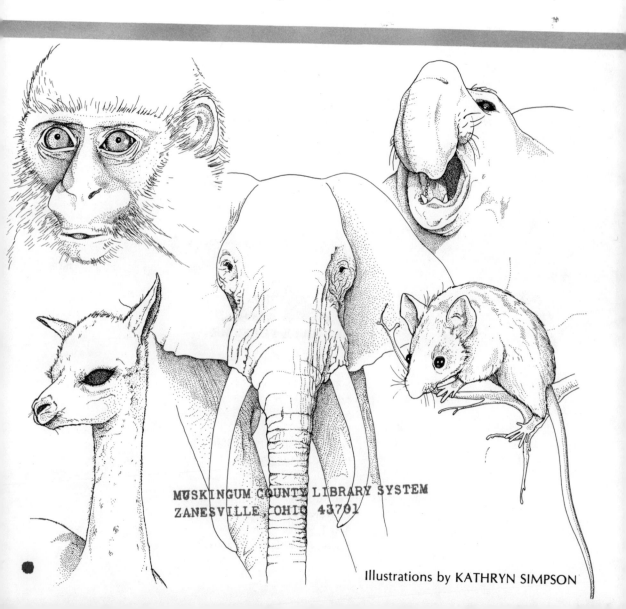

Illustrations by KATHRYN SIMPSON

DR. TIMOTHY E. LAWLOR is a Professor of Biology at Humboldt State University where his primary teaching responsibility is mammalogy. In addition, he has published and is actively conducting research on the taxonomy and evolution of mammals in general and of rodents in particular. He obtained his B.S. from Colorado State University (1961), his M.A. from The University of Kansas (1964), and his Ph.D. from The University of Michigan (1969).

KATHRYN SIMPSON drew the figures for Living Mammals. She also illustrated Vascular Plants for Mad River Press.

MAD RIVER PRESS INC.

© 1979 Timothy Lawlor

Second Edition
Published 1979 by
MAD RIVER PRESS
Rt. 1 Box 151-B
Eureka, California 95501
ISBN O-916422-16-X

Printed By
EUREKA PRINTING CO., INC.
106 T Street
Eureka, California 95501

TABLE OF CONTENTS

INTRODUCTION

The principal reason for writing this handbook to mammals is a pragmatic one. It has grown from needs expressed by students in mammalogy for keys and concise diagnoses of the orders and families of mammals. By themselves, keys do not provide enough characters or comparative information for a thorough diagnosis of a particular taxon. On the other hand, elaborate descriptions are usually tedious for the uninitiated student, contain a certain amount of redundancy, and often do not provide comparative information for closely related taxa. Moreover, the method of learning differs among students. Some enjoy the utility of keys, whereas others prefer diagnoses. In my opinion, the "best" method involves both approaches. In any case, both keys and diagnoses are provided here for completeness. Also provided is a brief section describing the skeletal system of mammals, without which the identification of mammals is impossible. Where appropriate, comparative information is presented so that an immediate appreciation of structural variation in mammals can be obtained. A glossary of terms not defined in the text is also provided.

Scope of the Keys and Accounts

Although I recognize that not all laboratories, museums, and universities are equipped with complete collections of mammals, the keys and accounts are worldwide in scope, covering all of the orders and families of extant mammals. Treatment of all groups is provided not only for completeness, but also because many of the listed characteristics are useful for identifying mammals illustrated in the literature (e.g., in Walker et al., 1975).

For compactness, statements listed in the **Recognition Characters** for each familial or

1

ordinal grouping are brief and in telegraphic style. They are presented in outline form in order to allow easy discrimination of characters. The accounts do not treat each group exhaustively. For greater detail and additional characters the student is urged to consult other literature (e.g., Anderson and Jones, 1967; Walker et al., 1975).

Use of the Keys and Accounts

The keys are dichotomous, requiring discrimination between individual characters or sets of characters in a couplet. Presumably such keys are familiar to all students of taxonomy. Practice in use of the keys may be required for the uninitiated. Whenever possible, both skeletal and external features are provided, but cranial characters are relied upon more heavily than others because of their diagnostic importance.

The accounts are intended to be as utilitarian as possible. An introduction for each order and family provides salient taxonomic features and peculiarities, and briefly summarizes known information on natural history. Diagnostic characteristics are identically numbered and are listed in the same sequence for all families within a particular major taxonomic grouping (suborder or order). Thus, a comparison of the condition of a character among different families in the same order or suborder can be made by simply referring to the correspondingly numbered trait in each family. This numbering scheme is also used for suborders and closely related or similar orders. In addition, other taxa similar to the one in question are listed at the end of each account. A list of representative genera accompanies all accounts of families, and where appropriate, pertinent literature and

taxonomic problems are identified or discussed. For each order and family I have cited representative references which reflect current knowledge of taxonomy and natural history of the group. For the most part, I have included only references which are recent and technical in content. Popular guides and obscure monographs have generally been omitted. With few exceptions, the arrangement of orders and families follows the phylogenetic scheme of Simpson (1945), which places closely related groups together, thus facilitating comparison. Distributions given include areas inhabited before exterminations or introductions by man.

The use of the characters provided in the diagnoses requires comment. Each diagnosis includes characters which singly or collectively distinguish all extant representatives of the group. Characteristics that are unique to a family are listed first and are written in bold face and identified by a solid circle (●) in the margin to the left of the trait. Other particularly useful diagnostic features are also in bold face. Exceptions to the individual characteristics usually are identified. External characters are indicated first, followed by features of the body skeleton, skull, dentition, and soft anatomy. The condition of a character becomes most meaningful when used in comparison with the corresponding character state in other groups. For example, the entries "Crown of cheekteeth simple" and "Claws unspecialized" become clear only when compared to the conditions of the cheekteeth and claws in other similar groups. Characters are completely reliable for adult specimens only, although many are also useful for immature individuals. Dental formulae disignate the number of teeth (upper/lower) on one side of the jaws. For example, the formula for humans, $\frac{2\ 1\ 2\ 3}{2\ 1\ 2\ 3} = 32$, refers to the presence of two incisors, one canine, two premolars, and three molars on *each* side of the upper and lower jaws, for a total of 16 teeth per side and 32 in the entire dentition. Digital formulae indicate the number of digits (toes) on each forelimb and hindlimb. For example, the statement "Digits 4-5" indicates four digits on *each* forefoot and five digits on *each* hindfoot. Where external measurements are provided, they refer to total length, i.e., the combined length of head, body, and tail.

Acknowledgements

I was inspired to write this book by students in mammalogy classes at Humboldt State University. Many improvements in language and structure of the keys and diagnoses resulted from their comments. I am also indebted to numerous graduate students for suggestions and criticisms of early drafts, including particularly Thor Holmes and Robert Sullivan. Dr. Warren J. Houck graciously commented on much of the manuscript and greatly improved the sections on pinnipeds and cetaceans.

I am indebted to the following persons and their respective institutions for allowing me to examine and illustrate specimens in their care: Drs. William Z. Lidicker and James L. Patton, Museum of Vertebrate Zoology, University of California, Berkeley; Dr. Guy G. Musser, American Museum of Natural History, New York; and Dr. Philip Myers, Museum of Zoology, University of Michigan, Ann Arbor.

Unnumbered figures are taken from Flower and Lydekker (An introduction to the Study of Mammals Living and Extinct; Adams and Charles Black, London, 763 pp., 1891).

Except for small cartilages at the ventral ends of the ribs, the adult mammalian skeleton is generally made entirely of bone. It consists of two principal parts, the axial and appendicular skeletons. The former includes the skull, vertebral column, ribs, and sternum; the limbs and girdles compose the latter.

Axial Skeleton

Skull

The skull consists of a series of bones encasing the brain and nasal cavities and forming the upper jaw, collectively making up the **cranium**, and the lower jaw, or **mandible**. Variations in overall shape of the skull among mammals results from evolutionary changes in jaw function and associated musculature, brain size and proportions, size and shape of of the bony housing of the ear (auditory bulla), and other features. With the exception of certain elements in the cranium of cetaceans, the bones making up the skull retain the same positions relative to one another. However, there is substantial variation in the size and shape of individual bones. Therefore, it is important to compare skull features for a variety of different mammals in order to appreciate the diversity of skull structure. For this reason skull outlines are provided for three distinctly different mammals (Fig. 1).

General features of the cranium

Braincase — That portion of the cranium encasing the brain. It is largest relative to other parts of the skull in primates (e.g., Hominidae).

Rostrum — That portion of the cranium extending anteriorly from the front edge of the orbits (see below) or base of the zygomatic arch (see below). It corresponds to the externally visible muzzle or snout, and includes the upper jaw and bones surrounding the nasal cavity. The rostrum is especially elongate in cetaceans (Mysticeti, Odontoceti), anteaters (Edentata: Myrmecophagidae), pangolins (Pholidota), bandicoots (Marsupialia: Peramelidae), and nectar-feeding bats (e.g., some phyllostomatids), among others.

Dorsal aspect of the cranium

Nasal bones — Paired bones forming the anteriormost roof of the nasal cavities. In some mammals these bones are absent (e.g., Sirenia: Dugongidae) or are very small and do not roof the nasal passages (Odontoceti; Fig. 1C).

Premaxillae (premaxillary bones) — A pair of bones forming the lower margin of the outer nasal openings and anteriormost portion of the roof of the mouth, or palate. The upper incisor teeth always reside on these bones. In most mammals each premaxilla has a elongate process extending along one side of the nasal cavity **(nasal process or branch)** and a second process meeting the other premaxilla at the midline of the palate **(palatal process or branch)**. In bats (Chiroptera) these processes are extremely variable; in one family (Megadermatidae) the premaxillae are absent altogether. The premaxillae fuse with the maxillae (see below) in some mammals (e.g., some primates and edentates).

Maxillae (maxillary bones) — These two tooth-bearing bones make up a large part of the sides of the rostrum and the palate posterior to and adjoining the premaxillae. They are especially large and elongate in cetaceans (Fig. 1C). The anterior base of each zygomatic arch (see below) usually consists of an extension of the maxilla, termed the **zygomatic process of the maxilla**.

Frontal bones — A pair of bones just posterior to the nasals and dorsal to the maxillae. They vary in size. In toothed whales (Odontoceti) only a small part of the frontals is exposed owing to a posterior expansion of the maxillae over them (Fig. 1C). The antlers and horns of artiodactyls are growths of the frontal bones. In many mammals, each frontal bone has a lateral pointed projection, the **postorbital process**, which marks the posterior border of the orbit. In some (e.g., Primates, Perissodactyla, some Artiodactyla) the postorbital process is joined with the zygomatic arch to form a **postorbital bar** or **plate**. In others (e.g., cetaceans) each frontal extends laterally as a broad wing over the entire orbit, termed a **supraorbital process**.

Parietal bones — Located posterior to the frontals, these paired bones form the bulk of the roof of the braincase. In certain primates (Anthropoidea) they are very large.

Interparietal bone — When distinct, this is a single, often triangular-shaped bone centrally located on the braincase at the posterior juncture of the parietal bones. Often it is fused with the occipital bone (see below) in adults. Rodents generally have a prominent interparietal (Fig. 1B).

Squamosal bones — Each of these two bones is located lateral and ventral to

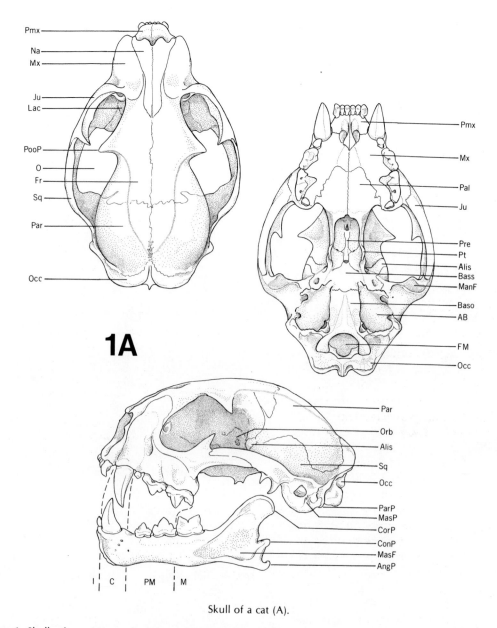

Skull of a cat (A).

Figure 1. Skulls of a cat (A), a rodent (B), and a porpoise (C). Abbreviations are as follows: AB, auditory bulla; Alis, alisphenoid; AngP, angular process; Baso, basioccipital; Bass, basisphenoid; C, canine; ConP, condyloid process; CorP, coronoid process; FM, foramen magnum, Fr, frontal; I, incisor; IC, infraorbital canal; Ju, jugal; Lac, lacrimal; M, molar; ManF, mandibular fossa; MasF, masseteric fossa; MasP, mastoid process; Mx, maxilla; Na, nasal; O, orbit; Occ, occipital; Orb, orbitosphenoid; PM, premolar; Pal, palatine; Par, parietal; ParP, paroccipital process; Pmx, premaxilla; PooP, postorbital process; Pre, presphenoid; Pt, pterygoid; Sq, squamosal; TemF, temporal fossa; Vo, vomer.

7

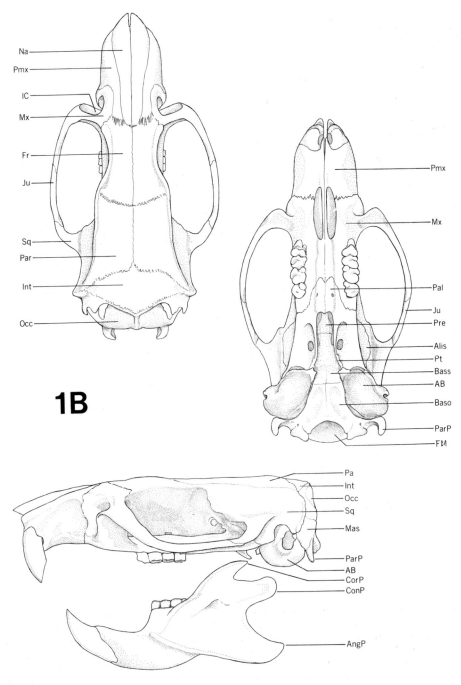

1B

Skull of a rodent (B).

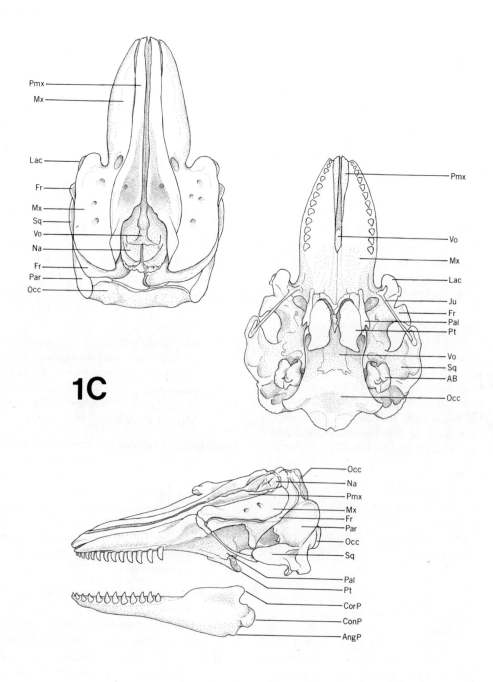

1C

Skull of a porpoise (C).

the corresponding parietal bone. Each squamosal bears a ventral articular surface, the **mandibular fossa**, that forms part of the hinge supporting the lower jaw. The posterior base of the zygomatic arch consists of the **zygomatic process of the squamosal**. When the squamosal is fused with the tympanic bone the complex is termed the **temporal bone**; this fusion is found in most mammals (exceptions include the marsupials and cetaceans).

Jugal bones — Each of these two bones forms the central portion of the zygomatic arch (see below) and is located between the zygomatic processes of the maxilla and squamosal. Occasionally the jugal also is in contact with the lacrimal bone (e.g., in many rodents) or the premaxilla (Sirenia: Dugongidae). In marsupials the jugal also makes up part of the mandibular fossa. When the zygomatic arch is absent or incomplete, the jugal often is absent (e.g., in some members of the Monotremata and Insectivora, and in Pholidota).

Zygomatic arches — Conspicuous arches on the sides of the cranium that form the lateral and ventral borders of the orbits and temporal fossae. Several bones, including the maxilla, jugal, squamosal, and lacrimal may contribute to each arch. Jaw muscles (masseters) have their origins on the surface of the arch. In mammals with reduced masseter musculature (e.g., Pholidota, cetaceans, and some Chiroptera, Insectivora, and Edentata), the arches are incomplete or absent. In many rodents the anterior portion of the arch is tilted upward

and forms a broad plate (**zygomatic plate**).

Orbits — The socket-like depressions, one on each side of the cranium, in which the eyes are housed. Each orbit is bordered anteriorly and laterally by the zygomatic arch (when present) and posteriorly by the temporal fossa.

Temporal fossae — These depressions are located posterior to the orbits and are bordered laterally by the zygomatic arches (when present). In some primates (Anthropoidea) and in horses (Perissodactyla: Equidae) the temporal fossa and orbit are separated by a postorbital plate, thus forming two compartments.

Lacrimal bones — Each of these bones is located on or adjacent to the anterior base of the zygomatic arch at its dorsal edge. Usually small, these bones can be identified by the presence in each of a **lacrimal foramen**, an opening for the tear duct. Lacrimal bones are absent in Monotremata and Pholidota.

Occipital (lambdoidal) crest — A ridge of variable size extending across the posterodorsal margin of the cranium. It is usually part of the supraoccipital bone (see below). This crest forms an area of attachment for neck muscles and ligaments in large-headed forms (e.g., Perissodactyla, Artiodactyla).

Sagittal crest — A vertical ridge extending along the dorsal midline of the posterior portion of the braincase. It is variable in extent, occurring to a lesser or greater degree on occipital, interparietal, and parietal bones, and is most prominent in mammals requiring an expanded surface area for large temporal muscles (e.g., Chiroptera, Carnivora).

Posterior aspect of the cranium

Foramen magnum — A large opening in the occipital bone through which pass the spinal cord and vertebral arteries.

Occipital bone — A large bone composing the posterior wall of the braincase that is formed by the fusion of the basioccipital, exoccipitals, and supraoccipital.

Supraoccipital bone — The part of the occipital bone overlying the foramen magnum. When present, the occipital crest is at the dorsal edge of this bone.

Basioccipital bone — A single bone ventral to the foramen magnum and extending anteriorly on the ventral surface of the cranium between the auditory bullae.

Exoccipital bones — Each of these bones is located lateral to the foramen magnum and bears an occipital condyle.

Occipital condyles — Paired swellings of the exoccipital bones adjacent to the foramen magnum, each of which articulates with the first cervical vertebra (atlas).

Paroccipital processes — Each of these processes is a ventrally extending projection of the occipital bone lying just posterior to and usually in close association with the auditory bulla (see below). Largest in herbivores (e.g., Artiodactyla, Perissodactyla, Rodentia) (Fig. 1B), these processes provide sites of origin for large digastric muscles necessary for grinding plant material.

Mastoid bones — Small, usually obscure bones adjacent to the paroccipital processes and at the posterior margins of the auditory bullae. The mastoid is a portion of the concealed periotic bone (a bone protecting the inner ear) exposed on the surface of the skull. In certain mammals it protrudes as the **mastoid process** (e.g., Carnivora) (Fig. 1A).

Ventral aspect of the cranium

Auditory bullae — Thin-walled, swollen capsules of bone on each side of the basioccipital bone and ventral to the squamosal. Each bulla consists of the **tympanic bone** or a fusion of the tympanic and **entotympanic bones**. The mastoid and alisphenoid (see below) may also participate in its formation. The bullae protect the middle-ear ossicles and facilitate efficient transmission of sound to the inner ear. They become enormously inflated in many mammals (particularly some groups of rodents) that are adapted to open plains or deserts and have acute hearing. In others the bullae are absent (e.g., Montremata) or are incomplete and the ear is surrounded by a bony ring made up of the tympanic bone (e.g., some insectivores). The bullae are very loosely attached to the skull in cetaceans, an adaptation that probably enhances reception of water-borne signals by reducing transmission of sound to the bulla from other parts of the skull.

11

Basisphenoid bone — A single bone in the midline just anterior to the basioccipital.

Presphenoid bone — A median bone which is usually visible anterior to the basisphenoid. It is fused with the **orbitosphenoids** which extend laterally into the posterior wall of the orbits.

Alisphenoid bones — Wing-like bones in the walls of the temporal fossae posterior to the frontal and orbitosphenoid bones and anterior to the squamosals. In marsupials the alisphenoids are very large and participate in the formation of the auditory bullae. An **alisphenoid canal**, which transmits part of the fifth cranial nerve, a diagnostic character in some mammals, may penetrate a bony shelf at the ventral base of the alisphenoid bone.

Pterygoid bones — Each of these bones lies posterior to the internal opening of the nasal passages. An elongate process (the **hamular process)** usually extends posteriorly from the ventral surface of each bone. The pterygoids are unusually large and distinctively shaped in odontocetes (Fig. 1C). They are often fused with the alisphenoid in other mammals.

Palatine bones — These are paired bones that form the posterior portion of the palate. They lie between the cheek-teeth (see below) and are posterior to the maxillae.

Vomer — The bone forming the postero-ventral part of the wall separating the two sides of the nasal passages. This bone is usually obscure but it appears occasionally as part of the palate.

Lower jaw or mandible

Dentary bones — The lower jaws consist of two halves, or dentary bones, united either firmly (most mammals) or loosely (e.g., Rodentia, Mysticeti) in a symphysis at the anterior end.

Coronoid process — The projection extending dorsally from each half of the jaw into the temporal fossa. It is largest in mammals with large temporal muscles (e.g., Carnivora) (Fig. 1A); it is small or absent in certain herbivores (e.g., some hystricomorph rodents).

Condyloid process — The projection on the upper rear portion of the mandible bearing the **mandibular condyle**. The latter articulates with the upper jaw at the mandibular fossa of the squamosal bone. The condyle varies substantially in shape because of differing patterns of jaw movement involved with different dietary requirements. In some carnivores (e.g., Mustelidae) the hinge formed at the joint is firmly constructed and the lower jaw can be removed from the upper jaw only with difficulty. This adaptation prevents disarticulation of the mandible as the predator struggles with its prey. In herbivores the joint tends to be loose in order to allow the flexibility of jaw motion necessary for grinding coarse vegetative matter.

Angular process — A process of variable size at the posteroventral edge of the lower jaw. It is enormous in some herbivores, particularly hystricomorph rodents, providing a large surface area for insertion of the masseter muscles. Marsupials and some rodents are characterized by an angular process that is markedly inflected (bent inward), thus providing a large area of insertion for the jaw muscles.

Masseteric fossa — The lateral depression of the lower jaw ventral to the coronoid process into which much of the masseter muscle inserts.

Teeth

Incisors — These teeth are the anteriormost teeth in the jaws of most mammals. The upper incisors reside wholly on the premaxillae. Incisors are ordinarily simple in structure but are modified in many mammals for grooming, cropping, cutting, and other functions.

Canines — There is one pair of these stabbing teeth on both the upper and lower jaws. On the upper jaw each canine is located at the suture between the premaxilla and maxilla. The tusks found in many mammals are usually modified canines. Some mammals, particularly herbivores (Rodentia, most perissodactyls and artiodactyls), lack canines and have a large gap, or **diastema**, between the incisors and premolars. In others (e.g., some members of the Insectivora and Primates) the canines are poorly developed and peg-like.

Cheekteeth — An inclusive term for all the teeth occurring in the cheek region. They include the premolars and molars of both jaws. The cheekteeth tend to be high-crowned (**hypsodont**) in mammals with course diets, such as grazers, and low-crowned (**brachydont**) in mammals with soft diets, such as

frugivores and omnivores. Details on these teeth follow.

Premolars — These teeth are located just posterior to the canines. On the upper jaw they reside in the maxillae. They are large in herbivores, where they often closely resemble the molars in size and complexity, and in certain omnivores and carnivores. In the latter, the last upper premolar and first lower molar combine when occluded to form the principal shearing teeth (the **carnassials**).

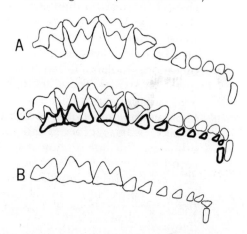

Figure 2. Upper (A) and lower (B) toothrows of an insectivore, and the fit of the teeth when occluded (C). Note the pattern of reversed triangles and the tritubercular upper molars. (After Romer, 1966.)

Molars — These are generally the most elaborate teeth in the dentition. In the upper jaw the molars are located in the maxillae. The molars are extremely variable in pattern. The three-cusped or **tritubercular (tribosphenic)** arrangement found in many marsupials, insectivores, and bats (Fig. 2), is considered primitive for mammals. The occlusal arrangement of such teeth is shown in Fig. 2. Each occluding pair of upper and lower molars functions as a set of "reversed triangles," with the apexes pointing in opposite directions. The lower molars are more complex than the upper molars, consisting of a triangular anterior portion, the **trigonid**, and a squared posterior crushing surface, the "tail" or **talonid**. Trituberclar teeth are all-purpose teeth, providing both shearing and crushing surfaces. The addition of another prominent cusp on the upper molars results in a four-cusped or **quadritubercular** molar (Fig. 3A), an arrangement common in some insectivores and primates. Omnivores frequently have **bunodont** molars. Often basically quadritubercular, these teeth have low, rounded cusps (Fig. 3B). Effective crushing devices, they are found in pigs, bears, raccoons, and many primates (including humans). The **secodont** dentition of carnivores (Fig. 3C) results from modification of certain cusps into an elaborate shearing mechanism. A **lophodont** dentition (Fig. 3D), present in most herbivores, is identified by ridges, or lophs, of enamel arranged in various ways between the cusps. The tooth may vary from having a simple ring-like ridge around the margin (e.g., Rodentia: Bathyergidae) to having a complex series of ridges and cross-ridges (e.g., Perissodactyla: Equidae). When the ridges are formed into two adjoining triangles or rings on the same tooth, the arrangement is called **bilophodont**, as in lagomorphs and some rodents. In most artiodactyls ridges of enamel take on a crescent shape, and for this reason the molars are termed **selenodont** (Fig.3E).

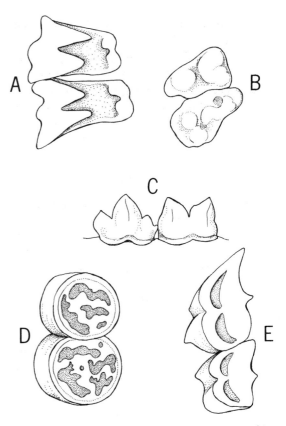

Figure 3. Occlusal views of crown patterns: quadritubercular (A); bunodont (B); secodont (in side view) (C); lophodont (D); selenodont (E).

Vertebral Column

In most mammals the vertebral column consists of five distinct regions or sets of vertebrae (Fig. 4B). In others the vertebrae appear to blend continuously into one another, and specific regions are difficult to identify (Fig. 4A). Flexibility of the vertebral column differs among mammals according to whether the vertebrae are elaborately interconnected (e.g., Edentata) or articulate loosely with each other (e.g., Sirenia, cetaceans). The following vertebrae and associated structures can be recognized.

14

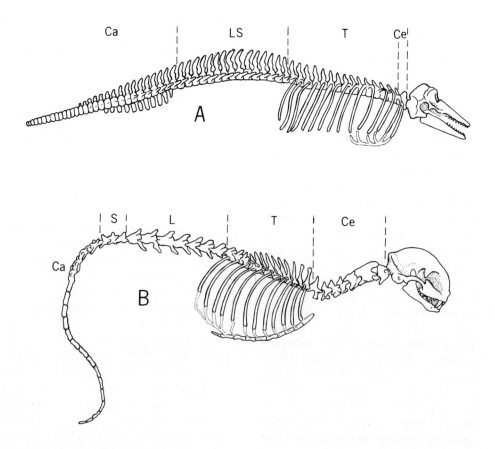

Figure 4. Axial skeletons of a porpoise (A) and a cat (B). Ca, caudal; Ce, cervical; L, lumbar; LS, lumbosacral; S, sacral; T, thoracic. Not drawn to scale.

Zygapophyses — The facets located on each end of a vertebra which articulate with the immediately preceding and succeeding vertebrae. They are best developed in the thoracic and lumbar regions.

Cervical vertebrae — These constitute the anteriormost group of vertebrae in the vertebral column. With rare exceptions, there are seven such vertebrae in mammals. Except for the first, and often the last, they can usually be identified by the presence of a foramen on each side of the centrum. The first vertebra, or **atlas**, has two large anterior depressions that articulate with the occipital condyles of the cranium. There is no body, or **centrum**, on this vertebra. The second vertebra, or **axis**, is identified by the **odontoid process**, a prominent projection extending anteriorly from the centrum into the atlas vertebra. Although usually a pointed, cone-like projection, the

15

odontoid process is crescent-shaped in some mammals (e.g., Artiodactyla: Cervidae). The cervical vertebrae are often compressed or fused into a single functional unit in fossorial, saltatorial, and aquatic mammals.

Thoracic vertebrae — Located posterior to the cervical vertebrae and usually 12-15 in number, these vertebrae are characterized by the presence of rib facets and generally by large posteriorly sloping dorsal **(neural)** spines (the latter are absent in bats). On each side of most anterior thoracic vertebrae there are three rib facets which accommodate the head and tubercle of the rib (see below). One is on the centrum at or near the junction of that centrum and the one just ahead, so that the head resides between successive centra. The second, for the tubercle, is on the wing-like **transverse process.** A third lies posteriorly on the centrum to articulate with the head of the next rib back. This facet is missing from the posterior thoracic vertebrae in many mammals. In perissodactyls and artiodactyls the thoracic vertebrae are especially large and have long spines for support of the large neck and head.

Lumbar vertebrae — These vertebrae lie posterior to the thoracic vertebrae. There are usually six or seven lumbars, but they may be numerous in some mammals (e.g., over 20 in some odontocetes). In saltators the neural spines are especially large and serve to support a long massive tail. The spines are upright or slope in an anterior direction, often converging with the thoracic spines in the posterior region of the thorax. Ordinarily, large lateral transverse processes extend anteroventrally on each side of the centrum. The presence of additional processes makes these vertebrae rather complex in appearance.

Sacral vertebrae — Located posterior to the lumbars, these 3-5 vertebrae generally are fused to form the **sacrum**, which provides a rigid support for the pelvic girdle and hind limbs. The number of sacral vertebrae is largest (up to 10) and fusion is most extensive in the Edentata. In contrast, the sacral vertebrae are simple and are not differentiated from the lumbar or caudal vertebrae in mammals with reduced hind limbs (cetaceans, Sirenia) (Fig. 4A).

Caudal vertebrae — The vertebrae of the tail are generally relatively simple in structure and vary greatly in number, the latter feature resulting from distinctly different functions of the tail in different mammals. In most long-tailed forms the anterior caudal vertebrae are short and broad, whereas the posterior vertebrae tend to become elongate and cylindrical in shape. However, in cetaceans the vertebrae are conspicuously flattened in the region of the flukes. The four caudal vertebrae in some Primates (Pongidae, Hominidae) are fused to form the **coccyx.**

Ribcage

Ribs — These elements consist of a series of elongate, curved, more or less compressed bones extending from the vertebral column laterally and ventrally to (or nearly to) the sternum. Usually ribs are attached only to the thoracic vertebrae, but there are exceptions (e.g., there are cervical ribs in sloths Edentata: Bradypodidae and monotremes). Each rib generally consists of two distinct parts: the dorsal, or **vertebral rib**, and the ventral, or **sternal rib**. The sternal ribs usually ossify more slowly than do the vertebral ribs. Occasionally an intermediate rib segment is also present. In some mammals (e.g., Edentata: Dasypodidae) the sternal ribs are quite large. In pangolins (Pholidota) the sternal ribs are modified into posteriorly directed processes from which muscles moving the protrusible tongue originate. Each vertebral rib, especially in the anterior thoracic region, typically has two processes by which it articulates with the vertebrae (see above). These are the tubercle, or **tuberculum**, which is the posterodorsal process, and the head, or **capitulum**, which is oriented anteroventrally when the rib is in place. Often the posteriormost ribs do not join at all with the sternum and hence are termed **floating ribs.** Floating ribs predominate in whales (Mysticeti, Odontoceti) (Fig. 4A) and these, together with loosely articulating vertebral ribs, facilitate compression of the ribcage during dives. Sloths (Edentata: Bradypodidae) have numerous (15-24) firmly articulated ribs.

Sternum — Consisting of a series of bony segments (**sternebrae**), this structure is located in the ventral midline of the thoracic region and forms the ventral portion of the ribcage. The sternal ribs attach to the sternum. The anteriormost segment (the **presternum** or **manubrium**) is large and commonly keeled in bats (Chiroptera) and many fossorial mammals (e.g., Insectivora: Talpidae) to provide a large surface area for attachment of the powerful pectoral muscles in these mammals. In strictly aquatic mammals the sternum is short and relatively simple, and few ribs articulate with it; only one element remains in the sternum of baleen whales (Mysticeti).

APPENDICULAR SKELETON

The limbs and girdles are variously adapted for many locomotor functions in mammals. Consequently, there is substantial variation in structure, although the same basic limb plan is common to all mammals. These differences are reflected, among other ways, in foot posture (Fig. 5). Ambulatory, arboreal, and fossorial mammals are **plantigrade**, a posture characterized by movement on the entire foot pad, from ankle or wrist to the digits (Fig. 5A). Man is a plantigrade mammal. **Digitigrade** mammals walk or run on the digits (Fig. 5B). Many cursorial (running) mammals (e.g., Carnivora: Felidae, Canidae, Hyaenidae) are digitigrade. Hoofed mammals (most artiodactyls, and perissodactyls) are **unguligrade**—only the hoof(s) of each limb contacts the ground (Fig. 5C).

The Girdles

Pectoral girdle (Fig. 6A)

Scapula — This is the large, typically

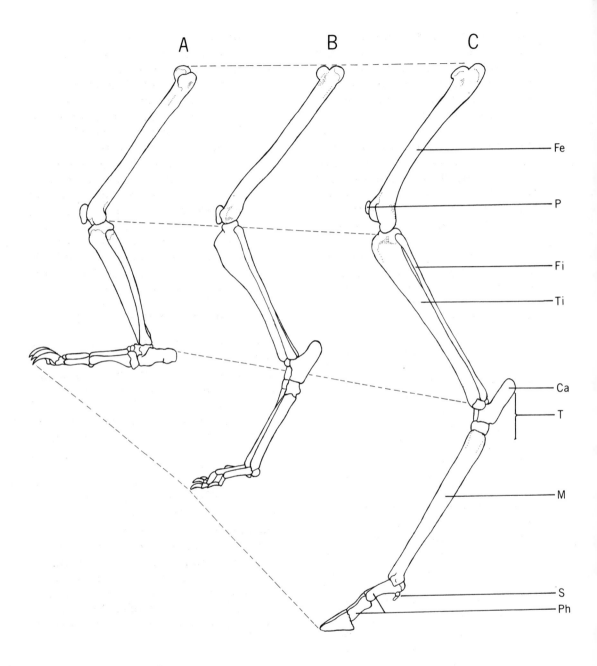

Figure 5. Hindlimbs of a bear (A), a dog (B), and a pronghorn (C), showing differences in foot posture and proportions of distal and proximal elements. Fe, femur; Fi, fibula; M, metatarsal; P, patella; Ph, phalanx; S, sesamoid bones; Ta, tarsal bones (tarsus); Ti, tibia. (After Hildebrand, 1974.)

flat bone extending dorsally and posteriorly from the proximal end of the forelimb. It articulates with the humerus (see below) at the anteroventral **glenoid fossa.** The outer surface of the scapula is generally divided into upper and lower concavities (**supraspinous** and **infraspinour fossae**) by a keel-like shelf or **spine**. This shelf and its associated processes are large and the scapula is broad in most fossorial mammals in order to provide a large surface area for muscle attachment. In mammals characterized by sprawling limbs (e.g., monotremes, moles) the supraspinous fossa and spine are small or absent. A projection at the anterior end of the spine, the **acromion process**, articulates with the clavicle.

Clavicle — If present, this is a rod-like bone extending from the acromion process of the scapula to the interclavicle (see below) (Monotremata) or sternum (all other mammals). It is prominent in arboreal, fossorial, aerial, and generalized mammals (e.g., Monotremata, Marsupialia, Insectivora, Chiroptera, Primates, Rodentia), but in cursorial and aquatic mammals it is reduced (e.g., Carnivora: Felidae and Canidae) or absent (Artiodactyla, Perissodactyla, Mysticeti, Odontoceti).

Coracoid — This is a distinct bone only in monotremes. It extends from the glenoid fossa to the sternum. In other mammals it is reduced in size and fused to the anteroventral border of the scapula as the **coracoid process**. It also contributes to the formation of the glenoid fossa.

Epicoracoid and interclavicle bones. — These bones also are found only in the Monotremata. The epicoracoid

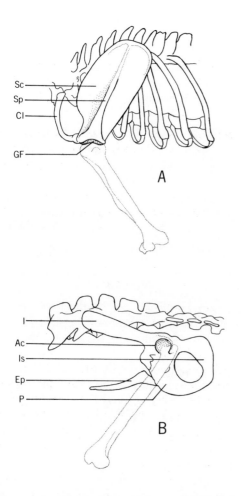

Figure 6. Pectoral girdle (A) and pelvic girdle (innominate bone) (B) of an opossum. Anterior is to the left. Ac, acetabulum; Cl, clavicle; GF, glenoid fossa; Ep, epipubic bone; I, ilium; Is, ischium; P, pubic bone; Sc, scapula; Sp, spine.

(also called the **precoracoid**) lies between the coracoid and clavicle and is dorsal to the interclavicle. It broadly overlaps its counterpart of the opposite side. The unpaired interclavicle is a T-shaped bone located in the midline just anterior to the presternum and ventral to the epicoracoids.

Pelvic girdle (Fig. 6B)

Innominate bones (pelvis) — The pelvic girdle is composed of two halves, or innominate bones, each of which consists of three bones fused into a single structure. It functions in transmitting the locomotor thrust from the hindlimb to the vertebral column, and in providing support for the limb and trunk musculature as well as for the ligaments of the penis and clitoris. The innominate bones articulate dorsally with the sacrum and ventrally with each other at the **pubic** (or **puboischiac**) **symphysis.** The symphysis varies in length and degree of fusion; there is no union of innominate bones in many insectivores (Talpidae, Chrysochloridae, Soricidae). Each innominate bone is perforated adjacent to the pubic symphysis by the **obturator foramen.** In whales and sirenians the innominate bones are reduced.

Acetabulum — The concavity more or less in the center of each innominate bone with which the head of the femur articulates. It also includes the point where all three of the principal bones of the innominate bone are joined.

Ilium — This relatively long, vertically flattened bone extends anterodor-sally from the acetabulum and articulates with the sacral vertebrae. Its elongate shape and position are distinctive for mammals.

Ischium — A bone surrounding most of the obturator foramen and extending posteriorly to form the rump and part of the puboischiac symphysis. The vestiges of the pelvic girdle in cetaceans probably are remnants of the two ischia.

Pubic bones — A bone which lies ante-roventral to the obturator foramen and meets its opposite at the pubic symphysis.

Epipubic bones (marsupial bones) — A pair of long, slender bones, each of which extends anteriorly from the pubic bone near the pubic symphysis. They are peculiar to monotremes and marsupials. The function of these bones is not precisely known.

Limbs

Both forelimbs and hindlimbs consist of three basic components (Figs. 5, 7): (1) a proximal segment, including the humerus (forelimb) and femur (hindlimb); (2) a middle segment, including radius and ulna (forelimb) and tibia and fibula (hindlimb); and (3) a distal segment, including carpals and metacarpals (forelimb), tarsals and metatarsals (hindlimb), and phalanges (both limbs). In cursorial mammals the metacarpals and metatarsals are very elongate and lightened, an adaptation promoting increased velocity of limb movement and lengthening of the stride. The metatarsals are similarly modified in saltatorial mammals. In contrast, the proximal parts of the limbs are proportionately larger in fossorial and ambulatory mammals for added strength. The forelimbs of aquatic mammals are modified to form flippers. Many other modifications have also been described. Suffice it to say that limb structure and mode of life are closely correlated in mammals. Certain additional peculiarities of specific limb elements are indicated below.

Forelimb

All mammals have forelimbs, although substantial modifications exist. The forelimbs exhibit greatest specialization relative to the hindlimbs in aerial, aquatic, and fossorial mammals (Fig. 7A, B, C). The following structures may be identified.

Humerus — This is the single, large, proximal bone of the forelimb. A few of its features are worthy of comment. The **head** is the smooth hemispherical projection that articulates with the glenoid fossa of the scapula. Adjacent to the head are two processes that serve for muscle attachments — a lateral one, the **greater tuberosity**, and a medial one, the **lesser tuberosity**. In bats these two structures are called the **trochiter** and **trochin**, respectively. In some bats, notably the Molossidae, they form a unique locking device that prevents over-extension of the wing and increases the efficiency of the power stroke during flight. The humerus is robust and heavily ridged for large muscular attachments in diggers (Fig. 7C). In extreme cases, it becomes virtually square and has two articulations with the pectoral girdle — with both the scapula and clavicle (Insectivora: Talpidae) — and movement at the joint is restricted to

one plane. The humerus is short, stout, and relatively simple in cetaceans (Fig. 7B) and pinnipeds.

Ulna — A long bone usually located on the lateral side of the forearm just distal to and articulating with the humerus. A proximal extension of this bone beyond the joint with the humerus is the **olecranon process**, or elbow. In specialized cursors (e.g., many artiodactyls) the ulna is almost directly posterior to the radius, thus restricting rotational movement of the forearm. The ulna and radius are sometimes fused for part of their length (e.g., Chiroptera) (Fig. 7A). Generally, however, the bones are free and the radius is allowed to rotate around the ulna, thereby enhancing flexibility in movement of the forelimbs.

Radius — A long, usually slender bone, located on the medial side of the forearm and somewhat anterior to the ulna. It articulates proximally with the humerus and distally with the carpal bones of the wrist. Although usually the smaller of the two forearm bones, it is the chief functional bone in the forearm of bats (Fig. 7A), and is more or less equal in size to the humerus in cetaceans (Fig. 7B).

Carpal bones — A group of small bones distal to the radius and ulna which collectively form the **carpus**, or wrist. In a few mammals these bones become quite specialized. For example, certain of the carpals and associated extra bones (sesamoid bones; see Glossary) in the giant panda (Carnivora: Ursidae) and moles (Insectivora: Talpidae) are sufficiently enlarged that the forefoot gives the appearance of having six, or even seven, digits.

Metacarpals — Elongate bones located between the carpus and phalanges. The number of metacarpals corresponds to the number of digits (toes) except in some cursors (e.g., many artiodactyls), in which the two functional metacarpals are fused into a single **cannon bone**, so named because early fossil hunters often discovered these bones projecting from the gound like cannons. The metacarpals are extremely elongate in bats (Chiroptera) and, together with similarly long phalanges, support the wing membrane (Fig. 7A).

Phalanges — a series of small bones extending distally from the tip of each metacarpal through each digit. In generalized mammals the first digit, or **pollex** ("thumb"), has two phalanges; each of the remaining four digits contains three. The digits in the flippers of whales often have more than the usual number (Fig. 7B), a condition called **hyperphalangy**. The number of phalanges in the digits of the wing in bats varies subtantially. The distalmost phalanx of each digit in most cats (Carnivora: Felidae) is specialized to house a retractile claw. The pollex in primates is opposable and functions importantly in grasping.

Hindlimb (Fig. 5)

The hindlimbs, or pelvic limbs, tend to be most highly modified relative to the forelimbs in runners and hoppers. In contrast, hindlimbs are absent or vestigial in cetaceans and sirenians, and are modified into a kind of tail in pinniped carnivores. The following features may be recognized.

Femur — The proximal long bone of the hindlimb that extends from the pelvic girdle to the knee joint. Like the humerus, it contains a rounded protuberance, or **head**. It articulates with the pelvic girdle at the acetabulum. On the lateral side of the head is a large projection, the **greater trochanter**. A smaller bump, the **lesser trochanter**, is located below the head on the posteromedial side of the femur. A **third trochanter** is also present in some mammals (e.g., some Lagomorpha, Rodentia, Edentata). These processes serve for muscle attachments. The presence of a third trochanter in perissodactyls distinguishes them from artiodactyls (see Fig. 10). In monotremes, the femur is distinctive in being quite flat and having a constricted shaft and broad ends.

Tibia — The larger of the two bones forming the lower hindlimb, it lies medial and/or anterior to the fibula. The tibia often tends to be triangular in cross-section because of a prominent ridge on the anterior surface.

Fibula — Normally long and narrow, this bone lies lateral to the tibia. It often is fused for part of its length with the tibia. The fibula is reduced in some mammals. The amount of reduction is positively correlated with the degree of specialization to a cursorial habit. For example, in most

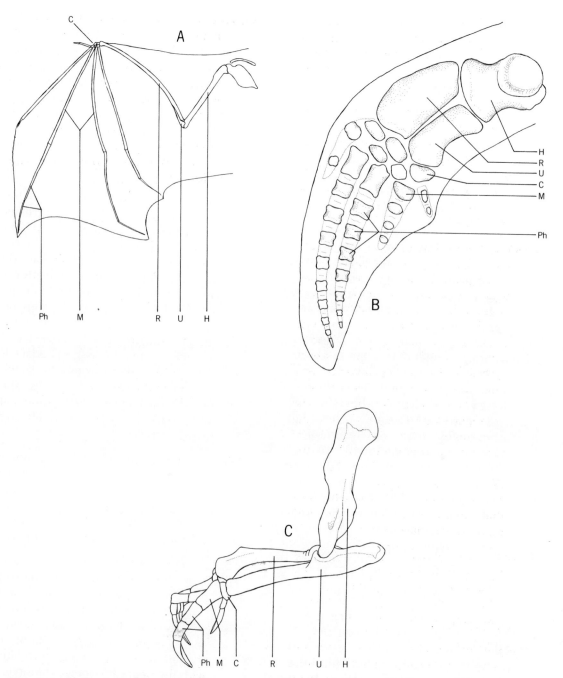

Figure 7. Forelimbs of a bat (A), a porpoise (B), and an armadillo (C), showing structural differences. C, carpal bones (carpus); H, humerus; M, metacarpal; Ph, phalanx; R, radius, U, ulna.

artiodactyls it is a small remnant near the distal end of the tibia. In contrast, the fibula is free of the tibia and well developed in arboreal mammals (e.g., Primates).

Patella — This sesamoid bone (see Glossary) is the knee-cap. It articulates loosely with the femur and develops separately from other limb bones in a tendon at the knee joint. Although usually well developed, it is very small or cartilaginous in many marsupials.

Tarsal bones — The counterpart of the carpal bones in the hindlimb. These bones form the **tarsus**, or ankle. Two proximal tarsal bones are noteworthy. The large **calcaneus**, or heel bone, has an elongate posterior process to which the tendon ("Achilles tendon") of the extensor muscles of the hindfoot attaches. In a few primates (e.g., *Tarsius*, the tarsier; and *Galago*, bushbabies) the calcaneus is very elongate, facilitating a springing type of locomotion without a reduction or loss of the grasping function of the hallux (see below). The **astragalus**, or **talus**, articulates most directly with the tibia, and usually lies medial and dorsal to the calcaneus.

Metatarsals — Elongate bones forming in the hindfoot the equivalent of the metacarpals in the forefoot. In saltators (e.g., some Marsupialia, Lagomorpha, Rodentia) and cursors (e.g., Artiodactyla, Perissodactyla), the metatarsals are elongate and often reduced in number. As in the forelimb, there may also be fusion to form a cannon bone (Fig. 5C).

Phalanges — The distalmost series of small bones in the hindfoot. Each digit of the hindfoot of generalized mammals has the same number of phalanges as the corresponding digit of the forefoot. However, there are only two phalanges in all digits of the hindfoot of disc-winged bats (Thyropteridae, Myzopodidae). The first digit of the hindfoot is called the **hallux** ("big toe").

Class Mammalia
  Subclass Prototheria
    Infraclass Eotheria
      Order *Triconodonta
            *Docodonta
    Infraclass Ornithodelphia
      Order Monotremata
    Infraclass Allotheria
      Order *Multituberculata
  Subclass Theria
    Infraclass Trituberculata
      Order *Symmetrodonta
            *Pantotheria
    Infraclass Metatheria
      Order Marsupialia
    Infraclass Eutheria
      Order Insectivora
            Dermoptera
            Chiroptera
            Primates
            *Tillodontia
            *Taeniodontia
            Edentata
            Pholidota
            Lagomorpha
            Rodentia
            *Creodonta
            Carnivora
            Pinnipedia
            *Archaeoceti
            Mysticeti
            Odontoceti
            *Notoungulata
            Tubulidentata
            *Amblypoda
            Proboscidea
            *Embrithopoda
            Hyracoidea
            Sirenia
            *Desmostylia
            Perissodactyla
            Artiodactyla
            Rhinogradentia

CLASSIFICATION OF MAMMALS

The classification of mammals, particularly at higher taxonomic levels, is in a state of flux because of uncertainties about the relationships of early mammals. The classification below follows that of Simpson (1945) and Romer (1966) as modified by Crompton and Jenkins (1973). Extinct orders are identified by an asterisk.

KEY TO ORDERS OF MAMMALS

1a.	Forelimbs modified into wings	**CHIROPTERA** (p. 76)
1b.	Forelimbs not modified into wings. 2	

2a (1b). Forelimbs modified into flippers 3
2b. Forelimbs not modified into flippers 6

3a (2a). Hindlimbs well-developed; teeth heterodont, with
prominent canines . . . . **PINNIPEDIA** (p.230)
3b. Hindlimbs absent (vestiges of pelvic girdle present in
some); teeth absent or, if present, homodont (rarely
heterodont), never with prominent canines 4

4a (3b). Nostrils located dorsally at end of snout; zygomatic
arch robust . . . . **SIRENIA** (p.260)
4b. Nostril (blowhole) or nostrils located on top of head;
zygomatic arch very slender. 5

5a (4b). Two external nostrils (blowholes) present; no teeth;
baleen present; skull ± symmetrical; nasals large,
roofing part of nasal passage . . . . **MYSTICETI** (p.240)
5b. One external nostril (blowhole) present; teeth pre-
sent; no baleen; skull often asymmetrical; nasals very
small, not roofing any part of nasal passage. . . . . **ODONTOCETI** (p.247)

6a (2b). No incisors or canines; cheekteeth absent or, if
present, peg like 7
6b. Incisors and/or canines present; cheekteeth always
present, rarely peg-like 10

7a (6a). Forefoot with 5 digits; epipubic bones present; no
auditory bulla . . . . **MONOTREMATA** (p. 30)
7b. Forefoot with 2-4 digits; no epipubic bones; auditory
bulla present 8

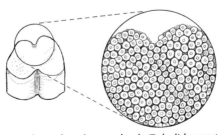

Figure 8. Enlarged view of a section of a molar of an aardvark (Tubulidentata), illustrating the numerous dentine tubes characteristic of the cheekteeth in members of this order.

8a (7b).   Forefoot with 4 principal digits, each with shovel-shaped nails; cheekteeth present, consisting of numerous vertical tubes of dentine (Fig. 8) . . . . **TUBULIDENTATA** (p.142)

8b.   Forefoot with 2-3 principal digits, each with long claws; cheekteeth absent or, if present, without vertical tubes of dentine 9

9a (8b).   Body covered with horny, overlapping scales; no jugal, lacrimal, or interparietal bones . . . . **PHOLIDOTA** (p.140)

9b.   Body well haired or covered with armor of bony skin (scutes); jugal, lacrimal, and interparietal bones present . . . . **EDENTATA** (p.132)

10a (6b).   Pouch (marsupium) or skin folds usually present on belly; braincase relatively small; jugal forming part of mandibular fossa (Fig. 9); angular process of lower jaw inflected . . . . **MARSUPIALIA** (p. 35)

10b.   No pouch; braincase relatively large; jugal only rarely forming part of mandibular fossa; angular process of lower jaw straight or deflected (rarely inflected) 11

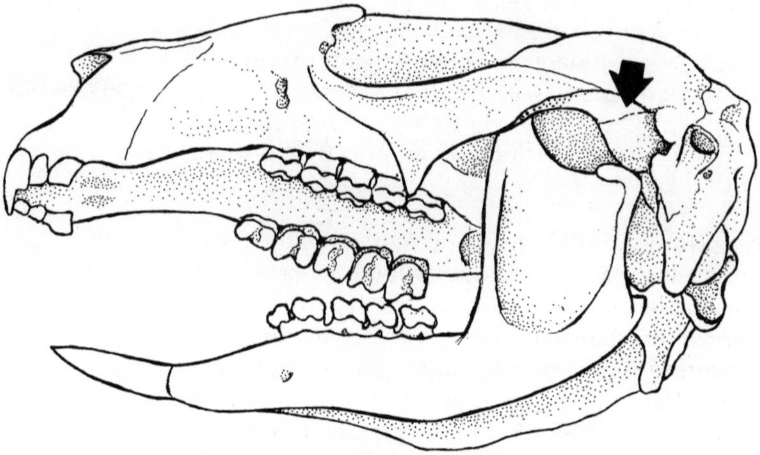

Figure 9. Lateral view of the cranium of a marsupial. Note participation of the jugal bone in mandibular fossa.

11a (10b). Skin (gliding) membrane surrounding entire body (between neck and forelimbs, forelimbs and hindlimbs, and hindlimbs and tail); cranium very shallow, flat; lower incisors procumbent and comb-like . . . . **DERMOPTERA** (p. 75)

11b.   No skin membrane surrounding body; skull not excessively shallow and flat; lower incisors only rarely procumbent and comb-like 12

12a (11b). Pollex opposable; braincase large, rounded; rostrum short; orbits directed forward . . . . **PRIMATES** (p.112)

12b. Pollex not opposable; braincase usually small to medium in size; rostrum usually long; orbits usually directed laterally 13

13a (12b). Size huge (weight of adults exceeding 4500 kg); snout extremely elongated into a proboscis (trunk); digits of feet wholly syndactylous and indistinct; only one functional cheektooth (or parts of two) per half jaw . . . **PROBOSCIDEA** (p.264)

13b. Size very small to large (weight much less than 4500 kg); snout never extremely elongated (occasionally a short proboscis present); digits of feet at least partly separated; more than one functional cheektooth per half jaw 14

14a (13b). Incisors 1/1 or 2/1 15
14b. Incisors not 1/1 or 2/1 16

15a (14a). Pinnae longer than tail; incisors 2/1 . . . . **LAGOMORPHA** (p.144)
15b. Pinnae usually shorter than tail; incisors 1/1 . . . . **RODENTIA** (p.148)

16a (14b). Digits largely syndactylous, with nails present on most; upper incisor tusk-like, no canines . . . . **HYRACOIDEA** (p.266)

16b. Digits not syndactylous, with claws or hooves (nails rarely present); upper incisors absent or, if present, not tusk-like; canines present or absent 17

17a (16b). Foot posture plantigrade or digitigrade; digits with claws; canines larger than other teeth or indistinct; cheekteeth tritubercular, quadritubercular, bunodont, or secodont 18

17b. Foot posture digitigrade or unguligrade; digits with nails or hoofs; canines absent, small, or large, triangular and tusk-like; cheekteeth bunodont, selenodont, or lophodont 19

18a (17a). Zygomatic arch present; auditory bulla present; canines prominent, conical, long; cheekteeth secodont or bunodont, never tritubercular or quadri-tubercular . . . . **CARNIVORA** (p.208)

18b. Zygomatic arch present or absent; auditory bulla present or absent; canines usually indistinct (if large, canines not conical); cheekteeth tritubercular or quadritubercular . . . . **INSECTIVORA** (p. 59)

19a (17b). Femur with a prominent ghird trochanter (Fig. 10A); nasal broadened posteriorly; alisphenoid canal present; crown patterns of upper premolars and molars similar . . . . **PERISSODACTYLA** (p.269)

19b. No third trochanter on femur (Fig. 10B); nasal usually not broadened posteriorly; no alisphenoid canal; crown pattern of upper molars more complex than that of premolars . . . . **ARTIODACTYLA** (p.276)

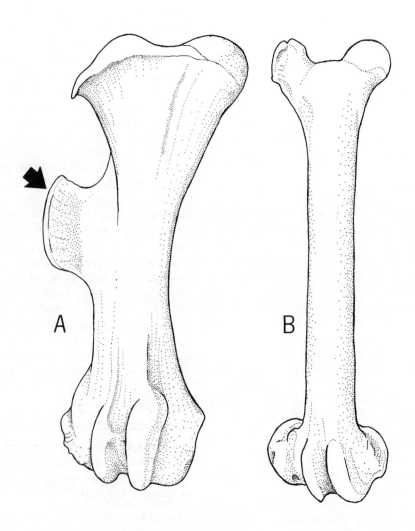

Figure 10. Presence (at arrow), in a perissodactyla (A), and absence, in an artiodactyl (B), of a third trochanter on the femur.

ACCOUNTS AND KEYS TO FAMILIES

ORDER MONOTREMATA

This order consists of six living species representing two families. A highly specialized, yet primitive group, it is composed of spiny anteater-like diggers (echidnas) in one family and a duck-billed aquatic form (platypus) in the other. Many characteristics are peculiar to this order. For example, all lay eggs. Hatchlings do not suckle; instead they are nurtured with milk exuded onto the surface of the skin of the female which they lap up. Certain characteristics of the order, such as the structure of the pectoral girdle, splayed limb posture, internal penis, and shell-covered eggs, are reptile-like. The presence of a cloaca is the basis for the name Monotremata, which literally means "single hole". Monotremes are endothermic, but their metabolic rates are low compared to those of most eutherian mammals. All hibernate or are periodically inactive in winter. Monotremes are long-lived—captive echidnas have lived 50 years. The fossil record extends back only as far as the Miocene (Woodburne and Tedford, 1975), but because of many primitive characters possessed by the group, monotremes are thought to be archaic, probably dating back to the Mesozoic. Prevailing opinion places then in a separate subclass from other living mammals (marsupials and eutherians).

Recognition Characters:

- **pectoral girdle with large epicoracoids, coracoids, and interclavicle** (these bones are absent in other mammals).
- **females lay eggs.**
  1. limbs modified for digging or swimming.
  2. ankle in males with a horny spur.

3. no vibrissae.
4. epipubic bone present (also found in marsupials).
5. skull bird-like in shape, sutures usually obliterated by fusion of bones in adults (Figs. 11, 12).
6. **no auditory bulla.**
7. premaxillae separated for at least part of their length (Figs. 11, 12).
8. jugal reduced or absent.
9. **no lacrimal**.
10. palate extending far posteriorly (Figs. 11, 12).

11. **no teeth in adults.**
12. cloaca present (absent in other mammals, with few exceptions).
13. penis within cloaca, used only for passage of sperm.
14. mammae without pendulous teats.

Remark: Summaries of many aspects of monotreme biology are provided by Augee (1978) and Griffiths (1978). Haltenorth (1958) reviewed classification.

KEY TO FAMILIES OF MONOTREMATA

1a. Pelage spiny; snout slender, long; tail very small; skull elongate, slender anteriorly; premaxillae narrow and separated except at anterior ends .... **TACHYGLOSSIDAE** (p. 32)

1b. Pelage consisting of soft hairs; snout broad, duck-billed; tail well developed, flattened; skull elongate relatively broad; premaxillae laterally expanded and separate anteriorly .... **ORNITHORHYNCHIDAE** (p. 34)

Family TACHYGLOSSIDAE
(Echidnas or spiny anteaters)

Echidnas are spiny terrestrial mammals equipped for rapid and powerful digging. They construct relatively shallow burrows and dig for termites, other insects, and worms. The tongue is long, sticky, and contractile. A unique food-grinding apparatus is located in the back of the mouth consisting of keratinized ridges at the base of the tongue and on the palate.

Spiny anteaters are usually solitary. They breed once a year, and normally lay one egg. The egg and young are brooded in a temporary brood pouch formed on the abdomen of the female. Offspring mature in one year.

Echidnas apparently have few natural predators, although they are eaten by natives of New Guinea.

Two genera, 5 species; Australia, Tasmania, New Guinea.

Recognition Characters:

1. **hair conspicuously spiny.**
2. **feet not webbed, modified for digging, with large claws.**
3. second digit of hindfoot elongate, modified for preening.
4. **snout slender, long.**
5. **pinna well developed.**
6. **tail very small.**
7. **tongue worm-like**.
8. cranium elongate, slender anteriorly (Fig. 11).
9. **premaxillae separated except at anterior ends** (Fig. 11).
10. lower jaw slender, rod-like (Fig. 11).

Dental formula: no teeth (Fig. 11).

Compare with: Ornithorhynchidae, Myrmecophagidae and Dasypodidae (Edentata), Manidae (Pholidota).

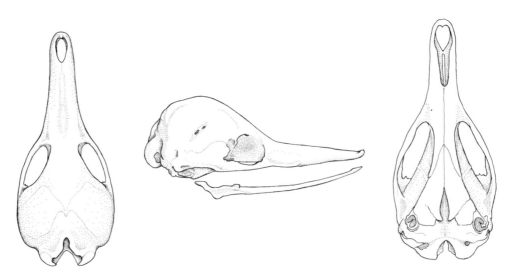

Figure 11. Skull of a tachyglossid (*Tachyglossus*, x ½).

Genera:

Tachyglossus (2) - Australian, Tasmanian echidnas; *T. aculeatus* is the most widespread species of echidna, occurring in both Australia and New Guinea.

Zaglossus (3) - New Guinean long-nosed echidnas.

Remarks: Accounts of habits and characteristics of spiny anteaters were provided by Griffiths (1968, 1978). Various aspects of their biology were also reviewed by Augee (1978).

Echidna.

Family ORNITHORHYNCHIDAE
(Duck-billed platypus)

One of the most bizarre mammals, the duck-billed platypus is the only living representative of this family. Platypuses are semi-aquatic. Their diet consists of freshwater invertebrates and vegetation, which they obtain mainly by probing the bottoms of streams and ponds with a flattened, leathery beak. The feet are webbed and well clawed. They construct burrows in banks.

Platypuses usually occur in pairs except during the breeding season, when, after intricate copulatory behavior, the female retreats to a nesting burrow where she lays two eggs (rarely one or three). She incubates the eggs by curling her body around them—there is no brood pouch. Young emerge from the burrow at four to five months of age and are sexually mature in one year.

Platypuses have few natural enemies. However, until protected by the Australian government they were actively sought for their pelts.

One genus, 1 species; eastern Australia, Tasmania.

Recognition Characters:

1. **pelage of soft hairs; no spines.**
2. **foot webbed, with moderately large claws.**
3. no distinct preening digits.
4. **snout broad, duck-billed.**
5. **no pinna.**
6. **tail well developed, flattened.**
7. **tongue flattened.**
8. cranium elongate, relatively broad (Fig. 12).
9. **premaxillae expanded laterally and separate anteriorly** (Fig. 12).
10. lower jaw of moderate size.

Dental formula: no teeth (horny plates, or "gum plates", present on jaws) (Fig. 12).

Compare with: Tachyglossidae.

Genus:

Ornithorhynchus (1) - *O. anatinus* is the duck-billed platypus.

Remarks: Burrell (1927) and Griffiths (1978) provided comprehensive treatments of the natural history of platypuses. Other aspects of their biology were reviewed by Augee (1978).

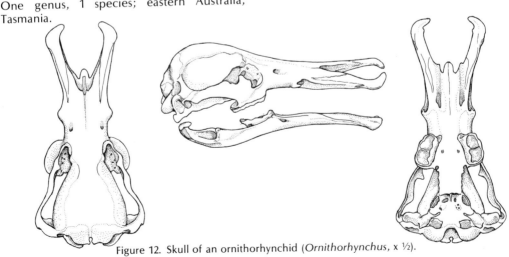

Figure 12. Skull of an ornithorhynchid (*Ornithorhynchus*, x ½).

ORDER MARSUPIALIA

Structurally, marsupials are set apart from other mammals in many ways, particularly in the urogenital and skeletal systems. They also have relatively few chromosomes (2n=10-32) compared to other mammals (Hayman, 1977). Rates of metabolism of marsupials are often lower than those of equivalently-sized eutherian mammals (but see McNab, 1978). Because of these characteristics marsupials are thought to have diverged from eutherians early in the evolutionary history of mammals, perhaps by mid-Cretaceous. The order exhibits considerable morphological, physiological, and behavioral diversification, resulting in many convergences in form and habits with other mammals. This diversity has also produced controversy about the relationships among marsupials. Hence, other classifications divide them into three or four orders (see reviews by Kirsch, 1977; and Kirsch and Calaby, 1977). Because the taxonomic arguments are not settled, the traditional arrangement, in which all are considered in a single order, is retained here.

The reproductive system is particularly interesting. Males have a penis which is forked and located posterior to the testes. Females of most species have an abdominal pouch (marsupium) for housing developing young which, compared to placental mammals, are born in a very immature condition. The gestation period in 8-40+ days. A yolk-sac placenta is present in most, but bandicoots (Peramelidae) have an allantoic placenta similar to that found in eutherians. At birth the fetus is expelled through a temporary birth canal which forms between the paired vaginae. The blind young move to the pouch (if present) or belly and attach to separate nipples.

Characteristics of the dentition and hindfeet have been used as convenient criteria for subdividing marsupials. The more primitive families (Didelphidae, Dasyuridae, Thylacinidae, Myrmecobiidae, and Caenolestidae) are **polyprotodont** (they have four or five upper incisors) and have separate digits on the hindfoot, whereas other families (Phalangeridae, Tarsipedidae, Phascolarctidae, Vombatidae, Macropodidae) are **diprotodont** (they have three or fewer upper incisors) and have two syndactylous digits (the second and third) on the hindfoot (Fig. 14). Bandicoots (Peramelidae) are intermediate—they are polyprotodont and syndactylous.

Marsupials occur in the tropics of the New World and in Australasia. They represent an extremely successful group in these areas, but evidently some are competitively inferior to placental mammals where they occur together, and extinctions of marsupials have apparently resulted from such interactions, especially in South America. The disjunct distribution of marsupials has inspired lively controversies about the origin and radiation of the group (see review by Keast, 1977). The oldest known fossils, referred to the family Didelphidae, are from the late Cretaceous and are very opossum-like. Clemens (1977) has argued convincingly for a North American origin of the order.

Except where noted, the classification of families follows that of Kirsch (1977).

Recognition Characters:

1. **marsupium (pouch) present or absent.**
2. **epipubic bone present** (also found in monotremes).
3. **braincase small.**
4. **jugal forming part of the mandibular fossa** (See Fig. 9).
5. alisphenoid large, forming part of the auditory bulla (if present).
6. **angular process of lower jaw inflected.**
7. vaginae paired.
8. cloaca absent or short.
9. penis external, forked, carrying both urine and sperm.
10. cerebrum relatively small.

Compare with: Monotremata, Insectivora.

Remarks: General treatments of Australian marsupials include those of Ride (1970) and Troughton (1947). None is available on American and New Guinean forms. Reviews of many aspects of marsupial biology were provided by Tyndall-Biscoe (1973), Stonehouse and Gilmore (1977), and Hunsaker (1977a). Haltenorth (1958) reviewed classification. Other important articles include Archer (1976a, 1976b), Kean (1961), Lillegraven (1974, 1976), Rowlands (1966), Sharman (1970), and Waring et al. (1966).

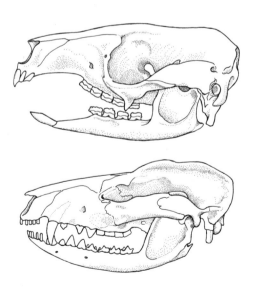

Figure 13. Skulls of two marsupials showing contrasting types of incisors.

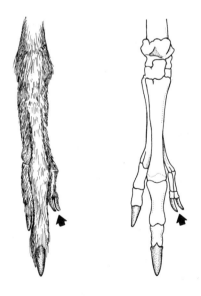

Figure 14. Syndactyly in the feet of a kangaroo.

KEY TO FAMILIES OF MARSUPIALIA

1a. First lower incisor very large and procumbent, other lower incisors small or absent; canines reduced or absent (Fig. 13) 2

1b. Lower incisors ± equal in size, not procumbent; canines prominent (Fig. 13)...7

2a (1a). No syndactylous digits on hindfoot; four upper incisors; 11-12 teeth on each half of lower jaw........ **CAENOLESTIDAE** (p. 48)

2b. Two digits of hindfoot syndactylous (Fig. 14); 1-3 upper incisors; 10 or fewer teeth on each half of lower jaw 3

3a (2b). Hallux rudimentary; zygomatic arch broadened vertically, flaring laterally; one upper incisor, chisel-like .... **VOMBATIDAE** (p. 54)

3b. Hallux absent or well developed; zygomatic arch slender to broad, usually not flaring laterally; two or three upper incisors, not chisel-like 4

4a (3b). Hindlimbs much larger than forelimbs; four digits on hindfoot; tail long, usually tapering from a stout base; masseteric fossa of lower jaw very deep; rostrum long .... **MACROPODIDAE** (p. 56)

4b. Hindlimbs and forelimbs ± equal in size; five digits on hindfoot; tail short or long, not tapering from a stout base; masseteric fossa of lower jaw shallow; rostrum usually short 5

5a (4b). Body form shrew-like; cranium very long, slender; dentition degenerate—incisors 2/1...................**TARSIPEDIDAE** (p. 50)

5b. Body form not shrew-like; cranium relatively short, broad; dentition not degenerate—incisors 3/1-3 6

6a (5b). Tail rudimentary; marsupium opening posteriorly; incisors 3/1..................................... **PHASCOLARCTIDAE** (p. 52)

6b. Tail well developed; marsupium opening anteriorly; incisors 3/2-3 .... **PHALANGERIDAE** (p. 49)

7a (1b). Forefoot with three functional digits; first two digits on hindfoot syndactylous; zygomatic arch slender; last lower incisor distinctly bicuspid .... **PERAMELIDAE** (p. 46)

7b. Forefoot with five functional digits; no syndactylous digits on hindfoot; zygomatic arch broad; last lower incisor unicuspid or faintly bicuspid...8

MARSUPIALIA

8a (7b).	Body form mole-like; no visible eyes or pinnae; horny shield present on nose; zygomatic arches converging anteriorly for entire length; incisors and canines small, often blunt	**NOTORYCTIDAE** (p. 44)
8b.	Body form not mole-like; eyes and pinnae visible; no horny shield on nose; zygomatic arches parallel for part of their length; incisors and canines small to large sharp 9	
9a (8b).	Tail long, naked for at least half its length; hallux well developed, opposable, clawless; incisors 5/4	**DIDELPHIDAE** (p. 39)
9b.	Tail long, well haired; hallux absent or weakly opposable and clawed; incisors 4/3 10	
10a (9b).	Body form anteater-like; dentition totaling 50 or more teeth	**MYRMECOBIIDAE** (p. 44)
10b.	Body form not anteater-like; dentition totaling 46 or fewer teeth 11	
11a (10b).	Body form fox-like; foot posture digitigrade; no hallux; sagittal crest prominent	**THYLACINIDAE** (p. 43)
11b.	Body form not fox-like; foot posture usually plantigrade; hallux present or absent; sagittal crest usually absent	**DASYURIDAE** (p. 41)

Family DIDELPHIDAE
(Opossums)

Didelphids are ancient, dating to the Cretaceous. Modern opossums often live as commensals of man. Most are small, although American opossums (*Didelphis*) may reach one meter in total length. The tail is usually long and is often prehensile. A pouch is well developed in several genera but is absent or poorly developed in most.

Opossums are normally ground-dwelling or arboreal. However, the water opossum (*Chironectes*) is adapted for an aquatic existence, the only marsupial so specialized. It has a streamlined body, webbed hindfeet, and a waterproof pouch. Others (e.g., *Lutreolina*) are weasel-like in form and habits. The diet of opossums is usually varied and includes fruit, insects and other invertebrates, small mammals, birds and their eggs, lizards, and carrion. A few species are strict carnivores.

Most species are solitary. Nests are constructed of leaves, grass, and twigs, in trees, under logs or rocks, and occasionally in burrows. Breeding is seasonal (most species) or year-long (some tropical species). Litter size varies from 1-20.

Fascination with the habits of opossums has inspired some interesting folklore. The common trait of "playing possum" is often considered an intent to feign death. The habit may actually impart survival value by its resemblance to death, but it is more likely an involuntary paralysis caused by fear that is also observed in other animals. The notion that opossums copulate and later give birth through the nose is imaginative but false. The idea probably stems from observations of the forked penis in males and the habit in females of frequently inspecting pouch young with the nose.

Twelve genera, about 70 species; southern Canada to South America.

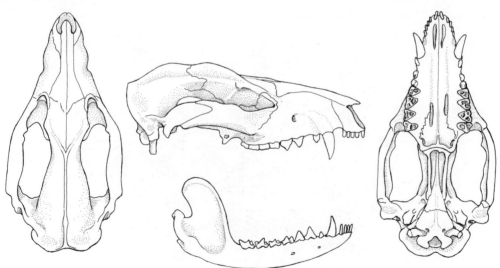

Figure 15. Skull of a didelphid (*Didelphis*, x ½).

MARSUPIALIA

Recognition Characters:

● **incisors 5/4**

1. body small to medium (18-104cm).
2. **marsupium, if present, opening anteriorly.**
3. **tail long**(short in *Monodelphis*), **usually mostly naked**, prehensile in some.
4. foot posture plantigrade.
5. digits 5-5; no syndactyly; digits ± equal in length.
6. **hallux well developed, opposable, without claw.**
7. cranium relatively long and slender (Fig. 15).
8. **sagittal crest often well developed.**
9. zygomatic arch relatively slender.
10. paroccipital process small.
11. **lower incisors ± equal in size, not procumbent** (Fig. 15).
12. canines well developed.
13. molars tritubercular.

Dental formula: $\frac{5}{4}\frac{1}{1}\frac{3}{3}\frac{4}{4} = 50$

Compare with: Dasyuridae, Thylacinidae.

Representative Genera:

Caluromys (3) - Woolly opossums.
Chironectes (1) - *C. minimus* is the water opossum.
Didelphis (3) - American opossums.
Dromiciops (1) - *D. australis* is the monito del monte.
Lutreolina (1) - *L. crassicaudata* is the thick-tailed opossum.
Marmosa (46) - Mouse opossums.
Metachirus (1) - *M. nudicaudatus* is the brown "four-eyed" opossum.
Monodelphis (10) - Short-tailed opossums.
Philander (2) - Gray "four-eyed" opossums.

Remarks: On the basis of serological evidence Kirsch (1977) placed *Dromiciops* in its own monotypic family (Microbiotheriidae).

Hartman (1952) provided a good general treatment of opossum fact and fancy. Gardner (1973) and Tate (1933) reviewed the systematics of *Didelphis* and *Marmosa*, respectively.

Opossum.

Family DASYURIDAE
(Marsupial mice and rats, native cats, Tasmanian devil)

Ecologically, the dasyurids are the Australasian equivalents of the didelphids and caenolestids of North and South America. The family contains species that vary widely in form and habits, resembling those of shrews (*Planigale*), mice (*Antechinus*, *Sminthopsis*), rats (*Phascogale*), and cats (*Dasyurus*). The Tasmanian devil (*Sarcophilus*), immortalized in cartoons as a sort of whirling dervish, resembles a small bear. Dasyurids occur in all major habitats from desert to tropical forest. Most species are ground-dwelling.

The tail is usually well haired and not prehensile. The pouch (if present) opens posteriorly and frequently is present only during the breeding season. The animals are largely insectivorous or carnivorous, but the Tasmanian devil is a scavenger. Desert-adapted species of certain genera (*Dasycercus*, *Sminthopsis*) parallel other desert-dwelling mammals in undergoing torpor or excreting a highly concentrated urine.

Nests of leaves, grass, twigs, or bark are located in burrows, caves, under rocks, or in holes in trees or logs. The number of pouch young is usually 3-12, but as many as two dozen offspring have been recorded. Sexual maturity is attained in one year. In males of several genera the penis has a secondary appendage (Woolley and Webb, 1977). Male antechinuses (*Antechinus*) breed only once, after which they spontaneously die. The basis for this peculiar trait is not known (but see Braithwaite and Lee, 1979), but it evidently is influenced by adrenal hormones (Lee et al., 1977).

Fourteen genera, about 50 species; Australia, Tasmania, New Guinea and some other associated islands.

Recognition Characters:

1. body small to relatively large (95-130 cm).
2. **marsupium, if present, opening posteriorly.**
3. **tail usually long** (relatively short in *Sarcophilus*) **and well haired** (nearly naked in *Murexia*), not prehensile.
4. foot posture plantigrade or digitigrade.
5. digits 5-4 or 5-5; no syndactyly; digits ± equal in length.
6. **hallux weakly opposable or absent, without claw.**
7. cranium short, blocky (*Sarcophilus*), or relatively long and slender (Fig. 16).
8. sagittal crest usually absent (present in *Sarcophilus*).
9. zygomatic arch relatively slender (robust in *Sarcophilus*).
10. paroccipital process small.
11. **lower incisors ± equal in size, not procumbent.**
12. canines well developed.
13. molars tritubercular.

Dental formula: $\frac{4\ 1\ 2\text{-}3\ 4}{3\ 1\ 2\text{-}3\ 4}$ = 42-46

Compare with: Didelphidae, Thylacinidae, Myrmecobiidae.

Representative Genera:

Atechinomys (1) - *A. laniger* is the narrow-footed marsupial mouse.

Antechinus (13) - Broad-footed marsupial mice or antechinuses.

Dasycercus (1) - *D. cristicauda* is the mulgara.

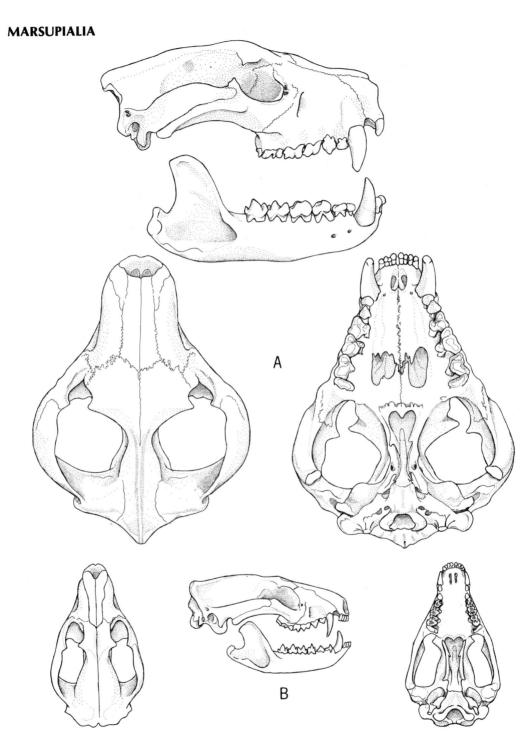

Figure 16. Skulls of dasyurids: A, *Sarcophilus*; B, *Dasyurus* (both x ½).

Dasyuroides (1) - *D. byrnei* is the crested-tailed marsupial rat or kowari.

Dasyurus (5) - Native cats.

Phascogale (2) - Phascogales or wambengers.

Planigale (5) - Planigales.

Sarcophilus (1) - *S. harrisii* is the Tasmanian devil.

Sminthopsis (12) - Narrow-footed marsupial mice or dunnarts.

Remarks: The Tasmanian wolf (*Thylacinus*) and banded anteater (*Myrmecobius*) (former members of the Dasyuridae) are placed here in separate families (Thylacinidae, below; and Myrmecobiidae, p. 44) following Kirsch (1977) and Ride (1964, 1970). New Guinean dasyurids are poorly known and future studies doubtless will produce taxonomic changes at the generic and species levels. Reproduction of dasyurids was reviewed by Woolley (1966). Buchmann and Guiler (1977) examined the ecology and behavior of *Sarcophilus*.

Family THYLACINIDAE
(Tasmanian wolf)

The single living representative of this group, the Tasmanian wolf (*Thylacinus cynocephalus*), is the largest living carnivorous marsupial (body and tail length approaching two meters). The short, gray or light brown pelage is interrupted along the lower back and rump by about 15 dark transverse stripes. Dog-like in general build, thylacines have a digitigrade foot posture, large canines, shearing premolars, and crushing molars.

Tasmanian wolves evidently are rather social. They prey on small and large

mammals, birds, and domestic livestock. Dens are located in rocks, at the bases of trees, or in hollow logs. Two to four offspring are produced.

Presently confined to forested areas of Tasmania, the species is exceedingly rare. Fossil remains are known from the mainland of Australia and from New Guinea.

One genus, 1 species; Tasmania.

Recognition Characters:

1. **body relatively large (to 170 cm), dog-like.**
2. marsupium present, opening posteriorly.
3. tail long, covered with short hairs.
4. **foot posture digitigrade.**
5. digits 5-4; no syndactyly; digits $\pm$ equal in length.
6. **no hallux.**
7. cranium relatively elongate.
8. sagittal crest present.
9. zygomatic arch relatively robust, wide.
10. paroccipital process relatively small.
11. lower incisors $\pm$ equal in size, not procument.
12. canines well developed.
13. molars tritubercular.

Dental formula: $\frac{4}{3}\frac{1}{1}\frac{3}{3}\frac{4}{4} = 46$

Compare with: Dasyuridae, Didelphidae, Canidae (Carnivora).

Genus:

Thylacinus (1) - *T. cynocephalus* is the Tasmanian wolf or thylacine.

Remarks: I follow Ride (1964, 1970) in placing the thylacine in its own distinct family. Some other authors (e.g., Van Deusen and Jones, 1967) retained it in the Dasyuridae.

Family MYRMECOBIIDAE
(Numbat or banded anteater)

The ground-dwelling numbat is a common inhabitant of termite-rich areas of Australia, particularly the southwestern forests. It is uniquely and attractively colored—the foreparts are usually reddish-brown and there is a series of alternating black and white transverse bars on the lower back and rump. The body fur is short and coarse, the tail bushy. Strong foreclaws aid in dislodging termites from decayed wood and soil. The snout is long and slender, and the tongue is extremely long, worm-like, and extensible. There is no pouch.

The teeth are mostly small and delicate. There are five or six upper and lower molars, so that the dentition totals 50-54 teeth, more than that of any other land mammal.

Unlike most other marsupials, banded anteaters are diurnal. They are solitary except during the breeding season. At this time the female digs a nesting burrow, where two to four young are raised. Dens are otherwise found in hollow logs.

One genus, 1 species; Australia.

Recognition Characters:

- **pelage grayish- or reddish-brown, with alternating white and black stripes on lower back and rump.**

- **five or six upper and lower molars; dentition totalling 50-54 teeth.**

1. size medium (31-45 cm).
2. **no marsupium.**
3. tail relatively long, well haired.
4. foot posture digitigrade.
5. digits 5/4; no syndactyly; digits ± equal in length.
6. **no hallux.**
7. **cranium long, slender.**
8. no sagittal crest.
9. zygomatic arch slender.
10. paroccipital process small.
11. lower incisors ± equal in size, not procumbent.
12. canines relatively small.
13. molars tritubercular.

Dental formula: $\frac{4}{3} \frac{1}{1} \frac{3}{3} \frac{5\text{-}6}{5\text{-}6} = 50\text{-}54$

Compare with: Dasyuridae.

Genus:

Myrmecobius (1) - *M. fasciatus* is the numbat or banded anteater.

Remarks: I follow Kirsch (1977) in assigning the banded anteater to its own family. Some other authors (e.g., Van Deusen and Jones, 1967) placed it in the family Dasyuridae.

Family NOTORYCTIDAE
(Marsupial moles)

Norotyctids are extraordinarily adapted for a fossorial life, as evidenced externally by the thick-set body, short limbs, blunt snout shielded with a horny plate, and a stubby, leathery tail. The third and fourth digits of the scoop-like forefeet bear large, triangular claws. There are no visible eyes, eyelids, or pinnae. Skeletal specializations include a conical skull, fused cervical vertebrae, and a firm connection between the sacral vertebrae and pelvic girdle. As in some other mole-like fossors (e.g., Insectivora: Chrysochloridae, p. 67), the fur is silky and iridescent. It varies in color from almost white to golden red.

Marsupial moles forage for insects and grubs by "swimming" through the substrate, causing the soil to fill in behind them. Their reproductive habits are unknown. The well-developed pouch contains two teats.

One genus, 1 species; southern, western Australia.

Recognition Characters:

● **eyes atrophied, not visible; no pinna.**

1. body small (10-21 cm), mole-like.
2. marsupium present, opening posteriorly.
3. **tail stubby, covered with leathery skin which is folded into concentric rings.**
4. foot posture plantigrade.
5. digits 5-5; no syndactyly; **digits highly modified for digging—third and fourth digits of forefoot greatly enlarged, bearing large triangular claws; remaining digits small, the first and second ones opposed to third and fourth.**
6. hallux well developed, with a short pointed nail.
7. **cranium elongate, conical.**
8. no sagittal crest.
9. zygomatic arch relatively robust, wide.
10. paroccipital process very small.
11. lower incisors ± equal in size, procumbent.
12. canines reduced.
13. molars simplified, not tritubercular.

Dental formula: $\frac{3\text{-}4}{3}\frac{1}{1}\frac{2}{3}\frac{4}{4}$ = 42 or 44

Compare with: Talpidae and Chrysochloridae (Insectivora).

Genus:

  Nortoryctes (1) - *N. typhlops* is the marsupial mole.

Family PERAMELIDAE
(Bandicoots)

Bandicoots are distinctive marsupials. Superfically resembling small wallabies (Macropodidae, p. 56), the long, tapered snout, polyprotodont dentition, and reduced number of digits on both forefeet and hindfeet collectively distinguish peramelids from related forms. The body varies in form from small and rather compact (*Isoodon*) to relatively large and delicate (*Macrotis*). A few species have very large rabbit-like ears.

Hayman (1977) described a curious condition in the chromosomes of peramelids. In virtually all species the somatic cells (e.g., those of liver, spleen, bone marrow) contain fewer chromosomes than germ cells (ovary, testis). The difference is the result of a loss of either the X or Y chromosome in somatic tissue occurring subsequent to fertilization. The mechanisms responsible for the change and the adaptive significance are not known.

These marsupials inhabit open grasslands, savannahs, swamps, and forests from lowlands to mountains. They feed on a varied diet of small vertebrates and invertebrates. Most do not burrow; instead, they construct ground nests of grass, twigs, and debris in thick vegetation. Those species which have been studied in detail are strongly territorial and solitary except for a brief period during the breeding season. One to six young are raised.

Bandicoots are eaten by natives of both New Guinea and Australia.

Eight genera, 18 species; Australia, Tasmania, New Guinea, Bismarck Archipelago, and some other islands.

Recognition Characters:

1. size small to medium (29-83 cm).
2. marsupium present, opening posteriorly.
3. tail short, sparsely haired or crested, not prehensile.
4. **foot posture digitigrade.**

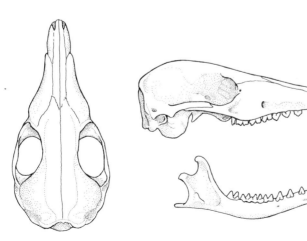
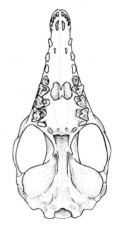

Figure 17. Skull of a peramelid (*Isoodon*, x 1).

5. **forefoot with three functional digits** (two in *Chaeropus*); **hindfoot with four main digits** (three in *Chaeropus*);**two innermost digits on hindfoot syndactylous, outer two large.**
6. **hallux vestigial or absent, without claw.**
7. **cranium very long, narrow** (Fig. 17).
8. no sagittal crest.
9. **zygomatic arch very slender** (Fig. 17).
10. paroccipital process small.
11. lower incisors ± equal in size, procumbent.
12. canines reduced.
13. molars tritubercular.

Dental formula: $\frac{4\text{-}5}{3}\frac{1}{1}\frac{3}{3}\frac{4}{4}$ = 46 or 48

Compare with: Macropodidae, Myrmecobiidae.

Representative Genera:

Chaeropus (1) - *C. ecaudatus* is the pig-footed bandicoot.
Echymipera (3) - Spiny bandicoots.
Isoodon (3) - Short-nosed bandicoots.
Parameles (4) - Long-nosed bandicoots.
Peroryctes (3) - New Guinean bandicoots.
Macrotis (2) - Rabbit-eared bandicoots.

Remarks: Archer and Kirsch (1977) suggested giving separate familial recognition to the rabbit-eared bandicoots (Thylacomidae). The taxonomy, ecology, reproduction, and behavior of bandicoots were examined by Stodart (1977), Heinsohn (1966), Smyth and Philpott (1968), and Tate (1948b).

Bandicoot.

Family CAENOLESTIDAE
(Shrew opossums)

Commonly called rat opossums, caenolestids are more shrew-like than rat-like in appearance. The similarity to shrews is evidenced in many ways. The feet are narrow and each foot bears five well-clawed digits. The head is elongate and conical, the eyes small, and the ears small and rounded. As in shrews, the teeth are sharp and cutting. The first lower incisors are large and procumbent (more so than in shrews), and each is followed by four or five unicuspids.

Anterior to the orbit there is a conspicuous opening between the nasal, maxillary, and frontal bones (Fig. 18). There is no pouch.

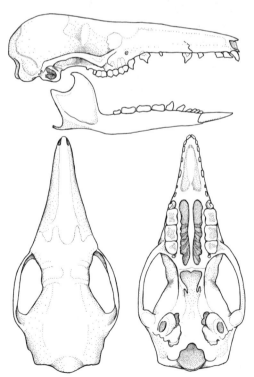

Figure 18. Skull of a coenolestid (*Orolestes*, x 2).

These terrestrial marsupials are restricted to coastal and mountain forests and clearings of western South America. They apparently feed on insects, their grubs, and other invertebrates, and are mostly nocturnal. Nothing is known of their reproductive habits.

Three genera, 7 species; western South America.

Recognition Characters:

1. **body small (15-28 cm), shrew-like.**
2. **no marsupium.**
3. tail long, sparsely haired.
4. foot posture plantigrade.
5. digits 5-5; no syndactyly; digits ± equal in length.
6. hallux present, weakly opposable, clawed.
7. cranium elongate (Fig. 18).
8. no sagittal crest.
9. zygomatic arch relatively slender.
10. paroccipital process very small.
11. **first lower incisor very large, extremely procumbent** (Fig. 18).
12. canines well developed or reduced in size.
13. molars quadritubercular.

Dental formula: $\frac{4}{3\text{-}4}\frac{1}{1}\frac{3}{3}\frac{4}{4}$ = 46 or 48

Compare with: Didelphidae, Dasyuridae, Soricidae (Insectivora).

Representative Genus:

Caenolestes (5) - Shrew opossums.

Remark: Some authors assigned this family to a separate order (Paucituberculata) (Ride, 1964; Kirsch, 1977; Kirsch and Calaby, 1977).

The taxonomy of *Caenolestes* was examined by Osgood (1921).

Family PHALANGERIDAE
(Possums, cuscuses, gliders, ringtails)

Phalangerids have the widest distribution of any of the Australasian marsupials. In size and appearance they vary from mouse-like to lemur-like. Although resembling didelphids (p. 39) and dasyurids (p. 41), they differ in several ways. All species have a pouch that opens anteriorly as in didelphids (it opens posteriorly in dasyurids). The hallux is well developed and opposable and lacks a claw as in didelphids (it is reduced and clawless in dasyurids), and the second and third digits of the hindfoot are syndactylous (they are separate in dasyurids and didelphids). Some small species (e.g., *Acrobates*, *Cercartetus*) have expanded pads at the ends of the digits. There are only three upper incisors (never four or five), and the first lower incisor is enlarged and procumbent (it is small and unspecialized in didelphids and dasyurids).

The tail of phalangerids is often prehensile. The pelage varies markedly in texture, color, and pattern. It is often dense and woolly. Phalangerids are uniform in color, are irregularly spotted, or have prominent or subtle stripes on the back or head. The skull is broad and flattened (Fig. 19).

Some interesting arboreal specializations are found in these marsupials. The limbs are united by a gliding membrane in gliders (*Petaurus*, *Schoinobates*, and *Acrobates*). In cuscuses (*Phalanger*) and ring-tailed possums (*Pseudocheirus*) the first two digits of the forefoot are opposable to the other three. In striped possums (*Dactylopsila*), an extreme elongation of the fourth digit of the front foot adapts them for extracting insects from bark or decayed wood. Striped possums are peculiar in having a partially divided marsupium and skunk-like color pattern and odor. Some of the small species (e.g., *Cercartetus*) undergo torpor during cold periods.

Phalangerids, which occur in lowland and mountain forests and scrub, are nocturnal and mostly arboreal. They find shelter in hollows of trees, abandoned

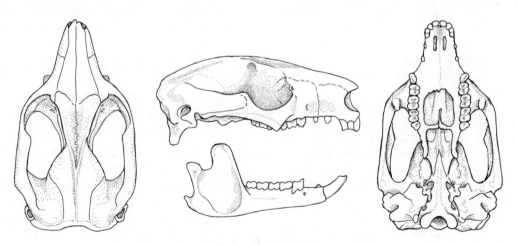

Figure 19. Skull of a phalangerid (*Phalanger*, x ½).

bird nests, rocks, caves, or burrows; *Trichosurus* and *Pseudocheirus* build nests in trees. Most species are herbivorous, but others are insectivorous or omnivorous.

These marsupials are usually solitary, but some (e.g., *Petaurus*) live in groups. Normally one to three young are produced, although a few small species (e.g., *Cercartetus*) give birth to five or six.

Several phalangerids are valued by natives for their fur or flesh.

Thirteen genera, about 40 species; Australia, Tasmania, New Guinea, the Bismarck Archipelago, Celebes, and many other associated islands.

Recognition Characters:

1. body small to medium in size (13-128cm).
2. marsupium present, opening anteriorly.
3. tail long, well haired or partly naked, prehensile in some.
4. foot posture plantigrade.
5. digits 5-5; second and third digits of hindfoot syndactylous; digits equal in length (except in *Dactylopsila*, striped possums, in which the fourth digit of forefoot is very elongate).
6. hallux well developed, opposable, without claw.
7. **cranium relatively broad** (Fig. 19).
8. sagittal crest often present.
9. **zygomatic arch robust, wide** (Fig. 19).
10. paroccipital process small to large.
11. **first lower incisor much larger than others, moderately to extremely procumbent** (Fig. 19).
12. canines reduced in size.
13. **molars quadritubercular, usually with rounded cusps.**

Dental formula: $\frac{2\text{-}3 \quad 1 \quad 1\text{-}3 \quad 3\text{-}4}{2\text{-}3 \quad 0 \quad 1\text{-}3 \quad 3\text{-}4} = 28\text{-}40$

Compare with: Tarsipedidae, Phascolarctidae.

Representative Genera:

Acrobates (1) - *A. pygmaeus* is the feather-tailed glider.

Burramys (1) - *B. parvus* is the pygmy possum.

Cercartetus (4) - Mundardas.

Dactylopsila (2) - Striped possums.

Petaurus (3) - Lesser gliding possums or sugar gliders.

Phalanger (7) - Cuscuses.

Pseudocheirus (13) - Ring-tailed possums.

Schoinobates (1) - *S. volans* is the greater gliding possum.

Trichosurus (3) - Brush-tailed possums; **T. vulpecula is distributed widely over most of Australia.**

Remarks: Kirsch (1968) and Ride (1970) divided the Phalangeridae into five distinct families—Phalangeridae, Petauridae, Burramyidae, Tarsipedidae, and Phascolarctidae. The last two families are recognized here as being distinct (see below and p. 52), but the Petauridae and Burramyidae are tentatively retained in the Phalangeridae. These three groups are not markedly different.

Family TARSIPEDIDAE
(Noolbenger or honey possum)

The single species, *Tarsipes spencerae*, is one of the most aberrant marsupials. Numerous specializations make noolbengers adept at climbing in foliage and feeding on the pollen and nectar of blossoms. They are small and mouse-like. As in other possums (Phalangeridae, p. 49), the first lower incisor is large and procumbent and the second and third digits of the hindfoot are syndactylous. Aside from the upper canines and first lower incisors, the dentition is degenerate. Except for the syndactylous toes, all digits are enlarged at the tips and bear small, blunt claws. The long, tubular snout houses a long, protrusible tongue that is brushed at the tip for gathering pollen. Ridges on the palate remove the pollen from the tongue. The tail is very long, almost hairless, and prehensile.

Honey possums are distinctively colored. The grayish-brown back is interrupted by three dark longitudinal stripes. The belly is yellowish. The number of chromosomes (2n=24) also sets this marsupial apart from other possums.

A pouch is present, opening anteriorly. Normally two young are reared.

One genus, 1 species; extreme southwestern Australia.

Recognition Characters:

1. **body very small (15-19 cm)**, mouse-like.
2. marsupium present, opening anteriorly.
3. tail long, sparsely haired.
4. foot posture plantigrade.
5. digits 5-5; second and third digits of hindfoot syndactylous; digits ± equal in length.
6. hallux well developed, opposable, without claw.
7. **cranium very long, narrow.**
8. no sagittal crest.
9. zygomatic arch very slender.
10. paroccipital process minute or absent.
11. **dentition degenerate—upper incisors small; lower incisor large, extremely procumbent.**
12. canines reduced in size.
13. **molars small, peg-like.**

Dental formula: $\dfrac{2\ 1\ 1\ 3}{1\ 0\ 0\ 3} = 22$

Genus:

Tarsipes (1) - *T. spencerae* is the noolbenger or honey possum.

Remark: I follow Kirsch (1968) and Ride (1970) in recognizing the Tarsipedidae as distinct from the Phalangeridae.

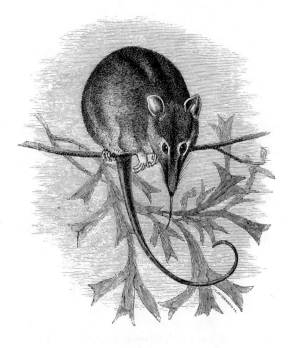

Noolbenger.

Family PHASCOLARCTIDAE
(Koala)

Identified by its "teddy bear" appearance, the well-known koala is confined to eucalyptus forests of Australia. It resembles some possums (Phalangeridae, p. 49) in having the first two digits of the forefoot opposed to the other three. However, the rudimentary tail, large furry ears, internal cheek pouches, and posteriorly opening pouch serve to make this marsupial distinctive. The combination of relatively long front limbs and long, curved claws suggests a resemblance to sloths (p.136).

Koalas are almost exclusively arboreal. They are strict vegetarians, foraging primarily on the leaves of a limited number of *Eucalyptus* species. Apparently soil is consumed as a digestive aid, for gravel is often found in the large caecum. Koalas live singly or in small groups. One offspring (rarely twins) is produced. Vocalizations include grunting and wailing sounds.

These marsupials are now strictly protected. They were once widely hunted for their luxurious pelts.

One genus, 1 species; southeastern Australia.

Recognition Characters:

1. **body relatively large (60-85 cm), teddy-bear-like.**
2. marsupium present, opening posteriorly.
3. **tail vestigial.**
4. foot posture plantigrade.
5. digits 5-5; second and third digits of hindfoot partly syndactylous; digits ± equal in length.
6. hallux well developed, opposable, without claw.
7. cranium robust, broad (Fig. 20).
8. no sagittal crest.
9. zygomatic arch robust, wide (Fig. 20).
10. paroccipital process large.
11. **first upper incisor much larger than other two,** lower incisor slightly procumbent.
12. **upper canine small.**
13. **molars squarish, with crescentic ridges.**

Dental formula: $\frac{3}{1}\frac{1}{0}\frac{1}{1}\frac{4}{4} = 30$

Compare with: Petauridae, Phalangeridae.

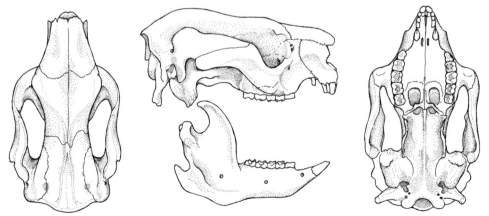

Figure 20. Skull of a phascolarctid (*Phascolarctus*, x ⅜).

Genus:

Phascolarctos (1) - *P. cinereus* is the koala.

Remark: I follow Kirsch (1968) and Ride (1970) in recognizing the Phascolarctidae as distinct from the Phalangeridae. The biology of koalas was reviewed by Bergin (1978).

Koala.

Family VOMBATIDAE
(Wombats)

Wombats are relatively large, thick-bodied marsupials that show adaptations similar to those of rodents, particularly in the dentition. The two gnawing incisors on the upper and lower jaws (Fig. 21) are chisel-shaped and enameled only on the front surfaces. There are no canines, and a large diastema separates the incisors and cheekteeth. The teeth are ever-growing, a feature which increases the lifespan of the dentition and enables the animals to feed on coarse plant matter. The robust, flattened skull is also similar to that of some of the larger rodents (Fig. 21). Wombats even have traces of cheek pouches.

These marsupials are powerful, efficient diggers. Adaptations that facilitate this habit include the heavy body, short stout limbs with well-clawed digits, and a reduced tail. They construct elaborate burrow systems, which are often long and very deep. Adjacent burrows may be interconnected and shared by more than one individual.

Wombats inhabit grasslands, savannah woodlands, and wet and dry forests. Mostly nocturnal, they feed on grasses, roots, bark, and fungi. One (rarely two) young is raised per breeding period.

Two genera, 4 species; Australia, Tasmania, and intermediate islands.

Recognition Characters:

● **incisors large, chisel-shaped** (Fig. 21).

1. body relatively large (70-120 cm), marmot-like.
2. marsupium present, opening posteriorly.
3. **tail vestigial.**
4. foot posture plantigrade.
5. digits 5-5; two innermost digits of hindfoot syndactylous; digits ± equal in length.
6. hallux vestigial.
7. **cranium robust, broad** (Fig. 21).
8. no sagittal crest.
9. zygomatic arch relatively robust, wide.
10. paroccipital process small.
11. **incisors as above; lower incisors procumbent** (Fig. 21).

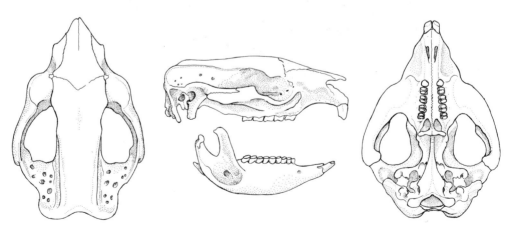

Figure 21. Skull of a vombatid (*Vombatus*, x ¼).

54

12. **no canines** (Fig. 21).
13. molars simple, bilophodont.

Dental formula: $\dfrac{1\ 0\ 1\ 4}{1\ 0\ 1\ 4} = 24$

Genera:

Lasiorhinus (3) - Hairy-nosed wombats.

Vombatus (1) - *V. ursinus* is the common wombat.

Remark: A taxonomic review of wombats was provided by Tate (1951).

Family MACROPODIDAE
(Kangaroos, wallabies, potoroos, and rat kangaroos)

Literally translated, Macropodidae means "bigfoot", an appropriate description of these saltatorial marsupials because of the relatively massive hindlimbs in most species. In the hindfoot the first digit (hallux) is normally absent, the second and third digits are small and syndactylous, and the greatly enlarged fourth and moderately large fifth digits transmit the main propulsive force for saltatorial locomotion. There are five subequal digits on the small front foot.

The tail is long and usually thickened at the base. It acts as a prop at rest and for balance during locomotion; rat kangaroos use it to carry nesting materials. The pelage varies in markings and coloration—it may be yellow or red to black, with striping or barring common on the face, back, hips, and tail. There is as much variation in chromosome number in this family (2n=10-32) as there is in the entire order.

Virtually all macropodids are strict vegetarians. The larger species of wallabies and kangaroos are the Australian equivalents of large browsing and grazing eutherians (e.g., antelope, buffalo, deer) found elsewhere. Like their eutherian counterparts, these marsupials possess some remarkable specializations for processing plant materials.

In some respects the dentition is like that of these eutherians; in some respects it is unique.The first upper and lower incisors in both groups are large and stout. There are no lower canines; upper canines are usually also absent. A large diastema is present between the incisors and cheekteeth. The cheekteeth are remarkably specialized. Young macopodids have two upper and lower premolars, but in adults these are usually replaced in both jaws by a single blade-like premolar (Fig. 22). In most species the grinding molars erupt sequentially. New molars appear at the posterior end of the toothrow and migrate anteriorly, causing a forward shift of the entire set of cheekteeth as the animal ages. In

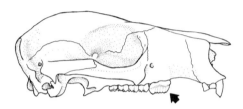

Figure 22. Cranium of a macropodid (*Bettongia*) showing the large blade-like premolar.

kangaroos and wallabies (*Macropus*) the front cheekteeth, including the cutting premolar (except in some wallabies), are progressively shed as they become worn. In others (e.g., *Bettongia, Lagostrophus*) the toothrow enlarges as teeth erupt but no teeth are shed. Normally a total of four upper and lower molars erupts. However, as many as nine molars may successively appear in the little rock wallaby (*Perodorcas*). The overall pattern of molar replacement is similar to that found in some eutherian herbivores (e.g., hyraxes, elephants). It appears to be an alternative to the evergrowing teeth present in many other herbivores (e.g., many rodents) as a means of extending the lifespan of the dentition.

Most macropodids have a complex stomach. The long side of the curved stomach has many sac-like folds, which add greatly to the total surface area. Like that of ruminants (Artiodactyla), the stomach contains many bacteria and protozoans. The stomach acts as a fermentation chamber in which cellulose and other plant products are converted to usable substances such as fatty acids. This process also conserves nitrogen and water because urea, formed during normal metabolic processes in the mammal, is passed to the stomach and is used by the bacteria to synthesize protein rather than being excreted in the urine.

Two genera depart from the picture described above. The tree kangaroos (*Dendrolagus*) resemble kangaroos in most features but have front and rear limbs of similar proportions, broad hindfeet, and a cylindrical (not tapered) tail as secondary adaptations for climbing trees. The musky rat kangaroo (*Hypsiprymnodon*) is the most unusual macropodid in that the hindlimbs are not enlarged, a well-developed hallux is present, and the tail is relatively naked and scaley. The diet of this animal is varied, consisting of berries, roots, and insects and other invertebrates. Since the food does not require the elaborate processing of leaves and grass, the stomach is simple.

Members of the family are distributed throughout the major habitats of Australia and New Guinea. They forage mostly at night, seeking shelter during the day in rocks, caves, beneath bushes, or in thickets. One species of *Bettongia* digs elaborate burrows. Most species are gregarious.

Females are polyestrous. In some of the smaller species there is more than one litter per year. The litter size is usually one (two in *Hypsiprymnodon*).

Macropodids are considered agricultural pests and are harvested for their meat or fur. Consequently, the populations of kangaroos and related species have been drastically reduced in size.

Fifteen genera, 47 species; Australia, Tasmania, New Guinea, Bismarck Archipelago, and some other islands.

Recognition Characters:

● **hindlimbs much longer than forelimbs** (± equal in size in other marsupials).

1. body medium to large (37-270 cm).
2. marsupium present, opening anteriorly.
3. tail long, well haired.
4. **foot posture digitigrade.**
5. **digits 5-4** (5-5 in *Hypsiprymnodon*, musky rat kangaroo); **two innermost digits** (second and third digits in *Hypsiprymnodon*) of hindfoot syndactylous and small, outer digits large.
6. **hallux vestigal or absent.**
7. cranium elongate (Fig. 23).
8. sagittal crest usually absent.
9. zygomatic arch relatively slender (Fig. 23).
10. **paroccipital process very large** (Fig. 23) .
11. upper incisors moderately large; lower incisors large, very procumbent (Fig. 23).
12. **upper canine, if present, relatively small** (e.g., in five genera of rat kangaroos).
13. molars bilophodont or quadrituber-cular.

Dental formula: $\dfrac{3}{1} \dfrac{0\text{-}1}{0} \dfrac{2}{2} \dfrac{4}{4} = 32$ or 34

Representative Genera:

Bettongia (4) - Rat kangaroos.
Dendrolagus (3) - Tree kangaroos.
Dorcopsis (3) - New Guinean forest wallabies.

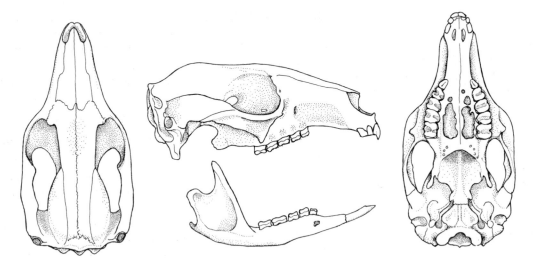

Figure 23. Skull of a macropodid (*Setonix*, x ½).

Hypsiprymnodon (1) - *H. moschatus* is the musky rat kangaroo.

Lagorchestes (4) - Hare wallabies.

Macropus (19) (including *Megaleia, Thylogale,* and *Wallabia*; see **Remarks** - Kangaroos and brush, scrub, and swamp wallabies; *M. giganteus*, the great gray kangaroo, is the largest species of marsupial.

Petrogale (3) - Rock wallabies.

Potorous (2) - Potoroos.

Setonix (1) - *S. brachyurus* is the quokka.

Remarks: The list of representative genera follows that of Kirsch and Calaby (1977) except for *Macropus*. I follow Van Gelder (1977) in combining *Megaleia, Thylogale,* and *Wallabia* under the name *Macropus*.

Good general references on kangaroos are Frith and Calaby (1969), and Russell (1974). Social organization and anatomy and phylogeny of macropodids were investigated by Kaufman (1974) and Tate (1948a), respectively.

ORDER INSECTIVORA

Insectivores constitute an assemblage of relatively primitive families of uncertain relationships to one another. The order is ancient, dating from the Cretaceous. Recent forms are diverse. Early representatives of the group form a generalized basal stock from which many other eutherian orders are derived. However, extant insectivores possess peculiar properties of their own, many of which obscure the primitive or generalized condition of earliest placental mammals. Consequently, it is practically impossible to present an exclusive diagnosis for the order.

This order can be divided conveniently into two groups, the lipotyphlans and menotyphlans. The lipotyphlans comprise shrews, moles, hedgehogs, and allied forms in which olfaction is the primary sense, the dentition is specialized for an insectivorous diet, and locomotion is of a generalized quadrupedal type. By contrast, menotyphlans, comprising tree shrews and elephant shrews, depend heavily on vision, have a dentition adapted for a more catholic diet, and exhibit more varied locomotor patterns. All members of the order have primitive brains—the cerebral hemispheres are relatively small and smooth.

With the exceptions of polar regions and most of Australasia and South America, insectivores occur throughout the world. There are perhaps 400 species. Despite their diversity and widespread occurrence, insectivores are poorly known because of their secretive habits.

Recognition Characters:
1. size very small to medium.
2. foot posture usually plantigrade.
3. snout generally elongate.
4. pelage usually consisting of only one kind of hair of ± uniform length.
5. cerebral hemispheres smooth, lacking complex folding.
6. **cheekteeth relatively simple, tritubercular or quadritubercular.**

Compare with: Marsupialia, Chiroptera, Primates, Dermoptera.

KEY TO FAMILIES OF INSECTIVORA

1a. Eyes relatively small; jugal reduced or absent; zygomatic arch complete or incomplete(**Lipotyphla**) 2
1b. Eyes relatively large; jugal well developed; zygomatic arch complete (**Menotyphla**) 8

2a (1a). Zygomatic arch complete 3
2b. Zygomatic arch incomplete 5

3a (2a). Eyes covered with skin, not visible; auditory bulla well developed; molars with a narrow V-shaped crown pattern .... **CHRYSOCHLORIDAE** (p. 67)
3b. Eyes present, visible; auditory bulla absent or incomplete; molars with cusps arranged in a W-shaped or quadritubercular pattern (Figs.2, 3) 4

INSECTIVORA

4a (3b). Pelage often spiny; pinna present; no auditory bulla; first upper incisor large, canine-like, directed downward; molars quadritubercular but always lacking W-shaped crown pattern .... **ERINACEIDAE** (p. 61)

4b. Pelage soft, never spiny; no pinna; auditory bulla present, incomplete; first upper incisor relatively large, not canine-like, directed backward; molars with W-shaped crown pattern (Figs. 2, 3) .... **TALPIDAE** (p. 63)

5a (2b). Alisphenoid canal present .... **SOLENODONTIDAE** (p. 68)

5b. No alisphenoid canal 6

6a (5b). Pelage short, soft; first upper incisor large, hook-like; molars quadritubercular .... **SORICIDAE** (p. 69)

6b. Pelage soft or coarse or spiny; first upper incisor not markedly enlarged or hook-like; molars trituber-cular 7

7a (6b). Body form otter-like; second and third digits of hindfoot syndactylous; molars with V- or W-shaped cusp pattern .... **POTAMOGALIDAE** (p. 66)

7b. Body form variable but not otter-like; second and third digits of hindfoot not syndactylous or all digits webbed; molars with V-shaped cusp pattern .... **TENRECIDAE** (p. 65)

8a (1b). Snout extended into proboscis; hindlimbs much longer than forelimbs; postorbital process small or absent; molars with four large cusps .... **MACROSCELIDIDAE** (p. 71)

8b. Snout not extended into a proboscis; hindlimbs and forelimbs ± equal in size; postorbital process large, contacting zygomatic arch; molars with three prin-cipal cusps .... **TUPAIIDAE** (p. 73)

SUBORDER LIPOTYPHLA

1. limbs relatively short; locomotion generalized, quadrupedal.
2. **vision poor, eyes small.**
3. olfaction well developed; olfactory lobes longer than rest of brain.
4. auditory bulla present or absent.
5. **lacrimal and palatine separated by maxilla.**
6. **jugal reduced or absent.**
7. **zygomatic arch often incomplete.**
8. innominate bones not united, or with short symphysis.

Family ERINACEIDAE
(Hedgehogs and gymnures)

This family comprises two groups: the gymnures, characterized by a rather strong ammonia-like odor and fur consisting of soft to coarse hair; and hedgehogs, which are only slightly odorous and which have a spiny pelage. With few exceptions (e.g., *Echinosorex*), the tail is short. In contrast to those of most other lipotyphlans, the eyes and ears are relatively large. The first upper incisors, and often the first lower incisors, are large and resemble canine teeth (Fig. 24). The cheekteeth are adapted for an omnivorous diet—the molars are squarish and less sharply cusped than in strictly insectivorous forms.

When alarmed, hedgehogs roll up in a ball. Well-developed muscles (panniculus carnosus) just beneath the skin tighten the skin around the body, erecting the spines.

Erinaceids are broadly distributed in temperate and tropical forests, deserts, and cultivated areas of the Old World. They are primarily nocturnal and terrestrial, although many are also good climbers. Animal matter, including carrion, is the preferred food, but a wide range of items makes up the diet. Shelters are located in a variety of places, including burrows, hollows in logs or beneath trees, piles of debris, or rocks. Erinaceids breed once or twice a year in most places; some reproduce year-round in tropical areas. The litter size is 1-7.

At least one species (*Erinaceus europaeus*) hibernates, and others estivate or become dormant for short periods.

Eight genera, 14 species; Africa, Europe, Asia as far south as Borneo.

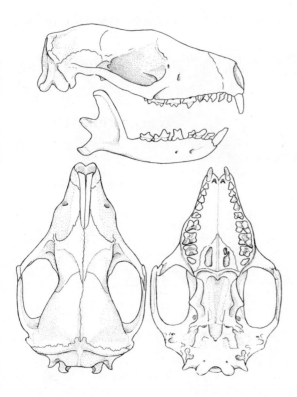

Figure 24. Skull of a erinaceid (*Erinaceus*, x 1).

INSECTIVORA

Recognition Characters:

1. size small to medium (15-65 cm).
2. eyes present, visible.
3. forefoot unspecialized.
4. **pelage with or without spines.**
5. pinna present, well developed.
6. **zygomatic arch present, slender** (Fig. 24).
7. no auditory bulla.
8. **first upper incisor large, canine-like** (Fig. 24).
9. **upper molars quadritubercular, with short, rounded cusps; crowns lacking W-shaped pattern of cusps** (Fig. 24).
10. pubic bones united in short symphysis.
11. no cloaca.

Dental formula: $\dfrac{2\text{-}3}{3}\dfrac{1}{1}\dfrac{3\text{-}4}{2\text{-}4}\dfrac{3}{3} = 36\text{-}44$

Compare with: Tenrecidae.

Representative Genera:

Echinosorex (1) - *E. gymnurus* is the greater gymnure.

Erinaceus (4) - Eurasian and African hedgehogs; *E. europaeus.* is the common European hedgehog.

Hemiechinus (2) - Long-eared desert hedgehogs.

Hylomys (1) - *H. suillus* is the lesser gymnure.

Paraechinus (3) - Desert hedgehogs.

Remark: The biology of hedgehogs (*E. europaeus*) was examined by Herter (1938).

Family TALPIDAE
(Moles and Desmans)

This family is noted mostly for its fossorial members, the moles. Yet it also contains aquatically-adapted species, the desmans, and shrew-like forms as well, the shrew moles. Despite these differences, all talpids share important features of the body, skull, and teeth (see below).

As in other fossorial mammals, the body of moles is fusiform, the limbs are short and stout, the tail is usually short, and the pelage is velvety. The eyes are minute, and pinnae are very small or absent. A keeled sternum provides a large surface area for attachment of enlarged pectoral muscles.

Some features of moles are not shared by other highly specialized fossors such as the Chrysochloridae (p. 67) or Notoryctidae (p. 44). The long tubular snout extends anteriorly well beyond the mouth, and the muzzle lacks a nose shield (except in *Condylura*, in which the muzzle is encircled by numerous fleshy "tentacles"). The skull is elongate and flattened (not conical) (Fig. 25). The broad paddle-shaped forefeet have five short digits, all of which bear large claws. The palms of the forefeet and the forearms are rotated outward and backward as a result of modifications in the nature of the articulations at the elbow and shoulder joints. The humerus is unusually blocky; it is doubly articulated with the pectoral girdle, meeting separately with both the scapula and clavicle.

Desmans are adapted for a semi-aquatic existence. Except for the extremely long, flexible snout, they are similar to muskrats (Rodentia: Muridae, p.164) in general appearance: the feet are webbed and the tail is laterally compressed. Several genera of talpids are aptly called shrew moles because in outward appearance they resemble shrews (p. 69). The forefeet in these animals are small (*Uropsilus*) or are only slightly broadened (*Neurotrichus, Urotrichus*).

Talpids are generally solitary, but in some species (e.g., *Talpa*) many individuals share tunnels. In all species, periods of activity occur during both day and night. Virtually all species are burrowers, although shrew-like forms are more active on the surface of the ground than are moles. The diet consists primarily of insects, worms, and other invertebrates. Breeding usually occurs in the spring, the gestation period is about a month, and 2-6 young are born in a nest chamber located deep in the burrow.

Many moles and desmans have a distinct, musky odor.

Twelve genera, about 22 species; North America, Eurasia.

Recognition Characters:

- **humerus usually blocky, often nearly as wide as long, articulating with scapula and clavicle.**

- **forefoot projecting outward and backward in most; elbow rotated upward.**

1. size small to rat-sized (8.5-43 cm).
2. eyes very small, visible.
3. **forefoot usually broad, paddle-shaped, adapted for digging** (unspecialized or webbed in some).
4. pelage short, soft, without spines.
5. **pinna very small or absent.**
6. **zygomatic arch present, slender** (Fig. 25).
7. **auditory bulla present, incomplete.**
8. incisors simple, **first upper incisor directed downward and backward** (Fig. 25).

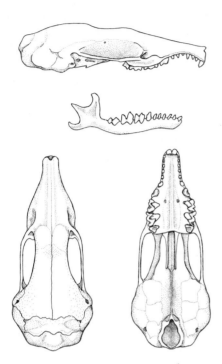

Figure 25. Skull of a talpid (*Scapanus*, x 1½).

9. **upper molars tritubercular to quad-ritubercular, with sharp cusps; crowns with W-shaped pattern of cusps** (Fig. 25).
10. pubic bones separate.
11. no cloaca.

Dental formula: $\dfrac{2\text{-}3}{1\text{-}3}\ \dfrac{1}{0\text{-}1}\ \dfrac{2\text{-}4}{2\text{-}4}\ \dfrac{3}{3}$ = 34-44

Compare with: Soricidae, Chrysochloridae, Notoryctidae (Marsupialia).

Representative Genera:

Condylura (1) - *C. cristata* is the star-nosed mole.
Desmana (1) - *D. moschata* is the Eurasian desman.
Neurotrichus (1) - *N. gibbsii* is the American shrew mole.

Scalopus (3) - Eastern American moles.
Scapanus (3) - Western American moles.
Talpa (5) - Old World moles.
Uropsilus (2) - Asiatic shrew moles.

Remark: General treatments of the natural history of Old World moles were provided by Godfrey and Crowcroft (1960) and Mellanby (1971).

Desman.

Family TENRECIDAE
(Tenrecs)

Tenrecs constitute a diverse group of insectivores confined to the island of Madagascar. In habits and outward appearance they resemble hedgehogs (p. 61) (several genera), moles (p. 63) (*Oryzorictes*), shrews (p. 69) (*Microgale*), and muskrats (p.164) (*Limnogale*). Two genera (*Echinops, Setifer*) have semi-arboreal tendencies.

The skull is relatively long and narrow and lacks jugal bones. The teeth vary in number, partly because the first molars are often shed before the eruption of the last molar. In *Tenrec* the canines are enlarged, especially in males.

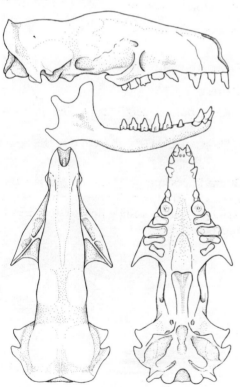

Figure 26. Skull of a tenrecid (*Setifer*, x 1¼).

The fur is soft, coarse, or spiny. As in true hedgehogs (Erinaceidae), a well-developed panniculus carnosus muscle underlies the skin in hedgehog tenrecs (*Echinops, Hemicentetes, Setifer*) which causes the spines to erect when these animals roll into a ball. In *Hemicentetes* and in young *Echinops* specially modified dorsal quills have a unique sound-producing function that coordinates movements between mother and offspring (Eisenberg and Gould, 1970).

Tenrecs occupy a wide variety of habitats, and retreat into burrows, hollow logs, or under rocks. They are mostly nocturnal and feed chiefly on invertebrates. Litter sizes in most species number 2-12; *Tenrec* is extraordinary in having two dozen or more offspring. Most tenrecs are heterothermic—both daily and seasonal periods of torpor are known.

Nine genera, 32 species; Madagascar.

Recognition Characters:

1. size very small to medium (9-58 cm).
2. eyes relatively small to large, visible.
3. forefoot unspecialized.
4. pelage soft or coarse, occasionally with spines.
5. pinna present, of moderate size.
6. **zygomatic arch incomplete (no jugal) (Fig. 26).**
7. no auditory bulla.
8. **incisors usually small, relatively simple.**
9. **upper molars tritubercular; crowns of upper molars usually with V-shaped pattern (Fig. 26).**
10. pubic bones united in short symphysis.
11. cloaca present.

INSECTIVORA

Dental formula: $\frac{2}{3}\frac{1}{1}\frac{3}{3}\frac{2\text{-}4}{2\text{-}3} = 34\text{-}40$

Compare with: Erinaceidae, Potamogalidae.

Representative Genera:

Echinops (1) - *E. telfairi* is the lesser hedgehog tenrec.
Hemicentetes (2) - Streaked tenrecs.
Limnogale (1) - *L. mergulus* is the web-footed tenrec.
Microgale (21) - Shrew tenrecs.
Oryzorictes (3) - Rice tenrecs.
Setifer (1) - *S. setosus* is the greater hedgehog tenrec.
Tenrec (1) - *T. ecaudatus* is the tenrec.

Remark: Aspects of the life history of tenrecs were described by Eisenberg and Gould (1970) and Gould and Eisenberg (1966).

Family POTAMOGALIDAE
(Otter shrews)

Potamogales are aquatically-adapted insectivores closely allied to tenrecs (p. 65). Externally they bear a remarkable resemblance to small otters. The body is streamlined, the snout rather blunt, and the limbs short. In *Potamogale* the tail is laterally compressed, and in one species of *Micropotamogale* the feet are webbed. Curiously, the second and third digits of the hindfoot are syndactylous as in some groups of marsupials. There is no clavicle, and the pubic bones are separate.

The habits of otter shrews are poorly known. Apparently they prefer to eat fish, frogs, and freshwater crustaceans.

Two genera, 3 species; west-central Africa.

Recognition Characters:
- **second and third digits of hindfoot syndactylous.**

1. size small to medium (30-65 cm).
2. eyes small.
3. forefoot relatively unspecialized or webbed.
4. pelage short, soft, without spines.
5. pinna present, small.
6. no zygomatic arch.
7. no auditory bulla.
8. incisors small, relatively simple.
9. upper molars tritubercular; crowns of upper molars with V-shaped (*Micropotamogale*) or W-shaped (*Potamogale*) pattern of cusps.
10. pubic bones separate.
11. cloaca present.

Dental formula: $\frac{2}{3}\frac{1}{1}\frac{3}{3}\frac{3}{3} = 38$

Compare with: Tenrecidae.

Genera:

Micropotamogale (2) - Dwarf otter shrews.
Potamogale (1) - *P. velox* is the giant otter shrew.

Remark: Some authors (e.g., Findley, 1967; Corbet, 1971; Vaughan, 1978) assigned the potamogales to the family Tenrecidae.

Family CHRYSOCHLORIDAE
(Golden moles)

Members of this family represent another highly specialized variation on a fossorial theme. The body is fusiform, the limbs are stocky, pinnae are absent, and the tail is short. In having large pick-like claws on two or three of the digits of the forefoot, iridescent fur, a leathery pad on the snout, minute eyes covered by skin, and a conical skull (Fig. 27), golden moles bear a remarkable resemblance to marsupial moles (p. 44). The bulky forelimbs are housed in a depression on each side of the ribcage, thus adding to the streamlining of the body. The lower cheekteeth are extremely high-crowned (Fig. 27). The pelage is often richly colored. Other unique features are indicated below.

Golden moles also resemble notoryctids in habits. Locomotion is by fore-and-aft movements of the forelimbs, in contrast to the lateral "swimming" motions of true moles (Talpidae). They inhabit grasslands, forests, and sandy areas, constructing shallow or deep burrows. The diet consists chiefly of insects and worms. Two young have been recorded.

Five genera, perhaps 16 species; southern Africa.

Recognition Characters:

- **digits 4/5** (5/5 or 5/4 in other Lipotyphla).
- **skull conical** (flattened in other Lipotyphla) (Fig. 27).
- **A pair of extra bones, called tabulars, present above and anterior to supraoccipital** (often fused with other bones in adults).

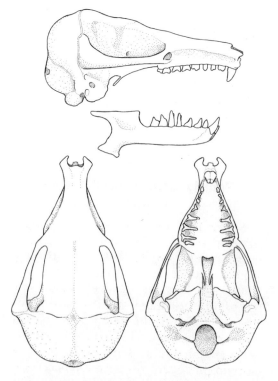

Figure 27. Skull of a chrysochlorid (*Amblysomus*, x 2).

1. size small (7.5-24 cm).
2. **eyes completely covered by skin, not visible externally.**
3. **forefoot with huge claws on two or three digits.**
4. pelage short, soft.
5. **no pinna.**
6. **zygomatic arch complete, formed by squamosal and long process of maxilla (no jugal).**
7. auditory bulla present or absent.
8. first upper incisor enlarged (Fig. 27).
9. **upper molars tritubercular; crowns with narrow V-shaped pattern (Fig. 27).**
10. pubic bones separate.

11. no cloaca.

Dental formula: $\frac{3}{3}\frac{1}{1}\frac{3}{3}\frac{3}{3} = 40$

Representative Genera:

Amblysomus (10) - African golden moles.

Chrysochloris (2) - Cape golden moles.

Eremitalpa (1) - *E. granti* is the desert golden mole.

Family SOLENODONTIDAE
(Solenodons)

Solenodons resemble large, ungainly, rat-like shrews. The tail and disproportionately large feet are sparsely haired, and the fur is coarse. The eyes are small; the ears are relatively large. The cusps of the upper molars have a V-shaped pattern; the outer two form a sharp cutting edge. The first upper incisor is enlarged and is separated from the second incisor by a short diastema. Toxic saliva from a gland located in the jaw is emitted through a groove in the second incisor.

As in shrews (Soricidae p. 69), vocalizations are high-pitched squeaks; these may function in echolocation.

These omnivorous mammals forage for invertebrates by unearthing them with the feet or by probing for them with the snout in the ground and in litter. Like that of other mammals with similar habits (e.g., pigs), the snout is long and moveable and has a small supportive bone at its tip. Solenodons seek shelter in openings in logs, trees, or burrows. One to three young are produced.

One genus, 2 species; Cuba and Haiti (recently extinct in Puerto Rico).

Recognition Characters:

● **Alisphenoid canal present** (absent in other Lipotyphla).

1. size medium (46-58 cm).
2. eyes relatively small, visible.
3. forefoot unspecialized.
4. pelage relatively long and coarse, without spines.
5. pinna present, well developed.
6. **zygomatic arch present, incomplete.**
7. no auditory bulla.
8. **first upper incisor greatly enlarged, directed slightly backward.**
9. **upper molars tritubercular; crowns with V-shaped pattern.**
10. pubic bones united in short symphysis.
11. no cloaca.

Dental formula: $\frac{3}{3}\frac{1}{1}\frac{3}{3}\frac{3}{3} = 40$

Genus:

Solenodon (2) - Solenodons.

Remark: The relationships of solenodons to other insectivores were examined by McDowell (1958).

Solenodon.

Family SORICIDAE
(Shrews)

This is the largest family of insectivores. The 300 or so species comprise a mixed lot of exceedingly small (two grams) to rat-sized forms. They are readily identified by general external appearance, by the large, beak-like first upper incisor and very procumbent first lower incisors (Fig. 28), and by two articular surfaces on the condyloid process of the lower jaw. In some genera (e.g., *Sorex, Cryptotis*) the teeth are a deep red color; only the occlusal surfaces are white. The body is cylindrical and the snout is relatively long and pointed. The legs are short, and the feet are small and pentadactyl. In aquatic forms the feet are webbed (*Nectogale*) or the digits are equipped with fringes of stiff hairs. The eyes and ears are small. Marked seasonal variation in size has been observed in some species (Pucek, 1970).

Because of their small size, shrews have the highest weight-specific rates of metabolism among mammals. They are quite vocal, emitting squeaks and other sounds, and at least some apparently echolocate (Gould et al., 1964). The saliva often is toxic and is used to immobilize prey. A musky odor is produced by skin glands in many species.

Shrews are mostly ground-dwelling inhabitants of moist grasslands, marshes, and forests. Members of several genera are aquatic (e.g., *Suncus, Sorex, Nectogale, Neomys, Chimarrogale*), and a few are desert dwellers (*Notiosorex, Diplomesodon*). They are active intermittently during both day and night, searching for their diet of animal matter (chiefly invertebrates) amongst leaves and debris or in surface tunnels. Some species construct burrows. Most are solitary except in the breeding period. Reproduction is seasonal (temperate areas) or year-round (tropical areas), and several litters may be produced per season. The litter size is 2-10.

Shrews have stimulated many superstitions. *Scutiosorex* (which has a peculiarly elaborate vertebral column; see Kingdon, 1974a) is known as the "hero" shrew because individuals of this genus allegedly confer protection on persons who wear parts of them as talismans.

Twenty four genera, approximately 300 species; worldwide except Antarctica, Australia, and central and southern South America.

Recognition Characters:

- **condyloid process of lower jaw with two condyles** (only one condyle in all other mammals).

1. size small (6-30 cm).
2. eyes small, visible.
3. forefoot unspecialized.
4. pelage short, soft.
5. pinna present, small.
6. **no zygomatic arch** (Fig. 28).
7. **no auditory bulla.**
8. **first upper incisor large, hooked, and with cusp at proximal base of tooth** (Fig. 28).
9. **upper molars tritubercular to quadritubercular, having sharp cusps; crowns with W-shaped pattern of cusps** (Fig. 28).
10. pubic bones separate.
11. shallow cloaca sometimes present.

Dental formula: $\dfrac{3}{1\text{-}2}\dfrac{1}{0\text{-}1}\dfrac{1\text{-}3}{1}\dfrac{3}{3} = 26\text{-}32$

(except for the large front incisors and molars, the identity of the teeth is uncertain).

INSECTIVORA

Compare with: Talpidae.

Representative Genera:

Blarina (2) - Short-tailed shrews.

Chimarrogale (8) - Asiatic water shrews.

Crocidura (160) - White-toothed shrews.

Cryptotis (30) - Small-eared shrews.

Diplomesodon (1) - *D. pulchellum* is the piebald shrew.

Microsorex (1) - *M. hoyi* is the pygmy shrew.

Myosorex (5) - Mouse shrews, mole shrews.

Nectogale (1) - *N. elegans* is the web-footed water shrew.

Neomys (2) - Old World water shrews.

Notiosorex (2) - Desert shrews.

Scutiosorex (1) - *S. somereni* is the hero shrew.

Sorex (40) - Long-tailed shrews.

Suncus (20) - Musk shrews.

Remarks: Fossil and recent families of shrews were reviewed by Repenning (1967). Crowcroft (1957) explored their life history.

Shrew.

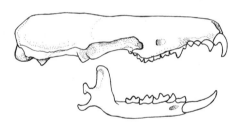

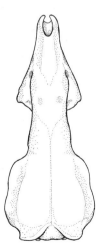
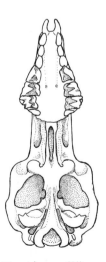

Figure 28. Skull of a soricid (*Crocidura*, x 1½).

70

SUBORDER MENOTYPHLA

1. limbs relatively long, adapted for hopping or climbing.
2. **vision acute, eyes large.**
3. olfaction moderately developed; olfactory lobes shorter than rest of brain.
4. auditory bulla present.
5. **lacrimal and palatine joined, not separated by maxilla.**
6. **jugal well developed.**
7. **zygomatic arch complete.**
8. innominate bones united in long symphysis.

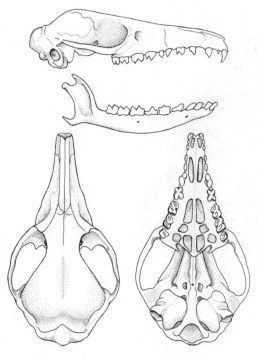

Figure 29. Skull of a macroscelidid (*Elephantulus*, x 1½).

Family MACROSCELIDIDAE
(Elephant shrews)

These menotyphlans are the only hopping insectivores. Adaptations for this habit include large hindlimbs bearing four or five elongate digits and a long tail. The snout is long, tubular, and flexible. Like those of other menotyphlans (Tupaiidae), the eyes and ears are well developed. The pelage is soft; there is a naked patch at the base of the tail. Certain features of the skull (Fig. 29) are distinctive (see below).

These mammals occur in habitats ranging from grasslands to tropical forest. Infrequently constructing their own burrows, they prefer to nest in rodent burrows, among rocks, under logs, or in dense vegetation. Their diet consists chiefly of ants and termites, but also includes other invertebrates and some plant material. The snout is used as a probe in search of food.

Large species (e.g., *Rhynchocyon*) prey on small birds and mammals. Elephant shrews occur singly, in pairs, or in small groups. One to two offspring are produced.

Five genera, approximately 30 species; Africa.

Recognition Characters:

1. body size (17.5-58cm) and form like that of kangaroo rat.
2. **hindlimbs much longer than forelimbs.**
3. **snout extended into long, movable proboscis.**
4. auditory bulla enlarged.
5. **palate containing a series of large perforations** (Fig. 29).

71

6. **postorbital process small or absent** (Fig. 29).
7. zygomatic arch not perforate.
8. molars with four large cusps.

Dental formula: $\dfrac{1\text{-}3}{3}\,\dfrac{1}{1}\,\dfrac{4}{4}\,\dfrac{2}{2\text{-}3} = 36\text{-}42$

Compare with: Tupaiidae.

Representative Genera:

Elephantulus (12) - Long-eared elephant shrews.

Petrodomus (1) - *P. tetradactylus* is the four-toed elephant shrew.

Rhynchocyon (3) - Giant elephant shrews.

Remarks: The relationships and taxonomy of elephant shrews were explored by Evans (1942) and Corbett and Hanks (1968). Kingdon (1974a) and Rathbun (in press) have examined behavior and natural history of these mammals.

Elephant shrew.

Family TUPAIIDAE
(Tree shrews)

This family contains forms that are squirrel-like in appearance and habits. Most are arboreal and diurnal. The limbs are about equal in size and have five digits bearing long curved claws. The snout is relatively long but not moveable. The tail is tufted, bushy, or covered with short hairs. The eyes and ears are prominent.

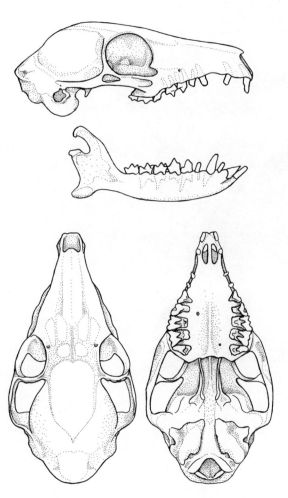

Figure 30. Skull of a tupaiid (*Tupaia*, x 1).

In contrast to macroscelidids (p. 71), tree shrews have tritubercular cheekteeth and a postorbital process that forms a bar between the frontal bone and zygomatic arch (Fig. 30). The palate is not extensively perforated.

Tupaiids inhabit dry or moist deciduous forests, nesting in trees, fallen logs, or holes in the ground or among roots of trees. They feed opportunistically on a wide variety of plant and animal matter. Most occur singly or in pairs, though social groupings are known in a few species. The breeding season appears to be year-round. The litter size is usually two.

Five genera, 15 species; southeastern Asia, including adjacent islands.

Recognition Characters:

1. body size (19-40cm) and form squirrel-like.
2. **hindlimbs and forelimbs ± equal in size.**
3. **snout moderately slender, pointed, not movable.**
4. auditory bulla not enlarged.
5. **palate without large perforations** (Fig. 30).
6. **postorbital process large, contacting zygomatic arch** (Fig. 30).
7. zygomatic arch perforate.
8. molars with three principal cusps (the fourth one is small).

Dental formula: $\dfrac{2}{3}\dfrac{1}{1}\dfrac{3}{3}\dfrac{3}{3} = 38$

Compare with: Macroscelididae.

Representative Genera:

Ptilocercus (1) - *P. lowii* is the pen-tailed tree shrew.
Tupaia (10) - Tree shrews.
Urogale (1) - *U. everetti* is the Philippine tree shrew.

INSECTIVORA

Remarks: Because they resemble primitive primates in some ways, tree shrews have inspired a lively controversy in the literature regarding the proper ordinal allocation of the group. Recently, Campbell (1974) showed that most purported resemblances to primates were based upon characters having little or no taxonomic value. I concur with him in placing the tupaiids in the Insectivora instead of the Primates.

Lyon (1913) provided a taxonomic account of the tupaiids.

Tree shrew.

ORDER DERMOPTERA

Family CYNOCEPHALIDAE
(Flying lemurs of colugos)

Colugos are a taxonomic enigma. Probably they represent an offshoot of a primitive insectivore stock that has become modified for a strictly arboreal existence. Specializations for this habit include gliding membranes, enlarged radius, reduced and partly ligamentous ulna, and keeled sternum. The face of flying lemurs is fox-like, the eyes are large, and the fur is soft. The skull and teeth are peculiar (see below and Fig. 31).

These animals hang sloth-like from branches, and move with slow deliberate motions. They eat leaves, flowers, and fruit. One young is born each year.

One genus, 2 species; Asia, including Burma, Indochina, Malaysia, Indonesia, Philippine Islands.

Recognition Characters:

- **membrane extending from neck to digits of forefeet, from forelimbs to digits of hindfeet, and from hindlimbs to tip of tail.**
- **two inner lower incisors on each side wide, comb-like, and procumbent; outer lower incisor multi-cusped** (Fig. 31).
  1. forelimbs and hindlimbs ± equal in size.
  2. soles of feet flat, resembling suction cups.
  3. **cranium broad, flattened** (Fig. 31).
  4. postorbital process well developed.
  5. temporal ridges prominent.
  6. upper incisors of left and right sides separated by large gap (Fig. 31).
  7. canines indistinct, premolar-like (Fig. 31).

Dental formula: $\frac{2}{3}\frac{1}{1}\frac{2}{2}\frac{3}{3} = 34$

Genus:
  Cynocephalus (2) - Flying lemurs.

Remarks: There are no general accounts of the natural history of this group. The osteology was described by Shufeldt (1911).

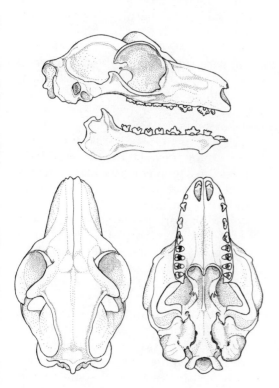

Figure 31. Skull of a cynocephalid (*Cynocephalus*, x ¾).

ORDER CHIROPTERA

Bats are an extremely successful group, second only to rodents in diversity (approximately 850 species). They are distributed worldwide but attain their greatest diversity and abundance in tropical areas. Bats are poorly known in the fossil record but extend back as far as the early Eocene. The diet varies according to species and consists of insects and other arthropods, fruit, nectar, pollen, flowers, small terrestrial vertebrates, fish, or blood. They are exceptionally long-lived—up to 20 or more years.

Bats are the only mammals exhibiting true flight. The wings consist of a naked membranous sandwich of two elastic skin layers enclosing blood vessels and nerves suspended on the delicate bones of the fingers like the ribs of an umbrella (see Figs. 7a, 32). Many other features of the morphology, physiology, and behavior of bats also are related to their unique locomotor patterns. For a discussion of morphological adaptions for flight see Vaughan (1970a, 1970b, 1970c, 1978).

Vision is well developed only in Old World fruit bats (Pteropodidae). In other bats, direction of flight is guided primarily by use of echolocation. Constant-frequency or frequency-modulated sounds, or a combination of both, are emitted at varying intensities through the mouth or (less frequently) the nose. Returning echoes are used to determine the distance of an object, its rate of movement, and its size and texture. Flying insects are captured with the feet, wing or tail membranes, or the mouth.

The intriguing variety of skin growths on the muzzles of many bats produces a kaleidoscope of distinctive facial expressions in these mammals (Fig. 33). Varying from simple bumps and leaf-like flaps ("noseleafs") to ornately patterned out-growths, these structures provide conspicuous species-recognition characters. They probably also serve to beam sounds produced by bats during flight.

Metabolic rates of bats vary both daily and seasonally. Most temperate bats are obligatory hibernators; a few species are migratory. Daily torpor is common to many species. Predictably, metabolic rates increase sharply during flight. Adequate oxygen is ensured by increased respiratory rates and a high oxygen-storage capacity of the blood (Thomas and Suthers, 1972). High heat loads produced during flight are released via the lungs and the highly vascularized wing membranes (ibid.).

Breeding patterns of bats are varied. Most exhibit distinct breeding periods. Species in temperate areas generally breed in the fall or early spring. In fall breeders, an overwinter delay in fertilization or implantation of the embryo often occurs. During feeding excursions young are either carried by the female or left behind in nurseries. Mother-young recognition takes place by vocal and olfactory cues (Brown, 1976; Kolb, 1977). Sexual dimorphism is occasionally present. Bats bear disproportionately large offspring—at birth they weigh up to one-half as much as the female. Females of some species have larger wings than males; probably these large wings enhance the flight capabilities of females heavily laden with young (Myers, 1978). The social behavior of bats is poorly known, but accumulating evidence indicates that it is complex (Bradbury, 1977a).

Bats avoid competition in a variety of ways. Insectivorous forms differ in their temporal foraging patterns, in the height at which they forage in flight, in the manner in which they forage (e.g., catching insects in flight or on the ground, or gleaning them from foliage), and in prey preference (Kunz, 1973; Black, 1974; Husar, 1976).

Bats are divided into two suborders. The Megachiroptera contain a single family of frugivorous forms. Because they orient largely by vision and have a generalized wing structure (i.e., the first and second digits are relatively free of the membrane and are clawed), megachiropterans are considered to be the most primitive living bats. The other suborder, Microchiroptera, contains 17 families. Echolocation is well developed in these bats and the wings are specialized in a variety of ways for different flight habits.

Bats have excited interest mainly as a source of superstitions and as carriers of diseases. Although there is a low incidence of rabies in New World bats, it does not occur in African or Australian species.

Recognition Characters:

● **forelimb modified for flight, with digits elongate and joined together by a membrane extending to side of body and hindlimb.**
1. ulna reduced, non-functional; radius relatively large.
2. **sternum usually keeled.**
3. clavicle present.
4. **glenoid fossa of scapula directed dorsally.**
5. **knee directed posteriorly owing to rotation of hindlimb for support of wing and tail membrane.**
6. cartilaginous rod (calcar) arising from inner side of ankle joint, supporting tail (interfemoral) membrane (occasionally absent).
7. bones light, tubular.
8. cervical and thoracic vertebrae without neural spines.
9. cranium domed, often inflated in region of braincase and concave in frontal region.
10. cheekteeth variable, but usually tritubercular.
11. incisors relatively small.

Remarks: General treatments of the natural history of bats include Allen (1939), Brosset (1966), and Yalden and Morris (1975). Review articles on behavior, taxonomy, origins, morphology, physiology, orientation, and diseases were provided in Wimsatt (1970a, 1970b, 1977) and Slaughter and Walton (1970). Echolocation was summarized by Griffin (1958) and Simmons et al.(1979). An old but excellent reference to the families and genera of bats is Miller (1907). For the most part, the numbers of genera and species in the following family accounts are taken from Koopman and Jones (1970).

KEY TO FAMILIES OF CHIROPTERA

1a.   Second digit of wing relatively independent of third digit, clawed (Fig. 32); rostrum long; postorbital process well developed; angular process of lower jaw absent, or broad and low **(Megachiroptera)** . . . . **PTEROPODIDAE** (p. 82)

1b.   Second digit of wing closely bound to third digit, not clawed (Fig. 32); rostrum short or long; postorbital process usually absent; angular process of lower jaw long and narrow **(Microchiroptera)** 2

2a (1b).   Postorbital process or large supraorbital process present 3

2b.   No postorbital process or supraorbital process 5

3a (2a).   No tail; tragus large, forked; no premaxilla; no upper incisors . . . . **MEGADERMATIDAE** (p. 91)

3b.   Tail present; tragus small, not forked; premaxilla present; upper incisors present 4

4a (3b).   Tail completely enclosed in tail membrane; deep concavity present on forehead between orbits; premaxillae with palatal branches only . . . . **NYCTERIDAE** (p. 89)

4b.   Tail protruding from dorsal surface of tail membrane; no concavity between orbits; premaxillae with nasal branches only . . . . **EMBALLONURIDAE** (p. 85)

5a (2b).   Distinct circular suction disc present on ventral surface of wrist and ankle; digits of hindfoot with two phalanges 6

5b.   No suction disc on wrist or ankle (rarely present); digits of hindfoot with three phalanges 7

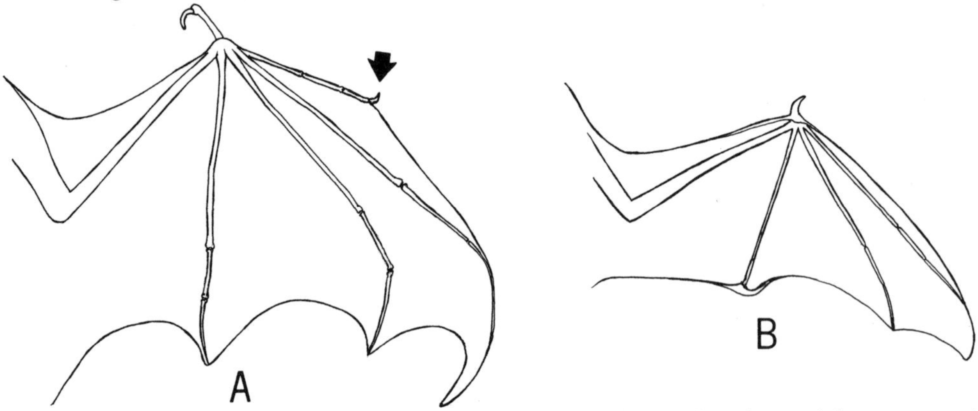

Figure 32. Wings of a megachiropteran (A) and a microchiropteran (B). Note clawed second digit (at arrow) in the megachiropteran.

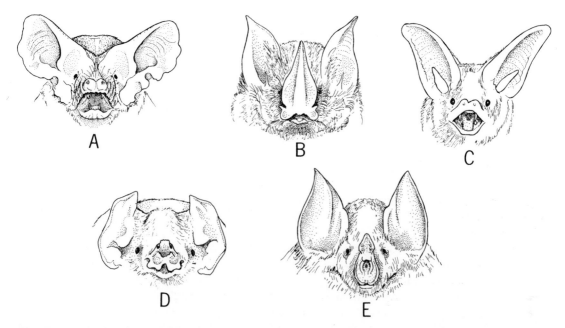

Figure 33. Faces of microchiropteran bats showing: a prominently ridged muzzle, a molossid (A); a pointed noseleaf, a phyllostomatid (B); a simple muzzle, a vespertilionid (C); a chin leaf, a mormoopid (D); a horseshoe-shaped noseleaf, a rhinolophid (E).

6a (5a).	Discs stalked; no mushroom-shaped structure adjacent to auditory opening in ear; pterygoids connected by a ridge on basisphenoid.................... **THYROPTERIDAE** (p.104)	
6b.	Discs not stalked; mushroom-shaped structure present adjacent to auditory opening in ear; pterygoids not connected by a ridge on basisphenoid .... **MYZOPODIDAE** (p.105)	
7a. (5b).	No tail; tail membrane very narrow; upper incisors and canines large, blade-like .... **DESMODONTIDAE** (p.100)	
7b.	Tail present or absent; tail membrane usually large; upper incisors and canines not abnormally large or blade-like..8	
8a (7b).	Noseleaf present, consisting of several distinct outgrowths or ridges (the latter often horseshoe-shaped) (Fig. 33E); premaxillae widely separated from maxillae and extending anteriorly from palate as a spatula-shaped process (Fig. 34A) .... **RHINOLOPHIDAE** (p. 93)	
8b.	Noseleaf present or absent, usually consisting of a single flap (Fig. 33B); premaxillae not spatula-shaped 9	

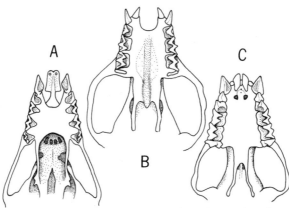

Figure 34. Palates of microchiropteran bats showing: a spatula-shaped extension of premaxillae, rhinolophid (A); prominent gap between premaxillae, a vespertilionid (B); fusion of premaxillae to produce a complete palate, a phyllostomid (C).

9a (8b.)   Muzzle terminating in a vertical pad surrounded by a ridge-like outgrowth; no calcar; rostrum with large swellings anterior to orbits 10

9b.   Muzzle without vertical pad and associated ridge; calcar usually present; rostrum without swellings anterior to orbits 11

10a (9a).   No tail; palatal branches of premaxillae fused anteriorly and posteriorly (no trace of suture) .... **CRASEONYCTERIDAE** (p. 85)

10b.   Tail present, long (± equal to length of body); palatal branches of premaxillae united anteriorly and posteriorly but not fused .... **RHINOPOMATIDAE** (p. 84)

11a (9b).   Tail extending well beyond tail membrane; legs and feet short and broad; first and fifth digits of feet bearing fringe of stiff bristles; rostrum broad, as wide long .... **MOLOSSIDAE** (p.110)

11b.   Tail extending to or only slightly beyond tail membrane; legs and feet relatively elongate; first and fifth digits of feet without fringe of bristles; rostrum longer than wide 12

12a (11b).   Premaxillae fused to one another and to maxillae— no premaxillary gap (slight notch may be present) (Fig. 34C) 13

12b.   Premaxillae separated—premaxillary gap present (Fig. 34B) 17

13a (12a).   Claws on pollex and digits of hindfoot with a basal talon; one upper incisor .... **MYSTACINIDAE** (p.108)

13b.   Claws lacking basal talon; two upper incisors 14

14a (13b). Anterior margin of palate with small V-shaped notch; three lower incisors .... **NATALIDAE** (p. 102)

14b. Palate entire, no notch in anterior margin (Fig. 34C, E); lower incisors 0, 1, or 2 15

15a (14b). Ventral margin of pinna extending anteriorly be-beath eye .... **MORMOOPIDAE** (p. 98)

15b. Ventral margin of pinna without anterior extension 16

16a (15b). Digits and claws of hindfoot much enlarged; no noseleaf; incisors 2/1 .... **NOCTILIONIDAE** (p. 88)

16b. Digits and claws of hindfoot not enlarged; noseleaf usually present; incisors 2/0, 2/1, or (usually) 2/2 (if 2/1, noseleaf is present) .... **PHYLLOSTOMIDAE** (p. 95)

17a (12b). Pollex rudimentary, with minute claw, enclosed in wing membrane; tragus small; maxillae extending forward between premaxillae as slender pointed process .... **FURIPTERIDAE** (p.104)

17b. Pollex prominent, well clawed, not enclosed in wing membrane; tragus large; maxilla lacking slender anterior process .... **VESPERTILIONIDAE** (p.107)

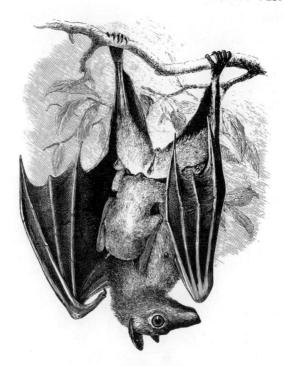

Fruit bat.

SUBORDER MEGACHIROPTERA

Recognition Characters:

1. **pinna simple, completely surrounding ear opening.**
2. no tragus in ear.
3. eyes well developed.
4. **second digit of forelimb relatively free of third digit and usually clawed.**
5. humerus with trochiter (greater tuberosity) and trochin (lesser tuberosity) small, never articulating with scapula.
6. **postorbital process large, forming a complete postorbital bar in some.**
7. **angular process of lower jaw absent or broad and low.**

Family PTEROPODIDAE
(Old World fruit bats)

These bats constitute the only family of megachiropterans. Several representatives of *Pteropus* are the largest species of bats and the only bats known to soar. The muzzle is simple. Only in *Nyctimene*, which has extensible tubular nostrils, are there growths on the snout. The mouse-like ears are simple and conspicuous. Climbing activities in foliage are aided by large hindlimbs which have well-clawed digits and by two clawed digits on the wings. In most species the dentition contains large canines and elongate, basin-shaped cheekteeth (Fig. 35); in specialized nectar-feeders these teeth are reduced, and in insect-feeding forms the cheekteeth are well cusped. The large postorbital processes are distinctive (Fig. 35).

In contrast to microchiropterans, which orient primarily by echolocation, the visual and olfactory senses of pteropodids

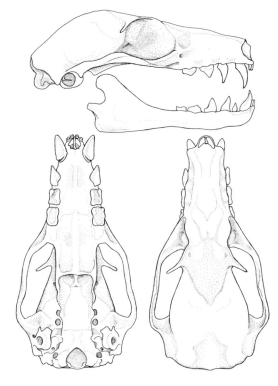

Figure 35. Skull of a pteropodid (*Epomophorus*, x 1½).

are well developed. Consequently, the head is disproportionately large in members of this family. Only *Rousettus* is known to echolocate.

Pteropodids are mostly nocturnal, but some species are active in the daytime. They feed upon fruit, nectar, pollen, and insects. Fruit is positioned in the mouth and crushed by the combined action of the tongue, teeth, and transverse corrugations on the palate. The pulp and juice are consumed and the remainder is spat out. Species that feed on nectar and pollen inadvertently serve as pollinating agents (Ayensu, 1974).

Behavioral habits of fruit bats vary widely. Sexual discrimination is made possible by marked sexual dimophism in many species. Males and females often differ in size, color, in the development of specialized glands on the shoulders and chest, and in the growth of tufts of hair (epaulettes) on the shoulders. Vocalizations are varied and are important in both solitary and colonial forms.

The hammerheaded bat, *Hypsignathus monstrosus*, is perhaps the most bizarre pteropodid. It has expanded nasal sinuses and a huge larynx. These chambers serve to amplify vocalizations, which resemble metallic croaks or honks. Males of this species gather and sing in "choirs" in order to attract females (Bradbury, 1977a, 1977b; Kingdon, 1974a).

These bats roost in trees, crevices, caves, or buildings. The small species are mostly solitary, whereas many of the large species congregate in colonies. Breeding is seasonal or aseasonal; 1-2 young are born per year. Pteropodids do not hibernate.

In many parts of their range, large species are prized as food by humans.

Thirty-eight genera, approximately 150 species; Old World from Africa to Australia and many islands in the south Pacific and Indian oceans.

Recognition Characters:

1. size medium to very large (wingspan up to 1.7m).
2. tail usually short or absent, never enclosed in a tail membrane (if membrane is present, it is narrow, and the tail is below it).
3. premaxillae usually with nasal branches only, fused to each other and to maxillae.
4. cheekteeth simple, cusps indistinct (Fig. 35).
5. other characters as per suborder.

Dental formula: $\frac{1\text{-}2 \ 1 \ 3 \ 1\text{-}2}{0\text{-}2 \ 1 \ 3 \ 2\text{-}3} = 24\text{-}34$

Representative Genera:

Acerodon (5) - Fruit bats.
Cynopterus (4) - Short-nosed fruit bats.
Dobsonia (7) - Naked-backed fruit bats.
Eidolon (1) - *E. helvum* is the straw-colored fruit bat.
Epomophorus (8) - Epauletted fruit bats.
Epomops (3) - Tailless epauletted fruit bats.
Hypsignathus (1) - *H. monstrosus* is the hammerheaded bat.
Macroglossus (3) - Australasian long-tongued fruit bats.
Megaloglossus (1) - *M. woermanni* is the African long-tongued fruit bat.
Micropteropus (3) - Dwarf epauletted fruit bats.
Myonycteris (2) - Little collared fruit bats.
Nyctimene (9) - Tube-nosed fruit bats.
Pteropus (65) - Flying foxes.
Rousettus (6) - Rousette bats.

Remark: Kingdon (1974a) summarized the general biology of many African pteropodids.

SUBORDER MICROCHIROPTERA

Recognition Characters:

1. **pinna often complicated, not completely surrounding ear opening.**
2. tragus usually present in ear.
3. eyes usually poorly developed.
4. **second digit of forelimb fully enclosed in wing membrane, not clawed.**
5. humerus with trochiter (greater tuberosity) and trochin (lesser tuberosity) large, often articulating with scapula.
6. **postorbital process usually absent.**
7. **angular process of lower jaw well developed.**

Family RHINOPOMATIDAE
(Mouse-tailed bats)

External features of the face and body and a long tail extending free of the narrow tail membrane distinguish these bats from all other microchiropterans. The body and limbs are slender, and facial and rump regions are sparsely haired. The dorsal surface of the muzzle contains a depression bordered on each side by a ridge. A small noseleaf is present. The large ears are connected across the forehead by a low bridge of tissue.

The skull is characterized by prominent dorsal swellings on the rostrum (Fig. 36). The teeth are adapted for an insectivorous diet.

Mouse-tailed bats roost in large colonies in caves, rock crevices, and buildings (e.g., pyramids). One young is produced per breeding season. These bats apparently do not hibernate, but fat deposits that accumulate in the hindquarters evidently provide sustenance during periods when insects are scarce.

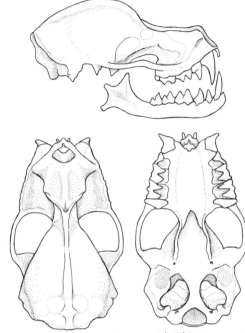

Figure 36. Skull of a rhinopomatid (*Rhinopoma*, x 2½).

One genus, 3 species; northern Africa, southern Asia.

Recognition Characters:

- **nostrils slit-like, valvular.**
- **tail very long, roughly equal to length of body, largely free of narrow membrane** (tail much shorter than length of body in other microchiropterans).

1. size medium (forearm to 67 cm).
2. **muzzle swollen laterally, terminating in a vertical pad which is surrounded by a ridge-like outgrowth.**
3. pinnae very large, rounded, united at bases, without ventral extension under eye.

4. tragus present, prominent.
5. no disc on wrist or ankle.
6. second digit of forelimb with two bony phalanges; third digit with two.
7. thumb relatively large.
8. hindlimb and hindfoot slender, with relatively large claws.
9. **no calcar.**
10. tail as described above.
11. humerus with trochiter smaller than trochin, not articulating with scapula.
12. premaxillae separated, not fused to surrounding bones; nasal and small palatal branches present.
13. no postorbital process.
14. cheekteeth tritubercular.

Dental formula: $\frac{1}{2}\frac{1}{1}\frac{1}{2}\frac{3}{3} = 28$

Compare with: Emballonuridae, Craseonycteridae.

Genus:

Rhinopoma (2) - Mouse-tailed bats.

Family CRASEONYCTERIDAE

Bats in this family were only recently discovered and described (J. Hill, 1974). They appear most similar to rhinopomatids (p. 84) but differ from then in the absence of a tail and in having an unusual modification of the premaxillae (see below). There is nothing known of the natural history of members of this family.

One genus, 1 species; Thailand.

Recognition Characters:

• **palatal branches of premaxillae fused anteriorly and posteriorly (no trace of suture), enclosing a large vacuity; nasal branches fused posteriorly, lying on nasals and maxillae.**

1. size small (forearm 22-26 mm).
2. **muzzle swollen laterally, and terminating in a vertical pad which is surrounded by a ridge-like outgrowth.**
3. pinnae very large, rounded, separate, without ventral extension under eye.
4. tragus present, prominent.
5. no disc on wrist or ankle.
6. second digit of forelimb with one bony phalanx only; third digit with two.
7. thumb relatively small.
8. hindlimb and hindfoot slender, with relatively large claws.
9. **no calcar.**
10. **no tail.**
11. humerus with trochiter and trochin ± equal in size, articulating with scapula.
12. premaxillae mostly separated (see above), not fused to surrounding bones; nasal and palatal branches present.
13. no postorbital process.
14. cheekteeth tritubercular.

Dental formula: $\frac{1}{2}\frac{1}{1}\frac{1}{2}\frac{3}{3} = 28$

Compare with: Rhinopomatidae, Emballonuridae.

Genus:

Craseonycteris (1) - *C. thonglongyai* is the only species.

Family EMBALLONURIDAE
(Sac-winged bats, sheath-tailed bats)

These insectivorous tropical bats are so named because of peculiarities of the wings and tail. The free portion of the tail projects above the dorsal surface of the tail membrane. The skin is loosely attached to the tail vertebrae so that, during flight, movements of the hindlimbs cause the skin to slide back and forth over the tail vertebrae, and the animal is said to "set sail." A glandular sac, which is most prominent in males, is often present in the wing membrane anterior to the elbow joint. One genus (*Taphozous*) has well-developed glands on the throat. The face is plain; there is no noseleaf. A postorbital process is present on the skull (Fig. 37).

Emballonurids shelter in many places, including caves, crevices, buildings, and hollow logs and trees. They are solitary or gregarious in small to large groups. Group members often fly in formation (usually in single file). Segregation of sexes is common. Breeding behavior is relatively complex and variable (Bradbury, 1977a). Males of *Saccopteryx bilineata* form exclusive year-round harems; their sexual displays are unique among microchiropterans (Bradbury and Emmons, 1974).

Reproduction is seasonal or aseasonal. One young is produced. Females of some species have false "fastening teats" to which the young attach. Emballonurids apparently do not hibernate.

Twelve genera, 44 species; tropics of Central and South America, South Africa, southern Australia, some Pacific islands.

Recognition Characters:

- **glandular sac present in wing membrane anterior to elbow join in some** (sac absent in other microchiropterans).

1. size small to medium (forearm 35-66 mm).
2. muzzle smooth — no special skin outgrowths.
3. pinnae moderately large, rounded, often united at bases, without ventral extension under eye.
4. tragus present, small.
5. no disc on wrist or ankle.
6. second digit of forelimb absent (well-developed metacarpal remaining); third digit with two phalanges.
7. thumb relatively large.
8. hindlimb and hindfoot slender, with relatively large claws.
9. calcar present, well developed.
10. **tail emerging from dorsal surface of relatively large membrane.**
11. humerus with trochiter smaller than trochin, not articulating with scapula.
12. premaxillae small, separated, not fused to surrounding bones; only nasal branches present.
13. **postorbital process present, prominent** (obscured by large supraorbital process in *Diclidurus*)(Fig. 37).

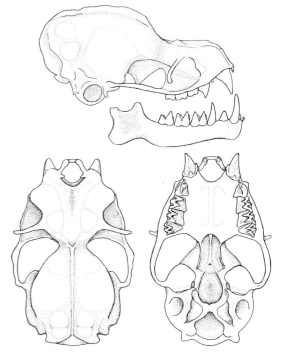

Figure 37. Skull of an emballonurid (*Peropteryx*, x 3).

14. cheekteeth tritubercular.

Dental formula: $\dfrac{1\text{-}2}{2\text{-}3}\dfrac{1}{1}\dfrac{2}{2}\dfrac{3}{3} = 30\text{-}34$

Compare with: Rhinopomatidae, Craseo-nycteridae.

Representative Genera:

Balantiopteryx (3) - Sac-winged bats.
Coleura (2) - African and Arabian sheath-tailed bats.
Diclidurus (3) - White bats.
Emballonura (10) - Old World sheath-tailed bats.
Peropteryx (3) - Dog-like bats.
Rhynchonycteris (1) - *R. naso* is the sharp-nosed bat.
Saccopteryx (4) - White-lined bats.
Taphozous (14) - Tomb bats.

Remark: Sanborn (1937) reviewed the taxonomy of members of this family.

Family NOCTILIONIDAE
(Bull-dog bats or fish-eating bats)

The unique appearance of the face, long hindlimbs, large feet, and long needle-sharp claws distinguishes these tropical bats. The muzzle lacks outgrowths, but the lips are large and fleshy, and the cheeks form pouches—hence the name "bull-dog bats." The ears are large and pointed. The skin is sparsely haired or naked. Often the fur is bright yellow, orange, or reddish, particularly in males. The skull is illustrated in Fig. 38.

Bull-dog bats commonly roost in colonies (often with other species), in hollow trees, rocky clefts, and caves. *Noctilio leporinus*, a piscivore, hunts by echolocating surface disturbances while skimming the water, the sharp claws of the hindfeet gaffing small fish (Bloedel, l955). It also eats insects and crustaceans. *N. albiventris* is insectivorous.

One young is normally produced per year. These bats do not hibernate.

One genus, 2 species; tropical areas of Central and South America.

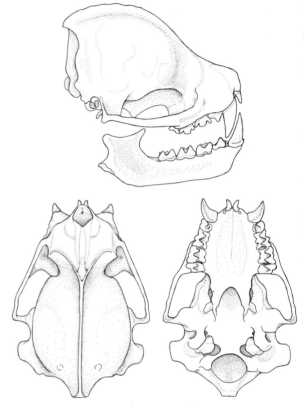

Figure 38. Skull of a noctilionid (*Noctilio*, x 2).

Recognition Characters:

● **lips thick, folded, with median cleft, and forming distinct cheek pouches.**

1. size medium (forearm 55-90 mm).
2. muzzle pointed, plain — no skin outgrowths.
3. pinnae large, pointed, separate, without ventral extension under eye.
4. tragus present, small.
5. no disc on wrist or ankle.
6. second digit of forelimb with one vestigial bony phalanx; third digit with two.
7. thumb large.
8. **hindlimb large; hindfoot with large, curved claws.**
9. calcar present, well developed.
10. **tail extending to middle of large membrane.**
11. humerus with trochiter much smaller than trochin, only slightly articulating with scapula.
12. premaxillae with palatal and nasal branches, fused to each other and to maxillae.
13. no postorbital process.
14. cheekteeth tritubercular.

Dental formula: $\frac{2}{1}\frac{1}{1}\frac{1}{2}\frac{3}{3} = 28$

Genus:

Noctilio (2) - Bull-dog bats, fish-eating bats.

Family NYCTERIDAE
(Hollow-faced bats)

These bats are characterized by a deep depression on the top of the muzzle (partly concealed by complex skin outgrowths) and by a correspondingly concave cranium (Fig. 39). The tail is peculiar in that it extends to the outer margin of the membrane, ending in a T-shaped process. The ears are very large. Females have accessory "fastening teats" to which the young attach during periods of activity of the mother.

Ordinarily gathering in small groups, hollow-faced bats find shelter in a wide variety of places, including the burrows of other mammals. They feed on insects and other arthropods, many of which they glean from tree trunks, foliage, or the ground.

One genus, 13 species; Africa, Near East, southeast Asia.

Recognition Characters:

- **tail long, fully enclosed in relatively large membrane, and terminating in T-shaped cartilaginous tip.**

- **fibula absent** (present in other microchiropterans).

- **cranium with large depression between orbits** (Fig. 39).

1. size small to medium (forearm 35-65 mm).
2. **top of muzzle with complex outgrowths of skin alongside a deep concavity.**
3. pinnae relatively large, rounded, separate, without ventral extension under eye.
4. tragus present, small.
5. no disc on wrist or ankle.
6. second digit of forelimb absent (well-developed metacarpal remaining); third digit with two phalanges.
7. thumb relatively large.
8. hindlimb and hindfoot slender; claws not enlarged.
9. calcar present, well developed.
10. tail as above.
11. humerus with trochiter and trochin ± equal in size; trochiter not articulating with scapula.
12. premaxillae represented by palatal branches only, fused to each other and to maxillae.
13. **postorbital process present, relatively small (obscured by large supraorbital ridge)** (Fig. 39).
14. cheekteeth tritubercular.

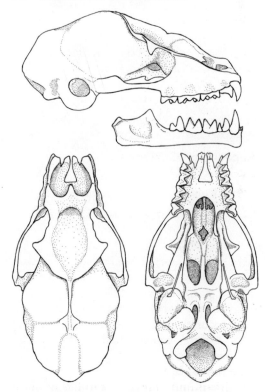

Figure 39. Skull of a nycterid (*Nycteris*, x 3).

CHIROPTERA

Dental formula: $\dfrac{2}{3}\dfrac{1}{1}\dfrac{1}{2}\dfrac{3}{3} = 32$

Compare with: Rhinolophidae, Megadermatidae.

Genus:

Nycteris (13) - Hollow-faced bats.

Family MEGADERMATIDAE
(False vampire bats, yellow-winged bat)

These relatively large bats are easily recognized by external and cranial characters. The wings are large and quite broad. The large rounded ears contain a long bifurcated tragus. A conspicuously large noseleaf is present. The front teeth are unique — there are no upper incisors, and the large protruding upper canine has a secondary cusp at its base (Fig. 40). Premaxillae are also absent.

The fur of megadermatids is long and soft. In the yellow-winged bat (*Lavia frons*) the noseleaf, ears, and wings are yellowish and the body is gray. A large gland on the back of males often discolors the fur, also giving it a yellowish cast.

Megadermatids feed upon insects, other arthropods, or small vertebrates, including fish (*Megaderma*) and bats (*Macroderma*). They roost singly or in colonies in caves, hollow trees, bushes, and buildings. *Lavia* is frequently active in the daytime. These bats probably breed once per year; they give birth to one young. As in several other families of bats, false teats on the abdomen of females provide a place of attachment for young.

Three genera, 5 species; Africa, southern Asia, Philippines, Australia.

Recognition Characters:

- **upper canine large, projecting noticeably forward, and with a large secondary cusp** (Fig. 40).

1. size medium to large (forearm to 107 mm).
2. muzzle with conspicuous long, erect noseleaf.
3. **pinnae large, rounded, connected across forehead by high ridge of skin,** without ventral extension under eye.
4. **tragus present, large, forked.**
5. no disc on wrist or ankle.
6. second digit of forelimb with one bony phalanx, third digit with two.
7. thumb relatively large.
8. hindlimb and hindfoot slender, with relatively large claws.
9. calcar present, well developed.
10. **tail short or absent;** tail membrane large.
11. humerus with trochiter and trochin ± equal in size; trochiter not articulating with scapula.

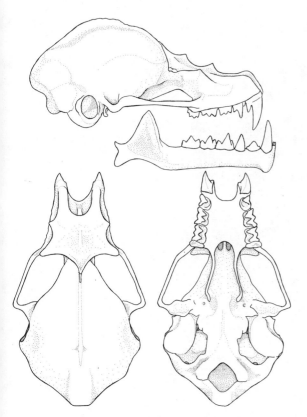

Figure 40. Skull of a megadermatid (*Lavia*, x 2½).

12. **no premaxillae, large gap between maxillae** (Fig. 40).
13. postorbital process present, small (often obscured by large supraorbital ridge).
14. cheekteeth tritubercular.

Dental formula: $\dfrac{0}{2}\dfrac{1}{1}\dfrac{1\text{-}2}{2}\dfrac{3}{3} = 26\text{-}28$

Compare with: Nycteridae, Rhinolophidae.

Representative Genera:

Lavia (1) - *L. frons* is the yellow bat.

Macroderma (1) - *M. gigas*, the Australian false vampire bat, is the largest species of insectivorous bat.

Megaderma (3) - Asian and African false vampire bats.

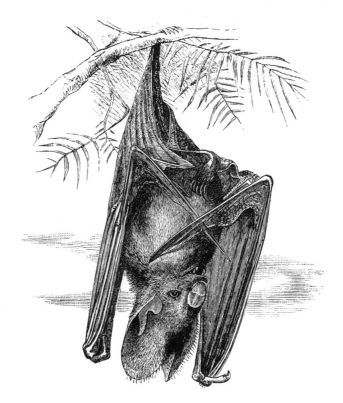

False vampire bat.

Family RHINOLOPHIDAE
(Horseshoe bats, noseleaf bats)

Members of this family are widespread in temperate, tropical, and desert regions of the Old World. They are identified by the peculiar shape of the complex noseleaf, part of which resembles a horseshoe (Fig. 33E). A sac-like gland, often larger in males, is located behind the noseleaf in many species. The ears are relatively large, but there is no tragus.

The skeleton also is unique. The fused premaxillae extend beyond the maxillae to form a conspicuous spatula-shaped process (Fig. 41). The pectoral and pelvic girdles are considerably strengthened. A bracing ring of bone is formed in the pectoral girdle by the fusion of the first two ribs with the manubrium of the sternum and the seventh cervical and first two thoracic vertebrae (to a lesser degree, this specialization also occurs in nycterids, p. 89, and megadermatids, p. 91).

Echolocation is highly developed in rhinolophids. Sounds are emitted through the nostrils and are beamed by the elaborate noseleaf (Moehres, 1953).

Rhinolophids seek shelter singly or in groups, in caves, buildings, trees, undergrowth, holes in the ground, or among rocks. They sleep cloaked in the wing membranes. Some species hibernate; others are migratory.

Breeding occurs once a year; one or two offspring are born. There is sexual dimorphism in size and color in some forms. Accessory "fastening teats" are present on the abdomen of females.

Eleven genera, about 130 species; Old World, from Europe and Africa to Japan, Philippines, and Australia.

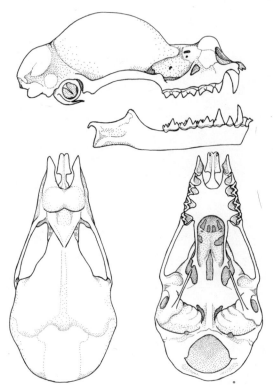

Figure 41. Skull of a rhinolophid (*Rhinolophus*, x 3 1/3).

Recognition Characters:

- **No tragus** (present in other microchiropterans).

- **premaxillae represented by palatal branches only, free of maxillae and extending anteriorly from palate as a spatula-like process** (Fig. 41).

1. size small to large (forearm 32-102 mm).
2. **muzzle with prominent outgrowths (often horseshoe-shaped) and depressions.**
3. pinnae small to large, pointed or rounded, united in some, without ventral extension under eye.
4. tragus as above.
5. no disc on wrist or ankle.

6. second digit of forelimb absent (well-developed metacarpal remaining); third digit with two phalanges.
7. thumb relatively large.
8. hindlimb and hindfoot slender, with only two phalanges per digit in some (*Hipposideros*), and with relatively large claws.
9. calcar present, well developed.
10. tail enclosed in membrane, small to moderate in size.
11. humerus with trochiter and trochin ± equal in size; trochiter not articulating with scapula.
12. premaxillae as above.
13. no postorbital process.
14. cheekteeth tritubercular.

Dental formula: $\frac{1}{2}\frac{1}{1}\frac{1\text{-}2}{2\text{-}3}\frac{3}{3}$ = 28-32

Compare with: Nycteridae, Megadermatidae.

Representative Genera:

Asellia (2) - Trident-noseleaf bats.
Hipposideros (44) - Old World noseleaf bats.
Rhinolophus (68) - Horseshoe bats.
Triaenops (4) - Triple-noseleaf bats.

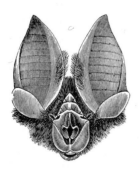

Horseshoe bat.

Family PHYLLOSTOMIDAE
(New World leaf-nosed bats)

This diverse family contains Neotropical ecological equivalents of the Old World fruit bats (Pteropodidae). The noseleaf is usually large, simple, and pointed. The eyes are relatively large. In other ways, leaf-nosed bats are highly variable. Diploid chromosome numbers vary from 16 to 46. The tail and tail membrane are absent to moderately or well developed. The fur varies from dull to brightly colored. In insectivorous and carnivorous species the cheekteeth are sharp and multi-cusped; in fruit-eaters, they are usually rounded or flattened; in pollen- and nectar-feeders they are simple and small (Fig. 42). A long snout and protrusible, brush-tipped tongue further characterize nectar- and pollen-feeding forms.

Phyllostomids live in caves, trees, buildings, culverts, and animal burrows. They occur singly or are gregarious in small to large colonies. Some (e.g., *Uroderma*) shelters of palm leaves by partly severing the frond and causing it to fold down in the form of a tent. Breeding is seasonal or aseasonal. One, occasionally two, young are produced.

Fifty genera, approximately 130 species; New World from northern Argentina to southwestern United States; mostly tropical.

Recognition Characters:

1. size variable, small to relatively large (forearm 25-110 mm).
2. **conspicuous erect noseleaf present on muzzle** (rudimentary in a few genera).
3. pinnae small to large, variable in form, usually separate, without ventral extension under eye.
4. tragus present, small.
5. no disc on wrist or ankle.
6. second digit of forelimb with one small bony phalanx; third digit with three.
7. thumb relatively large.
8. hindlimb and hindfoot slender, with relatively large claws.
9. calcar absent, small, or well developed.
10. tail variable; if present, it may be longer, shorter, or equal in length to tail membrane (the latter also variable in size).
11. humerus with trochiter smaller than trochin, articulating with scapula.
12. premaxillae with nasal and palatal branches, fused to each other and to maxillae.
13. no postorbital process.
14. cheekteeth variable, simple crushing type to tritubercular (Fig. 42).

Dental formula: $\frac{2}{0\text{-}2} \frac{1}{1} \frac{2\text{-}3}{2\text{-}3} \frac{2\text{-}3}{2\text{-}3} = 26\text{-}34$

Compare with: Desmodontidae, Mormoopidae.

Representative Genera:

Anoura (5) - Long-nosed bats.
Artibeus (8) - Neotropical fruit bats.
Carollia (4) - Short-tailed leaf-nosed bats.
Centurio (1) - *C. senex* is the wrinkle-faced bat.
Chiroderma (4) - White-lined bats.
Choeroniscus (5) - Long-nosed bats.
Ectophylla (2) - White bats.
Glossophaga (4) - Long-tongued bats.
Leptonycteris (3) - Long-nosed bats.
Macrotus (1) - *M. waterhousii* is the big-eared bat.
Micronycteris (10) - Little big-eared bats.
Mimon (2) - Spear-nosed bats.
Phyllonycteris (3) - Long-nosed bats.
Phyllostomus (4) - Spear-nosed bats.

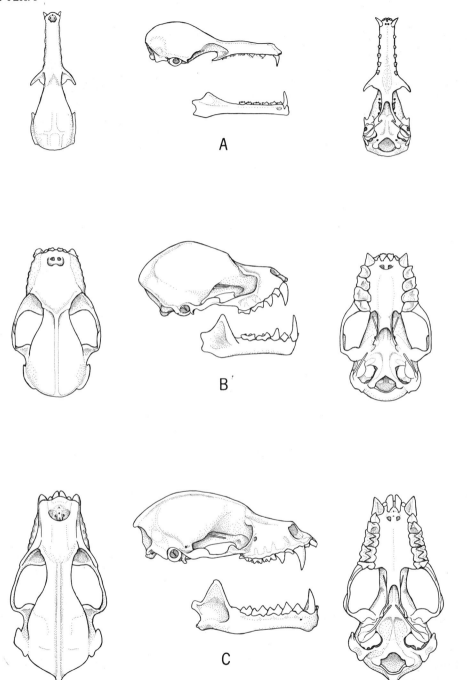

Figure 42. Skulls of phyllostomatids: A, *Choeronycteris*, a nectar-feeder; B, *Artibeus*, a frugivore; C, *Phyllostomus*, an omnivore (all x 1¼).

Sturnira (10) - Yellow-shouldered bats.
Tonatia (5) - Round-eared bats.
Uroderma (2) - Tent-making bats.
Vampyressa (5) - Yellow-eared bats.
Vampyrops (5) - White-lined bats.
Vampyrum (1) - *V. spectrum* is the false
   vampire, the largest New World bat.

Remark: Various aspects of the biology of phyllostomatids are reviewed in two volumes edited by Baker et al. (1976, 1977).

Long-nosed bat.

Family MORMOOPIDAE
(Leaf-chinned bats, moustached bats, naked-backed bats)

Formerly grouped with the phyllostomatids, these bats are distinguished by the absence of a noseleaf and by bumps and folds of skin on the upper and lower lips which nearly conceal the mouth and nostrils. The tragus has a peculiar shelf of skin projecting from the leading edge. The eyes are inconspicuous. In *Mormoops*, the skull is greatly shortened; the braincase is markedly elevated above the jaws and rostrum (Fig. 43).

In two species of *Pteronotus* the wing membranes extend to the middle of the back, giving the animals a naked-backed appearance, but fur is always present beneath the wing membranes.

These bats usually roost colonially in dark caves and tunnels. They are strictly insectivorous.

Two genera, 8 species; southwestern United States to Brazil, including West Indies.

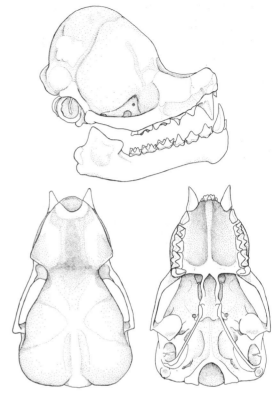

Figure 43. Skull of a mormoopid (*Mormoops*, x 3½).

Recognition Characters:

- **conspicuous leaf-like flap of skin on chin** (Fig. 33D).

- **pinnae large, rounded, often united at bases, with ventral extension under eye.**

1. size small to medium (forearm 37-63 mm).
2. noseleaf on muzzle rudimentary.
3. pinnae as above.
4. **tragus present, with secondary flap of skin on leading edge.**
5. no disc on wrist or ankle.
6. second digit of forelimb with one small bony phalanx; third digit with three.
7. thumb relatively large.
8. hindlimb and hindfoot slender, with relatively large claws.
9. calcar present, well developed.
10. **tail short, protruding from dorsal surface of large membrane.**
11. trochiter much smaller than trochin, not articulating with scapula.
12. premaxillae with nasal and palatal branches, fused to each other and to maxillae.
13. no postorbital process.
14. cheekteeth tritubercular.

Dental formula: $\frac{2\ 1\ 2\ 3}{2\ 1\ 3\ 3} = 34$

Compare with: Phyllostomidae, Desmodontidae.

Genera:

Mormoops (2) - Leaf-chinned bats.
Pteronotus (6) - Moustached bats, naked-
backed bats.

Remark: Smith (1972) recently reviewed
the taxonomic relationships of this family.

Leaf-chinned bat.

Family DESMODONTIDAE
(Vampire bats)

A source of many superstitions, these bats are uniquely specialized for a diet of fresh blood. The dentition is modified into a series of blade-like cutting teeth (Fig. 44) which are used to make small incisions in the skin of birds and mammals. The blood is lapped up by the tongue and transported through a tube formed by curling the tongue over a deep groove in the lower lip. Other diet-related peculiarities include a simple, elongate, sac-like stomach, and saliva that contains an anti-coagulant. Unlike most other bats, vampires are adept at rapid movement on horizontal surfaces. This habit is enhanced by the presence of large thumbs.

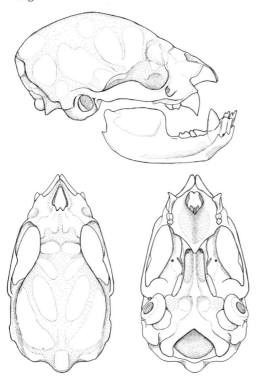

Figure 44. Skull of a desmodontid (*Desmodus*, x 2).

Efficient kidneys reduce the burden of transporting the large quantities of blood. As the bat feeds, much of the water in ingested blood is lost through the production of copious, dilute urine. Once the bat returns to the roost the kidneys shift to the production of a highly concentrated urine, conserving water and thus avoiding dehydration (Horst, 1969).

Vampires are generalized in other respects. They echolocate poorly compared to insectivorous forms. There is no tail, and the tail membrane is narrow. The eyes and ears are relatively small.

These bats frequent dark caves, tunnels, and hollow trees, sometimes in large groups. They are only rarely found in association with other species. Breeding appears to be aseasonal. The litter size is one.

Three genera, 3 species; tropics of New World.

Recognition Characters:

- **upper incisors and canines large, blade-like** (Fig. 44).
  1. size medium (forearm 52-65 mm).
  2. **muzzle relatively simple, with reduced noseleaf.**
  3. pinnae small, rounded, separate, without ventral extension under eye.
  4. tragus present, well developed.
  5. no disc on wrist or ankle.
  6. second digit of forelimb with one small bony phalanx; third digit with three.
  7. **thumb very large.**
  8. **hindlimb large and elongate;** hindfoot slender, with relatively large claws.
  9. calcar rudimentary.
  10. **no tail; tail membrane very narrow.**

11. humerus with trochiter and trochin ± equal in size; trochin slightly articulating with scapula.
12. premaxillae with nasal and palatal branches, fused to each other and to maxillae.
13. no postorbital process.
14. **cheekteeth small, blade-like**(Fig. 44).

Dental formula: $\dfrac{1\text{-}2}{2} \dfrac{1}{1} \dfrac{1\text{-}2}{2\text{-}3} \dfrac{0\text{-}2}{0\text{-}2} = 20\text{-}26$

Compare with: Phyllostomatidae.

Representative Genus:

Desmodus (1) - *D. rotundus* is the common vampire bat.

Remark: Recently several authors have relegated vampire bats to a subfamily in the Phyllostomatidae (see brief review in Smith, 1976).

A comprehensive treatment of the relationship of vampires and livestock was provided by Turner (1975).

Family NATALIDAE
(Funnel-eared bats)

Natalids are delicate slim-bodied bats with large wing and tail membranes which effect a fluttering, butterfly-like flight. They have a simple protruding snout and small eyes. The fur is long, soft, and buff to orange-red in color. A small triangular tragus is present in relatively large, funnel-shaped ears. The thumb is reduced, but it has a functional claw. The skull (Fig. 45) is small and thin-boned.

Peculiarities of the vertebral column include compressed thoracic vertebrae and fusion of the last thoracic and first several lumbar vertebrae. The ribs are also broadened to form a nearly complete sheet of bone across the thorax. These structural features lend rigidity to the skeleton.

Funnel-eared bats inhabit semi-tropical and tropical areas. They roost in moist, dark caves and mine shafts, usually in relatively large groups. They are insectivorous. Breeding is probably seasonal .

These bats are closely related to the Furipteridae (p.104) and Thyropteridae (p.104).

One genus, 4 species; northern Mexico to Brazil.

Recognition Characters:

1. **size small (forearm 27-42 mm).**
2. muzzle plain—no skin outgrowths.
3. **pinnae large, funnel-shaped,** separate, without ventral extension under eye.
4. **tragus present, small, triangular.**
5. no disc on wrist or ankle.
6. second digit of forelimb absent (metacarpal remaining); third digit with two phalanges.
7. thumb relatively small.
8. **hindlimb and hindfoot very slender, small, with relatively small claws.**
9. calcar present, well developed.
10. **tail long, fully enclosed in large membrane.**
11. humerus with trochiter nearly as large as trochin, articulating with scapula.
12. premaxillae with nasal and palatal branches, fused to each other and to maxillae.
13. no postorbital process.
14. cheekteeth tritubercular.

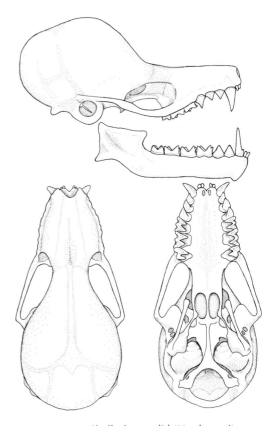

Figure 45. Skull of a natalid (*Natalus*, x 4).

Dental formula: $\frac{2}{3}\frac{1}{1}\frac{3}{3}\frac{3}{3}$ = 38

Compare with: Furipteridae, Thyropteridae.

Genus:

Natalus (4) - Funnel-eared bats.

Family FURIPTERIDAE
(Smoky bats)

Resembling natalids (p. 102) and thyropterids (below) in general appearance, these bats are small and delicate. The ears are funnel-shaped and contain a small triangular tragus. The tail is fully enclosed in the tail membrane. The common name derives from the usually slate-gray, coarse fur. The small, functionless thumb bears a minute claw and is mostly encased in the wing membrane. The skull is thin-boned and delicate (Fig. 46).

Little is known of the natural history of these bats. They apparently frequent caves.

Two genera, 2 species; South America.

Recognition Characters:
- **thumb much reduced, functionless, mostly enclosed in wing membrane.**
  1. **size small (forearm 30-40 mm).**
  2. muzzle plain—no skin outgrowths.
  3. **pinnae large, funnel-shaped, separate,** without ventral extension under eye.
  4. **tragus present, small, triangular.**
  5. no disc on wrist or ankle.
  6. second digit of forelimb absent (metacarpal remaining); third digit with two phalanges.
  7. thumb as above.
  8. hindlimb and hindfoot slender, small, with relatively small claws.
  9. calcar present, well developed.
  10. tail long, fully enclosed in large membrane.
  11. humerus with trochiter scarcely longer than trochin, articulating slightly with scapula.
  12. premaxillae with reduced and unossified palatal branches, fused to each other and to maxillae.

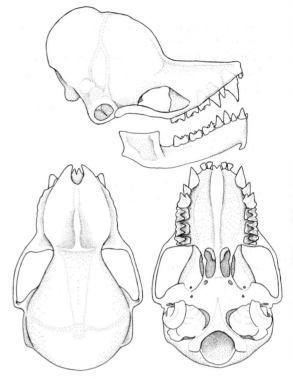

Figure 46. Skull of a furipterid (*Amorphochilus*, x 4½).

13. no postorbital process.
14. cheekteeth tritubercular.

Dental formula: $\frac{2}{3} \frac{1}{1} \frac{2}{3} \frac{3}{3} = 36$

Compare with: Natalidae, Thyropteridae.

Genera:

Amorphochilus (1) - *A. schnablii* is the smoky bat.
Furipterus (1) - *F. horrens* is also called the smoky bat.

Family THYROPTERIDAE
(Disc-winged bats)

These small bats resemble natalids (p.102) and furipterids (above) in having slim bodies, small eyes, and funnel-shaped ears each with a small triangular tragus. However, they differ in several respects. Circular suction discs elevated on short stalks are present on the wrists and ankles. The thumb is reduced but has a well-developed claw. Only two phalanges are present in the toes of the hindfoot, and the third and fourth digits are syndactylous. The lumbar vertebrae are distinct.

Disc-winged bats roost primarily in curled fronds of bananas and *Heliconia*. From one to eight individuals occur in the same leaf. The diet consists of insects.

One genus, 2 species; Central and South America.

Recognition Characters:

- **third and fourth digits of hindfoot (including claws) syndactylous.**

1. **size small (forearm 31-38 mm).**
2. muzzle plain—no skin outgrowths.
3. **pinnae large, funnel-shaped,** separate, without ventral extension under eye.
4. **tragus present, small.**
5. **prominent stalked adhesive disc present at wrist and ankle.**
6. second digit of forelimb absent (vestigial metacarpal remaining); third digit with three phalanges.
7. **thumb much reduced, but with well-developed claw.**
8. **hindlimb slender, hindfoot small—only two unfused phalanges per digit;** claws reduced.
9. calcar present, well developed.
10. tail extending slightly beyond relatively large membrane.
11. humerus with trochiter distinctly larger than trochin, articulating with scapula.
12. premaxillae with palatal and nasal branches, fused to each other and to maxillae.

13. no postorbital process.
14. cheekteeth tritubercular.

Dental formula: $\frac{2}{3}\frac{1}{1}\frac{3}{3}\frac{3}{3} = 38$

Compare with: Myzopodidae.

Genus:

Thyropterus (2) - Disc-winged bats.

Remarks: Locomotor adaptations of disc-winged bats were described by Wimsatt and Villa-R. (1970). Their biology and taxonomy were summarized by Wilson (1978) and Wilson and Findley (1977).

Family MYZOPODIDAE
(Sucker-footed bat)

Sucker-footed bats are the Old World counterparts of the Neotropical Thyropteridae. They may be recognized by the non-stalked discs on the wrists and ankles and the odd mushroom-shaped structure that partially blocks the ear opening. As in disc-winged bats (p.104), there are only two phalanges in the digits of the small hindfoot, but in myzopodids the phalanges in each toe are fused together and all digits are syndactylous.

These bats occur only in Madagascar. Their habits are poorly known.

One genus, 1 species; Madagascar.

Recognition Characters:

- **all digits of hindfoot (excluding claws) syndactylous.**
- **auditory opening partially closed by mushroom-shaped process.**

1. size small (forearm about 45 mm).
2. muzzle plain—no skin outgrowths.
3. pinnae very large, rounded, without ventral extension under eye.
4. **tragus present, bound to pinna.**

5. **prominent non-stalked adhesive disc on wrist and ankle.**
6. second digit of forelimb with one cartilaginous phalanx only; third digit with three bony phalanges.
7. **thumb much reduced, functionless, with minute claw.**
8. **hindlimb slender, hindfoot small— only two fused phalanges per digit, with small claws.**
9. calcar present, well developed.
10. tail completely enclosed in large membrane.
11. humerus with trochiter larger than trochin, articulating with scapula.
12. premaxillae with palatal and nasal branches, fused to each other and to maxillae.
13. no postorbital process.
14. cheekteeth tritubercular.

Dental formula: $\frac{2}{3}\frac{1}{1}\frac{3}{3}\frac{3}{3} = 38$

Compare with: Thyropteridae.

Genus:

Myzopoda (1) - *M. aurita* is the sucker-footed bat.

Remark: Known biology of *Myzopoda* was reviewed by Schlieman and Maas (1978).

Family VESPERTILIONIDAE
(Common bats)

Members of this widespread group are the most frequently observed bats, particularly in temperate areas. Most genera are rather generalized. The face is usually simple, the eyes are small, and the ears vary from small to very large. A tragus is present. The long tail extends to the edge of a wide tail membrane. Suction discs on the wrists and ankles are variously developed in several genera. Most species are some shade of brown, but species of some genera are spotted (e.g., *Euderma*, *Chalinolobus*) or brightly colored (e.g., *Kerivoula*). The skull is illustrated in Fig. 47.

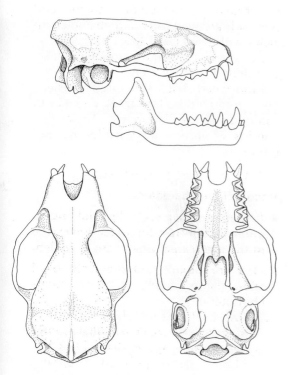

Figure 47. Skull of a vespertilionid (*Eptesicus*, x 2½).

Common bats inhabit shady or darkened places of all kinds. They may roost singly, in small groups, or in large colonies. Virtually all are insectivorous (*Pizonyx* is piscivorous).

Social behavior of vespertilionids is variable. Many species are sociable except at parturition, when the sexes segregate. Harems are recorded in several species (Bradbury, 1977a; Dwyer, 1970; Brosset, 1976). Breeding takes place in fall and/or spring. Usually 1-2 offspring are produced, but *Lasiurus* is unique among bats in having 3-4 young. Delayed implantation or delayed fertilization is common during winter periods. Hibernation is typical of temperate cave-dwellers, but some species migrate.

Thirty-four genera, approximately 280 species; virtually worldwide.

Recognition Characters:

1. size small to relatively large (forearm 24-90 mm).
2. muzzle plain—no skin outgrowths.
3. pinnae variable, small to large, pointed or rounded, usually separate, without ventral extension under eye.
4. **tragus present, prominent.**
5. small sucker-like pad on wrist or ankle (or both) in some (*Eudiscopus, Glischropus, Tylonycteris, Hesperoptenus,* some *Pipistrellus*).
6. second digit of forelimb with one small bony phalanx; third digit with two bony phalanges and a third cartilaginous one.
7. thumb relatively large.
8. hindlimb and hindfoot slender, usually with moderately large claws (very large in *Pizonyx*, fish-eating bat).
9. calcar present, well developed.

10. tail long, enclosed in relatively large membrane.
11. humerus with trochiter much larger than trochin, broadly articulating with scapula.
12. premaxillae separated, but fused to maxillae; only nasal branches present.
13. no postorbital process.
14. cheekteeth tritubercular.

Dental formula: $\dfrac{1\text{-}2}{2\text{-}3}\ \dfrac{1}{1}\ \dfrac{1\text{-}3}{2\text{-}3}\ \dfrac{3}{3}$ = 28-38

Compare with: Natalidae, Furipteridae, Thyropteridae, Myzopodidae.

Representative Genera:

Antrozous (3) - Pallid bats.
Chalinolobus (including *Glauconycteris*) (13) - Wattled bats.
Euderma (1) - *E. maculata* is the spotted bat.
Eptesicus (26) - Big brown bats, house bats, serotines.
Histiotus (3) - Big-eared brown bats.
Kerivoula (22) - Woolly bats, painted bats.
Lasionycteris (1) - *L. noctivagans* is the silver-haired bat.
Lasiurus (6) - Red bats, hoary bats, yellow bats.
Miniopterus (6) - Long-winged bats.
Murina (11) - Tube-nosed bats.
Myotis (68) - Little brown bats, mouse-eared bats; this is the most wide-spread genus of bats.
Nyctalus (9) - Noctule bats.
Nycticeius (12) - Evening bats, twilight bats.
Nyctophilus (7) - Australasian big-eared bats.
Pipistrellus (53) - Pipistrelles.
Pizonyx (1) - *P. vivesi* is the fish-eating bat.
Plecotus (5) - Long-eared bats.
Rhogeessa (3) - Little yellow bats.
Scotophilus (7) - House bats.
Tylonycteris (2) - Club-footed bats.
Vespertilio (3) - Frosted bats.

Family MYSTACINIDAE
(Short-tailed bat)

Found only in New Zealand, these bats are most closely related to the Molossidae. Similarities include a thick leathery skin forming the wing membranes, short thick legs, and broad feet, a relatively large thumb, and stiffened sensory hairs on the snout. Like molossids (p.110), they have adroit climbing abilities because of the peculiar wings (see below). Mystacinids differ from molossids in having a short tail emerging from the upper surface of the narrow tail membrane, a long pointed tragus, and feet with grooved soles and needle-sharp claws with prominent basal processes.

The fur is short and extremely dense. The dentition is tuberculo-sectorial.

Short-tailed bats are forest-dwellers. They frequent hollow trees and caves, roosting in small groups. Their diet consists of insects. Mystacinids do not hibernate.

One genus, 1 species; New Zealand.

Recognition Characters:

- **first phalanx of each digit folding to outer (rather than the usual inner) side of the metacarpal when wing is folded.**
- **claws of thumb and feet with basal talon** (talon absent in other micro-chiropterans).

1. size small (forearm about 43 mm).
2. **muzzle with small pad that houses hairs bearing spoon-shaped tips.**
3. pinnae large, pointed, separate, without ventral extension under eye.

4. **tragus present, long.**
5. no disc on wrist or ankle.
6. second digit of forelimb with one small bony phalanx; third digit with three.
7. thumb relatively large.
8. **hindlimb and hindfoot short, broad, with relatively large sharp claws and grooved soles.**
9. calcar present, well developed.
10. **tail short, protruding from dorsal surface of narrow tail membrane.**
11. **humerus with trochiter much larger than trochin, broadly articulating with scapula.**
12. premaxillae with nasal and palatal branches, fused to each other and to maxillae.
13. no postorbital process.
14. cheekteeth tritubercular.

Dental formula: $\frac{1}{1}\frac{1}{1}\frac{2}{2}\frac{3}{3} = 28$

Compare with: Molossidae, Vespertilionidae.

Genus:

Mystacina (1) - *M. tuberculata* is the short-tailed bat.

CHIROPTERA

Family MOLOSSIDAE
(Free-tailed bats)

Members of this insectivorous family exhibit the most advanced adaptations for flight. Among other things, a broad articulation of trochin and trochiter with the scapula forms a locking device that prevents hyperextension of the wing during the upstroke. It also adds to the power of the downstroke by involving the trunk muscles which insert on the scapula in the work of lowering the wing (Vaughan, 1966). The long, narrow wings are thick and leathery.

The common name derives from the protrusion of the tail beyond the trailing edge of the narrow tail membrane. The face is plain; it has a short, broad, obliquely truncate muzzle equipped with sensory hairs. The pelage is short and velvety. In *Cheiromeles* it is so short that the animals appear hairless. Because of the large thumb, short stout hindlimbs, and unusual way in which the wings fold, these bats, like mystacinids (p.109), are adept at moving on surfaces where they roost or forage, such as rock crevices or branches. There also are sensory bristles on the outer edges of the first and last toes of the feet. The skull is relatively unspecialized (Fig. 48), and a premaxillary gap may be present (Fig. 34B) or absent.

Molossids are swift and enduring fliers. They forage over large areas and ordinarily fly above the feeding range of other insectivorous forms. These bats do not hibernate; instead, they migrate or move about locally. They take shelter in many places, frequently inhabiting houses and other buildings. Some species occur in colonies of many thousands of individuals. One young (rarely two) are produced per breeding period.

Eleven genera, 82 species; extensive distribution in New and Old World (less common in north temperate areas).

Recognition Characters:

- **first phalanx of third finger folding to outer (rather than the usual inner) side of metacarpal when wing is folded.**
- **first and fifth digits of feet with fringe of stiff bristles.**

1. size medium (forearm 29-80 mm).
2. **muzzle plain, broad, with short hairs bearing spoon-shaped tips; muzzle often with tiny bumps or vertical wrinkles on upper surface.**
3. pinnae usually large, pointed or rounded, often united across forehead.
4. **tragus very small or absent.**
5. no disc on wrist or ankle.
6. second digit of forelimb with one bony phalanx; third digit with two.
7. thumb relatively large.
8. **hindlimb and hindfoot short, broad,** with relatively large claws.
9. calcar present, well developed.
10. **tail extending well beyond margin of relatively small membrane.**
11. humerus with trochiter much larger than trochin, broadly articulating with scapula.
12. premaxillae separated or united, fused to maxillae, with or without palatal branches.
13. no postorbital process.
14. cheekteeth tritubercular.

Dental formula: $\frac{1}{1\text{-}3}\frac{1}{1}\frac{1\text{-}2}{2}\frac{3}{3} = 26\text{-}32$

Compare with: Mystacinidae.

Representative Genera:

Cheiromeles (2) - Naked bats.
Eumops (10) - Mastiff bats.

Molossops (6) - No common name.
Molossus (5) - Velvety free-tailed bats.
Otomops (5) - Big-eared free-tailed bats.
Promops (3) - Domed-palate mastiff bats.
Tadarida (45) - Free-tailed bats.

Free-tailed bat.

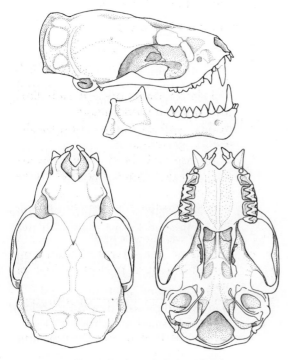

Figure 48. Skull of a molossid (*Tadarida*, x 3).

ORDER PRIMATES

Primates are one of the oldest orders of mammals, dating back as far as the Late Cretaceous. They are closely linked to insectivores. Members of the insectivore family Tupaiidae (p. 73), although not ancestral to primates, share morphological features with both orders.

The modern families of primates are characterized by features illustrating several evolutionary trends: (1) a progressive elaboration of the cerebral hemispheres of the brain; (2) regression in importance of olfaction and enhancement of visual acuity; and (3) improvements in mobility and dexterity of limbs and digits. According to Cartmill (1972, 1974) the origin and persistence of these arboreal adaptations resulted from visually directed predation on arboreal insects by ancestral nocturnal primates. Interestingly, virtually the entire range of chromosome numbers in mammals is found among primates (2n = 20-80).

Most primates are arboreal, although some (e.g., baboons, chimpanzees, humans) are secondarily terrestrial. Most are opportunistic feeders. With few exceptions, they have comparatively generalized teeth. Primates are most successful in tropical and subtropical areas.

There are ten extant families (only one of which is particularly diverse) composing two suborders—Prosimii and Anthropoidea. The anthropoids often are subdivided into two groups — Platyrrhini and Catarrhini — the former consisting of marmosets and New World monkeys, and the latter comprising Old World monkeys, apes, and man.

Partly because of anthropocentrism, primates have long been considered an important group of mammals and have provided a rich area for research. More has been written about them than about any other group of mammals.

Recognition Characters:

1. foot posture plantigrade.
2. soles of feet naked, with enlarged pads.
3. **nail almost always present on hallux, usually also on other digits.**
4. **pollex and/or hallux opposable, used in grasping.**
5. **braincase relatively large, housing well-developed cerebral hemispheres.**
6. radius and ulna, tibia and fibula separate.
7. clavicle well developed.
8. orbit large and separated from temporal fossa by a postorbital bar or plate.
9. molars tritubercular or quadritubercular.

Compare with: Insectivora, Dermoptera.

Remarks: The literature dealing with primates is enormous and widely scattered. A general review of primate biology was provided by Fiedler (1956), Hill (1972), and Schultz (1969). Clark (1971) reviewed structure and evolution. Taxonomy and comparative anatomy were thoroughly explored in the multivolume works of Hill (1953, 1955, 1957, 1960, 1962, 1966, 1970, 1974) and Elliott (1913) and in Napier and Napier (1967). Selected sources for other aspects of primate biology are: locomotion (Jenkins, 1974); behavior (Crook, 1970; Devore,

1965; Jay, 1968; Jolly, 1972); feeding ecology (Clutton-Brock, 1977); myths and relation to man (Morris and Morris, 1966); conservation and use by man (H.S.H. Prince Rainier III of Monaco and Bourne, 1977; Bermant and Lindburg, 1975). The journals *Primates* and *Folia Primatologica* are devoted to studies of this order of mammals.

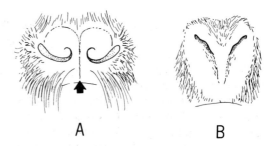

A   B

Figure 49. Anterior views of the snout of prosimian (A) and anthropoid (B) primates showing divided (at arrow) and undivided upper lips, respectively. (After Hershkovitz, 1978.)

KEY TO FAMILIES OF PRIMATES

1a.	Upper lip divided (Fig. 49A); postorbital bar complete, but orbit and temporal fossa largely continuous deep to it; lacrimal foramen opening outside orbit **(Prosimii)** 2
1b.	Upper lip not divided (Fig. 49B); orbit and temporal fossa separated by a bony plate; lacrimal foramen opening inside orbit **(Anthropoidea)** 6
2a (1a).	Third digit on forefoot much longer than other digits; incisors 1/1, chisel-shaped; premolars 1/0 .. **DAUBENTONIIDAE** (p. 117)
2b.	Third digit on forefoot not markedly longer than other digits; incisors more than 1/1, not chisel-shaped; premolars 2/2 or 3/3 3
3a (2b).	Digits extremely elongate, terminating in enlarged discs; auditory bulla extending laterally as a bony tube; no gap between upper incisors of opposite sides; molars tritubercular............................ **TARSIIDAE** (p.120)
3b.	Digits only moderately elongate, not terminating in enlarged discs; auditory bulla not extending laterally as a bony tube; distinct gap between upper incisors of opposite sides; molars quadritubercular 4
4a (3b).	Digits webbed; all digits with nails; upper incisors present, enlarged, and unequal in size; lower premolars 2/2, first one canine-like; 30 or fewer total teeth .... **INDRIDAE** (p.116)
4b.	Digits not webbed; claw present on at least one digit of hindfoot; upper incisors absent or very small and ± equal in size; lower premolars 3/3, none canine-like; more than 30 total teeth 5

5a (4b). Second digit of forefoot short or absent; snout and rostrum short; braincase globular .... **LORISIDAE** (p.118)

5b. Second digit of forefoot prominent; snout and rostrum elongate; braincase elongate .... **LEMURIDAE** (p.115)

6a (1b). Nostrils well separated, directed laterally; auditory bulla not extending laterally as a bony tube (Fig. 50A) (**Platyrrhini**)..7

6b. Nostrils close together, directed forward or downward; auditory bulla extending laterally as a bony tube (Fig. 50B) (**Catarrhini**) 9

7a (6a). All digits with flattened or narrow, keeled nails; cheekteeth 6/6 .... **CEBIDAE** (p.122)

7b. Claws present on all digits except hallux, which bears a nail; cheekteeth 5/5 or 6/6 8

8a (7b). Cheekteeth 5/5 .... **CALLITRICHIDAE** (p.124)
8b. Cheekteeth 6/6 ....**CALLIMICONIDAE** (p.123)

9a (6b). Hallux not opposable; no ischial callosities; braincase enormous; toothrows forming rounded arch; canines relatively small, scarcely longer than other teeth .... **HOMINIDAE** (p.130)

9b. Hallux opposable; ischial callosities usually present; braincase moderately large; toothrows ± parallel; canines well developed, much longer than other teeth 10

10a (9b). Tail usually present; ischial callosities well developed; no bony shelf on posterior border of jaw symphysis
....**CERCOPITHECIDAE** (p.126)

10b. No tail; ischial callosities small or absent; bony shelf present on posterior border of jaw symphysis ....**PONGIDAE** (p.128)

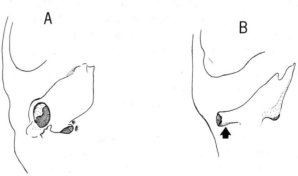

Figure 50. Absence, a cebid (A), and presence, a cercopithecid (B), of a tubular extension of the bulla.

SUBORDER PROSIMII

1. muzzle with rhinarium (except Tarsiidae).
2. **upper lip divided** (except Tarsiidae) (Fig. 49A).
3. **orbit and temporal fossa largely continuous.**
4. **lacrimal foramen opening outside orbit.**
5. braincase relatively small.
6. foramen magnum ± directed posteriorly.

Family LEMURIDAE
(Lemurs)

Lemurs may be easily distinguished from other prosimian primates by a combination of roughly equally proportioned limbs, a long well-haired tail, an elongate muzzle, and separate digits. The skull is also unusual — the rostrum and cranium are elongate, the upper incisors are minute or absent, the lower canine is indistinct, and the cheekteeth are tritubercular (Fig. 51).

These primitive primates inhabit wet or dry tropical forests. They are herbivorous, insectivorous, or omnivorous. Most are arboreal and nocturnal, but the ring-tailed lemur (*Lemur catta*) is frequently active on the ground during the day. They are agile climbers. Lemurs rest in rock crevices, in hollow trees, or in nests which they construct of leaves or grass.

Lemurs occur singly, in pairs, or in groups of up to 20 individuals. They engage in mutual grooming and scent marking. *L. catta* has "stink-fights" (Jolly, 1966). Social forms have sharply defined territories. Lemurs emit a variety of shrieking and grunting sounds.

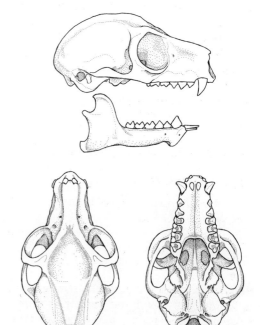

Figure 51. Skull of a lemur (*Lemur*, x ½).

Breeding normally occurs once a year. Usually one or two young are born, but multiple births also occur.

Lemurs are sometimes eaten by humans; hawks also prey on them.

Five genera, 15 species; Madagascar.

Recognition Characters:

● **braincase elongate** (globular in other prosimians) (Fig. 51).
1. size small to medium (24-96 cm).
2. limbs ± equal in length.
3. **digits each bearing a nail except for second digit of hindfoot, which bears a claw.**
4. tail long, furred.
5. fur woolly.
6. **rostrum elongate** (Fig. 51).

115

7. orbits large, usually with prominent ridge around each.
8. **upper incisors absent or uniformly very small, peg-like, and separated from incisors of opposite side by a prominent gap;** lower incisors comb-like, procumbent (Fig. 51).
9. molars tritubercular.

Dental formula: $\dfrac{0\text{-}2\ 1\ 3\ 3}{2\ 1\ 3\ 3} = 32\text{-}36$

Compare with: Indridae, Lorisidae.

Representative Genera:

Cheirogaleus (2) - Dwarf lemurs.
Lemur (5) - Lemurs.
Lepilemur (1) - *L. mustelinus* is the sportive lemur.
Microcebus (2) - Mouse lemurs.

Remarks: Various aspects of the biology of lemurs were explored by Tattersall and Sussman (1975). Jolly (1966) examined the behavior of lemurs, and Hill (1953) treated anatomy and taxonomy.

Family INDRIDAE
(Sifakas, endrinas, woolly lemurs)

These primates are recognizable externally by the relatively short hairless muzzle and long woolly or silky fur. Because the hindlimbs are relied upon for most propulsion and grasping, they are disproportionately large, and the hindfoot is large and elongate. The well-developed hallux opposes the other four toes, which are webbed at their bases. The total of 30 teeth in the dentition is unique among primates.

Indrids are strict herbivores. Morphological indications of this habit include a long caecum and well-developed salivary glands. They are the Madagascaran equivalents of anthropoid leaf-eaters of Africa (e.g., *Colobus, Presbytis*) and South America (e.g., *Alouatta*).

Indrids occur in tropical forests and brushy woodlands. They are relatively sluggish, deliberate climbers, generally travelling on the ground or in an upright fashion in trees. Movements are by leaps or hops. They shelter in tree holes.

There is one breeding period per year, at which time a single offspring is born. Indrids produce varied sounds. Endrinas (*Indri*) utter howls that are amplified by special laryngeal sacs.

Three genera, 4 species; Madagascar.

Recognition Charaters:

● **bases of digits on hindfoot (except hallus) united by skin.**
1. size medium (63-160 cm).
2. **hindlimbs much longer than forelimbs.**
3. **all digits with nails.**
4. tail vestigial or long, furred.
5. fur soft, often woolly.
6. rostrum relatively short.
7. orbits large, with prominent ridge around each.
8. **upper incisors enlarged, unequal in size, separated from incisors of opposite side by a small gap;** lower incisors comb-like, procumbent.
9. molars quadritubercular.

Dental formula: $\dfrac{2\ 1\ 2\ 3}{2\ 0\ 2\ 3} = 30$

Compare with: Lemuridae, Lorisidae.

Representative Genera:

Indri (1) - *I. indri* is the endrina.
Propithecus (2) - Sifakas.

Remarks: Hill (1953) reviewed taxonomy and anatomy of indrids.

Family DAUBENTONIIDAE
(Aye-aye)

Like lemurs (p.115) and indris (p.116), these curious prosimians are restricted to Madagascar. They possess peculiar specializations that enable them to subsist on a diet of wood-boring insects and their larvae. The dentition is reduced and rodent-like (see below and Fig. 52). The digits on the forefeet are long and clawed. The third finger is extremely elongate and wire-like, and, together with the incisor teeth, it is used to probe and chip away bark and wood for insects. The fur is coarse, the tail bushy, and the ears large.

Little is known of aye-aye habits. They are secretive, nocturnal animals of tropical forest, occurring solitarily or in pairs. They rest in nests or in hollow trees. The only known vocalization is a sharp shriek.

One genus, 2 species; Madagascar.

Recognition Characters:
- **third digit on forefoot slender, longer than other digits.**
- **upper and lower incisors large, chisel-shaped** (Fig. 52).

1. size medium (86-104 cm).
2. hindlimbs longer than forelimbs.
3. digits each bearing a claw except for hallux, which bears a flat nail.
4. tail long, bushy.
5. **pelage with short woolly underfur and long coarse guard hairs.**
6. rostrum very short.
7. **orbits medium-sized, without prominent orbital ridges** (Fig. 52).
8. incisors as described above.
9. **molars basically quadritubercular with flat crowns and indistinct cusps** (Fig. 52).

Dental formula: $\frac{1}{1}\frac{0\text{-}1}{0}\frac{1}{0}\frac{3}{3}$ = 18-20

Genus:

Daubentonia (1) - *D. madagascariensis* is the aye-aye.

Remarks: The most authoritative account of aye-aye biology is that of Petter (1977).

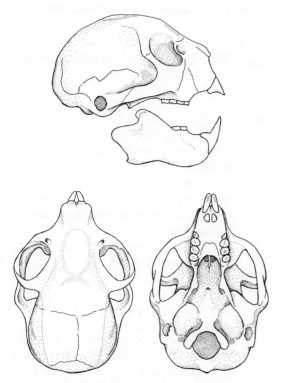

Figure 52. Skull of a daubentoniid (*Daubentonia*, x 1). (After Elliott, 1913.)

Family LORISIDAE
(Lorises, pottos, galagos)

Although superficially resembling lemurs (p.115), these forest-dwelling primates are distinguished by several external features of the limbs and snout (see below). The tail and ears vary in size. The fur is soft, thick, and variable in color, and sexes of some species (e.g., lorises) exhibit color dimorphism. The eyes are prominent. In galagos the hindlimbs are proportionately larger than those in other lorisids. The skull is illustrated in Fig. 53.

Other peculiar adaptations are present. The fingers are richly supplied with blood vessels; this arrangement apparently results in improved gaseous exchange and reduced muscle fatigue during climbing

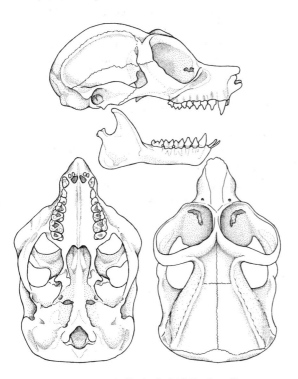

Figure 53. Skull of a lorisid (*Loris*, x 1).

activities. In pottos (*Perodictus*), the elongate spinous processes of the cervical vertebrae are visible where they protrude through the skin of the dorsal surface of the neck. The function of this curious condition is not known, although it may serve as a protective device or as a secondary sexual characteristic. Like cebid monkeys (p.122), lorisids practice "urine washing" of the hands.

Lorisids are nocturnal and arboreal. Lorises and pottos usually progress with slow, deliberate motions. In contrast, galagos are prodigious leapers; as in tarsiers, their tarsal bones are lengthened. Lorisids eat insects and other invertebrates, small vertebrates, eggs, resin, and fruit. They find shelter in tree holes, forks of branches, foliage, or abandoned nests.

Breeding apparently occurs twice a year. One to three young are produced.

Six genera, 11 species; southeast Asia, India, Ceylon, East Indies, and Africa south of the Sahara.

Recognition Characters:

1. size relatively small (18-80 cm).
2. **hindlimbs much longer than forelimbs.**
3. **digits each bearing a nail except for second digit of hindfoot, which bears a claw.**
4. **tail usually very small or absent (long in bushbabies).**
5. fur soft, dense, somewhat woolly.
6. rostrum short.
7. orbits large, usually with prominent ridge around each (Fig. 53).
8. **upper incisors uniformly very small, peg-like, and separated from incisors of opposite side by a prominent gap;** lower incisors usually comb-like, procumbent (Fig. 53).

9. molars quadritubercular (Fig. 53).

Dental formula: $\frac{1\text{-}2}{2}\frac{1}{1}\frac{3}{3}\frac{3}{3} = 34\text{-}36$

Compare with: Lemuridae, Indridae.

Representative Genera:

Galago (4) - Galagos, bushbabies.
Loris (1) - *L. tardigradus* is the slender loris.
Nycticebus (2) - Slow lorises.
Perodictus (1) - *P. potto* is the potto.

Remarks: Some authors (e.g., Kingdon, 1971; Hershkovitz, 1978; Vaughan, 1978) relegated bushbabies to a separate family (Galagidae).

A good source of information on ecology and behavior of lorisids is Charles-Dominique (1977). Anatomy and taxonomy were reviewed by Hill (1953).

Slow loris.

Family TARSIIDAE
(Tarsiers)

Tarsiers have long confused tax-onomists. Structurally they combine characters of both suborders of primates, prompting some authors (e.g., Hershkovitz, 1978) to place them in a group also including anthropoid families (Haplorrhini), or others (e.g., Romer, 1966) to erect a separate suborder for them (Tarsiiformes). Despite taxonomic difficulties, tarsiers are easily distinguished from other primates because of the squat body, rounded head dominated by huge eyes, and long naked tail. Two clawed grooming digits on the hindfoot and large mobile ears are also peculiar. The diploid chromosome number (2n = 80) is one of the largest recorded for mammals.

Tarsiers are nocturnal and mainly arboreal, progressing by leaps from branch to branch. Adaptations for this habit include the presence of elongate tarsal bones in the hindfoot and relatively large hindlimbs. Grasping is enhanced by the presence of flattened pads at the ends of the digits. Tarsiers rest while clinging to vertical limbs.

Insects compose the bulk of the diet. Breeding is apparently aseasonal; one young is produced. Tarsiers are territorial (at least during the mating period) and occur in pairs.

One genus, 3 species; Sumatra, the Philippines, and some other islands.

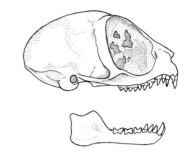

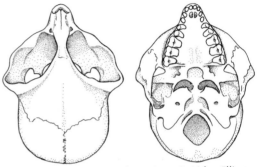

Figure 54. Skull of a tarsiid (*Tarsier*, x 1). (After Elliott, 1913.)

Recognition Characters:

● **no rhinarium** (present in all other prosimians.

● **digits very elongate, terminating in enlarged discs.**

● **auditory bulla extending laterally as a bony tube** (tube absent in other prosimians) (Fig. 54).

1. size relatively small (22-43 cm).
2. hindlimbs longer than forelimbs.
3. **claws on second and third digits of hindfoot and nails on remaining digits.**
4. **tail long, naked or sparsely haired, often tufted at end.**
5. **fur silky, wavy.**
6. rostrum short.
7. **orbits enormous, with prominent ridge around each** (Fig. 54).
8. **upper and lower incisors well developed, not equal in size; upper incisors not separated from incisors of opposite side; lower incisors vertical** (Fig. 54).
9. **molars tritubercular.**

Dental formula: $\dfrac{2}{1}\dfrac{1}{1}\dfrac{3}{3}\dfrac{3}{3} = 34$

Genus:

Tarsius (3)- Tarsiers.

Remarks: Hill (1955) summarized the anatomy and taxonomy of tarsiers.

SUBORDER ANTHROPOIDEA

Characters:
1. muzzle without rhinarium.
2. **upper lip undivided** (Fig. 49B).
3. **orbit and temporal fossa separated by postorbital plate.**
4. **lacrimal foramen opening inside orbit.**
5. braincase relatively large.
6. foramen magnum ± directed ventrally.

Family CEBIDAE
(New World monkeys)

Members of this family constitute the largest group of New World primates. The absence of rump calluses, an opposable thumb, and bony ear tubes, and the presence of nostrils which open laterally, nails on the digits, and six cheekteeth per jaw set cebids apart from closely related families. The tail is prehensile in some genera. The skull is shown in Fig. 55.

Cebids are mostly diurnal (*Aotus* is nocturnal). They are active and graceful, progressing through trees with agile swinging and leaping movements. Most live in territorial family units. Their diet consists of insects and other invertebrates, small vertebrates, fruit, shoots, and leaves. Social behavior is relatively complex, and communication is achieved by varied vocalizations, facial expressions, and other gestures. In howler monkeys (*Alouatta*) the larynx is modified (especially in males) into a large resonating chamber. Howlers emit a loud, penetrating roar.

Breeding takes place at any time of year. Females bear one young.

Eleven genera, 29 species; Mexico, Central and South America.

Recognition Characters:
1. size small to medium (63-183 cm).
2. forelimbs longer or shorter than hindlimbs.
3. **pollex only slightly opposable or absent;** hallux opposable.
4. digits each bearing a flattened or narrow and keeled nail.
5. tail short (*Cacajao*) or long, **prehensile in some** (e.g., *Ateles, Alouatta, Lagothrix*).
6. no ischial callosities (rump patches).
7. **nostrils well separated, directed laterally.**

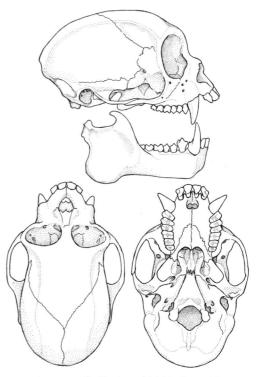

Figure 55. Skull of a cebid (*Ateles*, x ½).

8. **auditory bulla not extending laterally as a bony tube** (Fig. 55).

Dental formula: $\frac{2\ 1\ 3\ 3}{2\ 1\ 3\ 3} = 36$

Compare with: Callitrichidae, Cercopithecidae, Callimiconidae.

Representative Genera:

Alouatta (5) - Howler monkeys.

Aotus (1) - *A. trivirgatus*, is the night monkey.

Ateles (4) - Spider monkeys.

Cacajao (3) - Uakari monkeys.

Callicebus (3) - Titi monkeys.

Cebus (4) - Capuchins.

Lagothrix (2) - Woolly monkeys.

Saimiri (2) - Squirrel monkeys.

Remarks: Comparative anatomy and taxonomy of cebids were treated by Hill (1960, 1962). Behavior, ecology, and conservation were examined in volumes edited by Moynihan (1976) and Thorington and Heltne (1976). Rosenblum and Cooper (1968) summarized the biology of squirrel monkeys. Carpenter's (1934) study on howler monkeys was one of the first thorough field studies of primates.

Family CALLIMICONIDAE
(Callimico)

This family is represented by only one living species. Because it shares characters with both callitrichids (p.124) and cebids (p.122), the callimico has been a taxonomic enigma. The number of cheekteeth and some details of the skull are cebid-like, whereas external features (long silky pelage, non-opposable thumb, clawed digits, and general size and form) are reminiscent of marmosets. The form of the cheekteeth is intermediate between those of cebids and callitrichids.

Almost nothing is known of the habits of callimicos in the wild. Studies of captive animals (Lorenz, 1972) indicate that they are omnivorous. The family is the basic social unit. They bear only one young.

One genus, 1 species; Upper Amazon basin of Peru and Colombia.

Recognition Characters:

1. size small (48-56 cm).
2. forelimbs shorter than hindlimbs.
3. pollex not opposable; hallux opposable.
4. **digits each bearing a claw except for hallux, which bears a flat nail.**
5. tail long, not prehensile.
6. no ischial callosities.
7. nostrils well separated, directed laterally.
8. auditory bulla not extended laterally as a bony tube.

Dental formula: $\frac{2\ 1\ 3\ 3}{2\ 1\ 3\ 3} = 36$

Compare with: Cebidae, Callitrichidae.

Genus:

Callimico (1) - *C. goeldii* is the callimico.

Remarks: The foregoing account is based largely on Hershkovitz' (1978) summary of the taxonomy and biology of *Callimico*. The anatomy of this mammal was described by Hill (1959).

Family CALLITRICHIDAE
(Marmosets, tamarins)

This family contains the smaller New World primates. Their small size, thick silky fur, non-opposable thumb, clawed digits, and dental characters (described below) are distinguishing features. The tail is long but not prehensile. The pelage is often strikingly colored or variegated, and the head in some forms is adorned with manes, mustaches, or ear tufts. The skull is illustrated in Fig. 56.

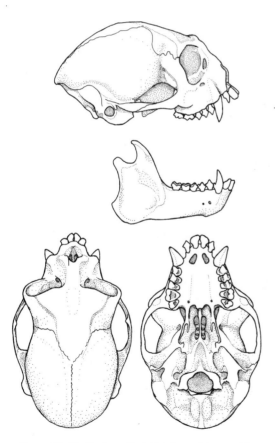

Figure 56. Skull of a callitrichid (*Leontideus*, x ¾).

Marmosets are diurnal primates of dry scrub and rainforest. They do not brachiate; instead, they use all four limbs to scramble over branches in squirrel-like fashion. Movements are quick and jerky. The diet consists chiefly of insects and fruit. But small vertebrates, tree sap, and leaves are consumed also.

Callitrichids are social, occurring chiefly in family groups, and are territorial. Reproduction is seasonal. Partition coincides with the onset of the rainy season. Females usually bear twins.

Four genera, 14 species; Panama and South America.

Recognition Characters:

● **molars tritubercular** (quadritubercular in other anthropoids) (Fig. 56).

1. size small (30-89 cm).
2. forelimbs slightly longer or shorter than hindlimbs.
3. **pollex not opposable;** hallux opposable.
4. **digits each bearing a claw except for hallux, which bears a flat nail.**
5. tail long, not prehensile.
6. no ischial callosities.
7. nostrils well separated, directed laterally.
8. auditory bulla not extending laterally as a bony tube.

Dental formula: $\frac{2}{2}\frac{1}{1}\frac{3}{3}\frac{2}{2} = 32$

Compare with: Cebidae, Cercopithecidae Callimiconidae.

Genera:

Callithrix (3) - True marmosets.
Cebuella (1) - *C. pygmaea* is the pygmy marmoset.
Leontopithecus (1) - *L. rosalia* is the lion marmoset.
Saguinus (9) - Tamarins.

Remarks: Hershkovitz (1978) provided an excellent review of the taxonomy and biology of marmosets. Other useful references include Hill (1957), Kleiman (1977), Moynihan (1976), and Thorington and Heltne (1976).

Marmoset.

Family CERCOPITHECIDAE
(Old World monkeys)

This is the largest and most diverse family of primates. Arboreal or secondarily terrestrial, cercopithecids range widely over Africa and Asia. All digits have nails. Both hallux and pollex are strongly opposable. Prominent, often brightly colored calluses are present on the rump. The skull of cercopithecids is distinguished from that of marmosets (p.124) and New World monkeys (p.122) by the presence of prominent bony ear canals (Fig. 57). All can stand upright but most progress quadrupedally.

Social interactions are complex and varied. Communication is achieved chiefly by varied calls and visual cues. Facial expressions are relatively well developed—the face is nearly naked, usually dark in color (infrequently yellow, red, or blue), and has well-developed musculature. Mustaches, beards, manes, or other crests of hair on the foreparts aid visual communication. Cercopithecids usually occur in family units, are often territorial and aggressive (particularly terrestrial forms), have a well-defined social structure, and are often sexually dimorphic.

Cercopithecids are mostly diurnal. Some (*Cercopithecus*) are omnivorous; others (e.g., *Colobus, Presbytis*) are herbivorous. Colobus monkeys and langurs are especially agile brachiators. Cercopithecids shelter in trees, rocks, or caves.

Breeding is seasonal or aseasonal. Normally one young is produced. A menstrual cycle is probably present in all cercopithecids. The life span may exceed two decades.

Members of this family are widely used for food, as pets, and as subjects of medical research (e.g., rhesus monkey, *Cercopithecus mulatta*).

Six genera, about 60 species; Gibraltar, Africa, southern Arabia, southeast Asia and adjacent islands, Japan.

Recognition Characters:

1. size medium (70-185 cm).
2. forelimbs slightly longer than hindlimbs.
3. pollex opposable (unless reduced or absent); hallux opposable.
4. **digits each with flattened nail.**
5. **tail absent or, if present, short or long, not prehensile.**
6. ischial callosities present.
7. nostrils close together, directed forward or downward.
8. **auditory bulla extending laterally as a bony tube** (Fig. 57).

Dental formula: $\frac{2}{2} \frac{1}{1} \frac{3}{3} \frac{2}{2} = 32$

Compare with: Pongidae, Cebidae.

Representative Genera:

Cercopithecus (including *Cercocebus, Cynopithecus, Erythrocebus, Macaca, Mandrillus, Miopithecus, Papio,* and *Theropithecus*; see **Remarks**) (40) - Guenons, vervets, macaques, talapoin, baboons, mandrills, mangabeys, and patas monkeys.

Colobus (3) - Colobus monkeys.

Nasalis (1) - *N. larvatus* is the proboscis monkey.

Presbytis (13) - Langurs, leaf-eating monkeys.

Remarks: Van Gelder (1977) presented evidence of natural and artificial hybridization among many species of Old World monkeys. I follow him in relegating the currently recognized genera of macaque-like cercopithecids to one genus, *Cercopithecus* (see above).

The literature on Old World monkeys is extensive and scattered. A few samples are Hill (1966, 1970, 1974) and Napier and Napier (1970). Many other articles dealing with cercopithecid biology are included in volumns cited above for primates as a whole (p.112).

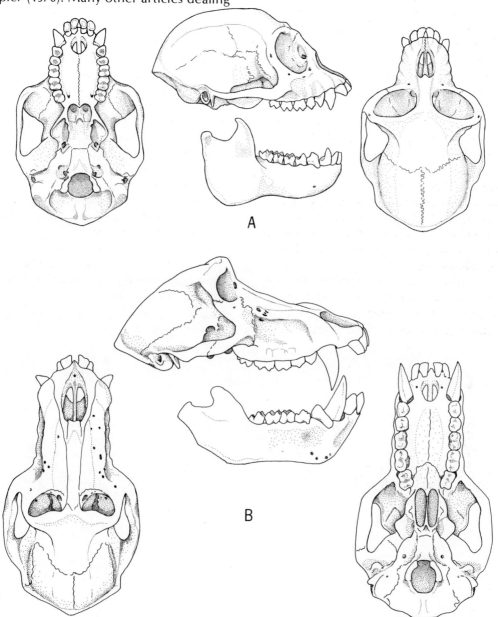

Figure 57. Skulls of cercopithecids: A, *Colobus* (x ¼); B, *Cercopithecus* (x 1/3).

Family PONGIDAE
(Great Apes)

Pongids are primates specialized for great strength (gorillas, chimpanzees, and orangutans) and agility and speed in trees (gibbons). The forelimbs are long, and dexterity of the feet is pronounced. The forefeet of gibbons are peculiar—instead of grasping branches while brachiating, the hands glide in hook-like fashion over the surface of the limb as the body swings underneath. Pongids have no tail. The skull of all forms is relatively massive and heavily ridged (Fig 58). A supportive bridge of bone (the "simian shelf") connects the two sides of the lower jaw where they join.

Vision and hearing are the best developed senses. Vocalizations are varied and are amplified in gibbons by a distensible throat sac.

Pongids occur in family groups consisting of one dominant adult male and one to several females and offspring. Usually there is sexual dimorphism in size or color. As in cercopithecids (p.126), facial expressions play important roles in social interactions, and the face is relatively naked and well muscled. Chimpanzees use simple tools fashioned from natural objects (e.g., twigs) or which they fabricate themselves for a particular use.

Apes are diurnal and are mainly vegetarians, although animal matter also is taken. Chimpanzees and gorillas are mostly terrestrial, whereas gibbons and orangutans are arboreal. Pongids rest on branches in trees (*Hylobates*), in stick nests on the ground (*Gorilla*), or in trees (*Chimpansee, Pongo*). Females bear a single young at any time of year.

These primates are favored by man as a source of food, for zoo exhibits, and for medical research. Some species (e.g., gorillas, orangutans) have declined markedly in numbers because of exploitation of their preferred habitats for timber and agriculture.

Four genera, 8 species; Africa, southeast Asia and adjacent islands.

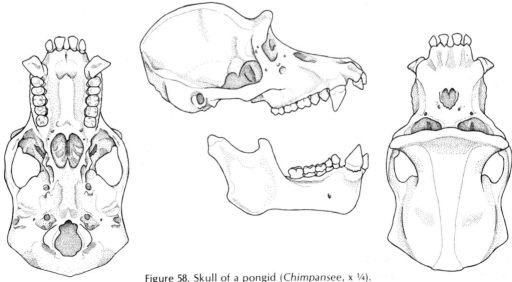

Figure 58. Skull of a pongid (*Chimpansee*, x ¼).

Recognition Characters:

- **bony shelf present at posterior border of jaw symphysis.**

1. size medium to large (to standing height of 180 cm).
2. **forelimbs much longer than hindlimbs.**
3. pollex opposable (unless reduced); hallux opposable.
4. **digits each bearing a flattened or slightly keeled nail (except for hallux and pollex in gibbons, which lack claws or nails).**
5. **no tail.**
6. ischial callosities small (*Hylobates*) or absent.
7. nostrils close together, opening forward or downward.
8. auditory bulla extending laterally as a bony tube (Fig. 58).

Dental formula: $\frac{2}{2} \frac{1}{1} \frac{2}{2} \frac{3}{3} = 32$

Genera:

Chimpansee (=Pan) (1) - *C. troglodytes* is the chimpanzee.

Gorilla (1) - *G. gorilla* includes the mountain and coastal gorillas.

Hylobates (including *Symphalangus*) (6) - Gibbons.

Pongo (1) - *P. pygmaeus* is the orangutan.

Remarks: The gibbons (*Hylobates*) have been placed in a separate family by some authors (e.g., Elliott, 1913; Napier and Napier, 1967). While they do exhibit traits not common to other pongids (such as habitual bipedal locomotion on the ground, extremely long forelimbs, and ischial callosities), they closely resemble great apes in other features.

An older but still useful general reference to pongids is Yerkes and Yerkes (1929). More specific works include: Schaller (1963) on *Gorilla*; Bourne (1969-1972) and van Lawick-Goodall (1968) on *Chimpansee*; and Carpenter (1940) and Chivers (1974) on *Hylobates*.

Gibbon.

Family HOMINIDAE
(Humans)

The primary features distinguishing hominids from other mammals are bipedalism and the extraordinary enlargement of the brain and associated braincase (Fig. 59). This evolutionary development afforded humans the capacity to develop complex cultures, spoken languages, and the ability to control many aspects of their environment. Numerous skeletal and muscular peculiarities that assist in support and balance are associated with the upright stance. The habits of many groups of humans, such as the food-gathering tribes of South America, the Philippines, New Guinea, Africa, and Australia, are not far removed from those of many other mammals. However, a complete discussion of the many and varied activities of humans is beyond the scope of this book.

Females usually give birth to one young, though multiple births of up to five or more are recorded. Humans are sexually dimorphic.

One genus, 1 species; worldwide.

Recognition Characters:

- **braincase enormously inflated** (Fig. 59).

- **toothrows forming rounded arch** ($\pm$ parallel in other anthropoids) (Fig. 59)

- **canines small, scarcely (if at all) longer than other teeth** (large in other anthropoids) (Fig. 59).

1. size large (to standing height of 200 cm).
2. hindlimbs longer than forelimbs.
3. **pollex highly opposable; hallux not opposable.**

4. digits with flattened nails.
5. **no tail.**
6. no ischial callosities.
7. nostrils close together, opening downward.
8. auditory bulla extending laterally as a bony tube.

Dental formula: $\frac{2\ 1\ 2\ 3}{2\ 1\ 2\ 3} = 32$

Compare with: Pongidae.

Genus:

Homo (1) - *H. sapiens* is the only species of human.

Remarks: Some authors consider humans to be no more than relatively specialized pongids. Anderson (1967) implied that were it not for the anthropocentric nature of most scientists, humans would properly be classified in a single family with the great apes.

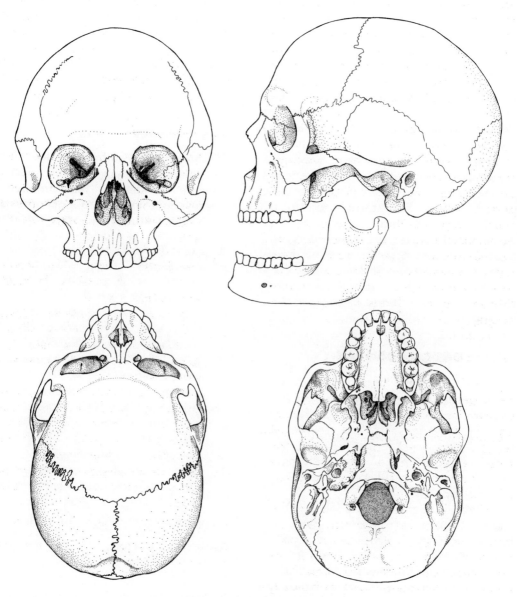

Figure 59. Skull of a hominid (*Homo*, x ⅜).

ORDERS EDENTATA, PHOLIDOTA, AND TUBULIDENTATA

In early classifications of mammals, anteaters, armadillos, sloths, pangolins, and aardvarks were commonly grouped together in a single order. Indeed, the aardvark and giant anteater were once placed in the same genus (*Myrmecophaga*). It is now clear, however, that these mammals form distinct assemblages and that, whereas pholidotes and edentates are relatively closely related and probably share a common ancestor, the affinities of the tubulidentates seem to be with the early ancestors of ungulates. Although there are morphological differences among living forms, the fossil history of the orders offers few clues to their relationships. Despite differences in degree of relatedness, the three orders are treated together here because of their superficial similarities, making it possible to separate them more effectively than if the orders were scattered throughout the book.

ORDER EDENTATA

Living edentates are morphologically heterogeneous, consisting of arboreal and terrestrial forms of rather different features and habits. When they are considered together with fossil forms, however, the close relationships of the seemingly distinctive sloths, armadillos, and anteaters become apparent.

The name Edentata, meaning without teeth, is somewhat misleading because only anteaters (Myrmecophagidae) wholly lack teeth. However, incisors and canines are always absent in other members of the order, and remaining teeth are usually homodont, simple, and without enamel.

Only one of two suborders (Xenarthra) survives, so named because of accessory zygapophyses (xenarthrism) present on the thoracic and lumbar vertebra. This group evolved in South America and was widespread in North America until the end of the Pleistocene. In addition to modern forms, the suborder includes the extinct turtle-like glyptodonts and giant ground sloths.

Recognition Characters:

1. size small to medium-large (15-210 cm).
2. body covered with hair or scutes.
3. **forefoot with two or three principal digits, each bearing long claws;** hindfoot with 2-5 digits.
4. no incisors or canines.
5. **cheekteeth absent** (Myrmecophagidae), **or if present, homodont and without enamel.**
6. zygomatic arch complete (*Dasypodidae*) or incomplete (*Bradypodidae, Myrmecophagidae*).
7. **jugal, lacrimal, and interparietal bones present.**
8. pterygoid bones variable, either separate (Bradypodidae, Dasypodidae) or meeting at midline to form part of palate (Myrmecophagidae) (See Figs. 60-62).
9. **extra zygapophyses present on posterior thoracic and lumbar vertebrae.**

Compare with: Pholidota, Tubulidentata.

Remark: Characters of edentates were examined by Pocock (1924).

KEY TO FAMILIES OF EDENTATA

1a.   Teeth present; jugal well developed; pterygoids usually separate and not forming part of palate (Figs. 61, 62) 2

1b.   Teeth absent; jugal small; pterygoids meeting at midline, forming posterior portion of palate (Fig. 60) . . . . **MYRMECOPHAGIDAE** (p.134)

2a (1a).   Body covered with horny scutes; limbs short; tail long; rostrum long, slender; teeth homodont . . . . **DASYPODIDAE** (p.138)

2b.   Body well haired; limbs long; tail very short; rostrum very short; teeth heterodont . . . . **BRADYPODIDAE** (p.136)

Family MYRMECOPHAGIDAE
(Anteaters)

This is the only family of edentates which has lost all teeth. The elongate snout, acute sense of smell, long tongue, and sharp, powerful claws equip these animals for tearing open termite and ant nests and for probing for and catching insects. The internal support for the worm-like protrusible tongue extends to the posterior portion of the sternum. The mouth is small—in *Tamandua*, the opening is reduced to the size of a pencil. The large salivary glands produce copious quantities of mucus that cause insects to adhere to the tongue.

Anteaters are arboreal *(Cyclopes)*, terrestrial *(Myrmecophaga)*, or both *(Tamandua)*. Mobility of the two arboreal forms is assisted by a prehensile tail. They are diurnal *(Myrmecophaga)* or nocturnal and are generally solitary. The diet is mostly termites, ants, and beetles.

Apparently one young is produced per breeding effort.

Three genera, 4 species; southern Mexico to Argentina.

Recognition Characters:

● **no teeth** (teeth present in other edentate families) (Fig. 60).

1. forelimbs and hindlimbs ± equal in size.
2. **tongue very long, protrusible, worm-like.**
3. **skull elongate; rostrum very long and curving downward** (Fig. 60).
4. **zygomatic arch incomplete** (Fig. 60).
5. teeth as above.
6. premaxilla very small.
7. **jugal small.**

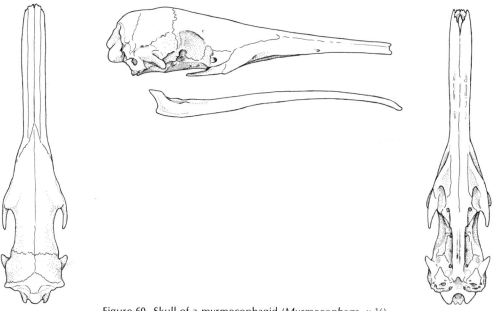

Figure 60. Skull of a myrmecophagid (*Myrmecophaga*, x ¼).

8. **pterygoids meeting at midline, extending palate posteriorly to auditory bullae** (Fig. 60).

Dental formula: no teeth (Fig. 60).

Compare with: Dasypodidae, Manidae (Pholidota), Tachyglossidae (Monotremata).

Genera:

Cyclopes (1) - *C. didactylus* is the silky anteater.

Myrmecophaga (1) - *M. tridactyla* is the giant anteater.

Tamandua (1) - *T. tetradactyla* is the tamandua or collared anteater.

Collared anteater.

Family BRADYPODIDAE
(Sloths)

These arboreal endentates are probably best known for their slow, methodical movements and upside-down posture. The ungainly appearance of sloths is accentuated by relatively long forelimbs, a rounded head with small face and inconspicuous ears, and a stubby tail. The narrow feet are syndactylous. The digits, together with the long claws, form a hook-like appendage. Bradypodids share a skeletal peculiarity with sirenians — the number of cervical vertebrae departs from the usual seven (in sloths it is six or nine).

The shaggy pelage of sloths contains an interesting community of organisms. Red and green algae, which reside on the surface of or in longitudinal grooves in the hairs, impart a greenish hue to the animal, especially on the body parts most exposed to moisture. In addition to providing protective coloration for the sloth, these algae provide a source of food for small pyralidid moths that also inhabit the fur.

Members of this family are heterothermic. They are strictly leaf-eaters and are relatively long-lived. Births have been recorded at all times of the year. Females bear one young. *Bradypus* is sexually dimorphic—males have a conspicuous oval patch between the shoulder blades consisting of pale to orange hairs bordering a median dark stripe.

Two genera, 6 species; Central America to Argentina.

Recognition Characters:

● **tail very small** (long in other edentates).

● **skull blocky, snout blunt** (both are long in other edentates) (Fig. 61).

1. **forelimbs much longer than hindlimbs.**
2. tongue unspecialized.
3. skull as above.

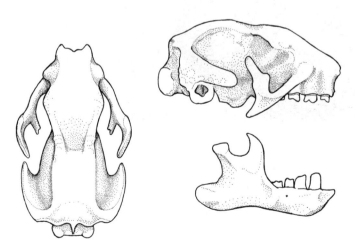
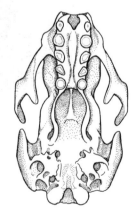

Figure 61. Skull of a bradypodid (*Bradypus*, x 2/3).

4. zygomatic arch incomplete.
5. **first pair of cheekteeth canine-like, otherwise homodont** (Fig. 61).
6. premaxilla very small.
7. jugal well developed.
8. pterygoids separate, not forming part of palate (Fig. 61).

Dental formula: $\dfrac{0}{0}\dfrac{0}{0}\dfrac{5}{4\text{-}5}$ = 18-20

(premolars and molars not distinguishable).

Genera:

Bradypus (4) - Three-toed sloths.
Choloepus (2) - Two-toed sloths.

Remarks: Bradypodid biology was summarized by Britton (1941). The life history of three-toed sloths was explored by Beebe (1926), and their anatomy has been described by Sonntag (1921).

Two-toed sloth

Family DASYPODIDAE
(Armadillos)

Members of this family are the most widespread of the edentates. They are most common in arid or semi-arid grasslands and savannahs of the New World.

Armadillos are easily identified by the shell-like protective carapace covering the body. It consists of several plate-like shields covering the head, back, and rump which are separated by transverse bands. The shields and bands are composed of squarish bony scutes overlain by hardened epidermal tissue and connected by flexible skin. The banded portion of the shell contains 2-18 rings of scutes. The entire carapace is attached to the body by well-developed tegumentary muscles and connective tissue. It is supported by the axial skeleton. The degree of attachment and support differs from species to species. Scutes are also present on the limbs and tail.

In many aspects of their morphology and life style, armadillos are similar to anteaters (p.134). The limbs are stout and are equipped with large curved claws (some armadillos walk wholly on these claws), the snout is usually long, and the tongue is long and protrusible. Teeth are present: they are all small, peg-like, and sometimes numerous (up to 100 total teeth in *Priodontes*).

Armadillos are terrestrial and diurnal or nocturnal. They occur singly, in pairs, or in small bands. They construct shallow or deep burrows, which they may share with several other individuals. Most are omnivorous, feeding on insects and other invertebrates, small vertebrates, and vegetation. Protective behavior includes

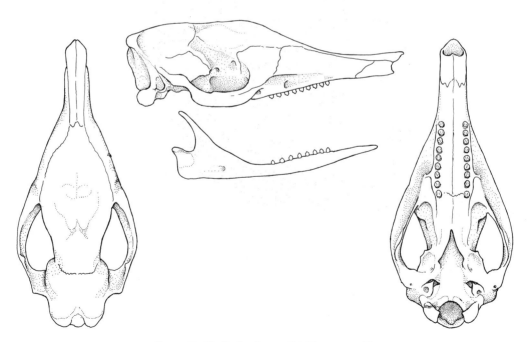

Figure 62. Skull of a dasypodid (*Dasypus*, x ¾).

rolling up in a ball, wedging themselves in burrows, or simply crouching on the ground.

Reproduction in armadillos is peculiar. Females are polyembryonic; that is, all litter mates originate from division of a single zygote (Patterson, 1913). Up to a dozen identical offspring of the same sex are produced, although the usual number is one to four. Delayed implantation is also common.

Nine genera, 21 species; central United States to Argentina.

Recognition Characters:

- **body covered with horny scutes** (body well-haired in other edentate families).

1. forelimbs and hindlimbs about equal in size.
2. tongue long and protrusible.
3. **skull elongate, flattened; rostrum elongate** (Fig. 62).
4. zygomatic arch complete.
5. **cheekteeth homodont.**
6. premaxilla well developed.
7. jugal well developed.
8. pterygoids usually separate, not forming part of palate (joined at midline in *Dasypus*) (Fig. 62).

Dental formula: $\dfrac{0\ 0\ 7\text{-}25}{0\ 0\ 7\text{-}25}$ = 28-100

(premolars and molars indistinguishable).

Compare with: Myrmecophagidae, Manidae (Pholidota).

Representative Genera:

Cabossous (5) - Naked-tailed armadillos.
Chlamyphorus (1) - *C. truncatus* is the pygmy armadillo.
Dasypus (6) - Nine-banded armadillos.

Priodontes (1) - *P. giganteus* is the giant armadillo.
Tolypeutes (2) - Three-banded armadillos.
Zaedyus (1) - *Z. pichiy* is the pichi.

Remark: Taber (1945) studied the natural history of *Dasypus*.

ORDER PHOLIDOTA
Family MANIDAE
(Pangolins or scaly anteaters)

Superficially these mammals show convergences in form and habits toward New World anteaters (p.134) and armadillos (p.138). However, they differ from the latter both externally and internally. In outward appearance they resemble an animated pine cone that tapers gradually toward both ends. Numerous overlapping scales cover the upper parts, head, tail, and limbs (except the forelimbs in two species). The scales are sharp-edged and keeled or striated. The belly is furred. They lack teeth and several cranial bones which are common to most other mammals (see below). The skull is shown in Fig. 63.

Pangolins are nocturnal and arboreal or terrestrial. Arboreal forms have a prehensile tail. They shelter in tree hollows or burrows. The diet consists of ants and termites, which are obtained by the extremely long tongue connected at its base to long posterior processes of the sternum. Gravel in the gizzard-like stomach aids digestion. Pangolins roll up into a ball to protect themselves.

These animals occur singly or in pairs. Males are larger than females. One (occasionally two) young are produced.

Pangolins are prized as food by man. Their scales are used for medicinal and ornamental purposes.

One genus, 8 species; southeast Asia, Africa south of the Sahara.

Recognition Characters:

1. size medium (65-175 cm).
2. **body covered with large overlapping scale-like plates.**

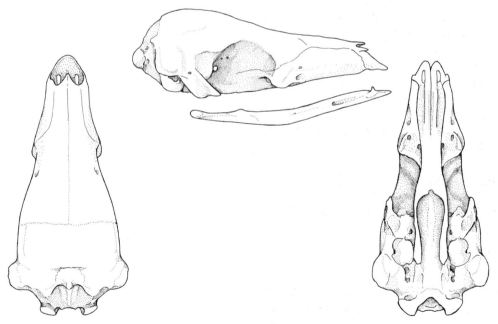

Figure 63. Skull of a manid (*Manis*, x 2/3).

140

3. **forefoot with three principal digits, hindfoot with five; all digits well clawed.**

4-5. **no teeth** (Fig. 63).

6. zygomatic arch incomplete (Fig. 63).

7. **no jugal, lacrimal, or interparietal bones.**

8. pterygoids separate, not forming part of palate (Fig. 63).

9. no extra zygapophyses on vertebrae.

Dental formula: no teeth.

Compare with: Myrmecophagidae and Dasypodidae (Edentata).

Genus:

Manis (8) - Pangolins or scaly anteaters; *M. gigantea* is the giant pangolin of Africa.

Remark: Kingdon (1971a) summarized the habits of African species.

Pangolin.

ORDER TUBULIDENTATA
Family ORYCTEROPODIDAE
(Aardvark)

The common name, aardvark (Afrikaans for "earth-pig"), and the ordinal name, Tubulidentata (referring to "tubule-teeth"), identify two of the most distinguishing features of these mammals. Superficial features include a slender head and snout, large closable ears, and muscular tail and limbs. The digits are partially syndactylous. The structure of the teeth is unique (see below and Fig.8). The permanent cheekteeth are ever-growing; since they do not erupt at the same time, they are seldom present simultaneously. Weighing as much as 80 kg (about 200 lbs), aardvarks are the most massive termite-eaters.

Aardvarks have a highly developed sense of smell. The peculiar shape of the cranium (Fig. 64) is due to an enlargement of the anterior portion of the brain cavity and an elongation and expansion of the nasal cavities, which house, respectively, the large olfactory lobes of the brain and the elongate curled turbinal bones which are covered by the olfactory mucosa. The blunt end of the snout is soft and mobile, and the nostrils are surrounded by dense hairs and sensory tentacle-like vibrissae.

In habits, aardvarks are primarily nocturnal and solitary, and are most common in open grasslands and savannahs where termites and ants are abundant. Aardvarks excavate their own elaborate burrows, termite mounds, and anthills. Females generally bear one young.

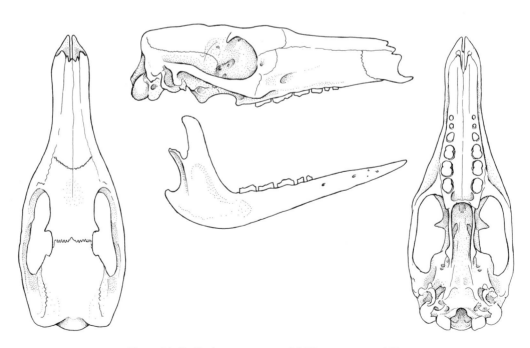

Figure 64. Skull of an orycteropodid (*Orycteropus*, x 1/3).

One genus, 1 species; Africa south of the Sahara.

Recognition Characters:

● **cheekteeth homodont, columnar, consisting of numerous vertical tubes of dentine in a matrix of pulp** (Figs. 8, 64).
1. **size medium-large (145-220 cm), piglike.**
2. **body covered with bristly hairs.**
3. **digits 4-5, with shovel-shaped nails.**
4. no incisors or canines.
5. cheekteeth as described above.
6. zygomatic arch complete (Fig. 64).
7. **jugal and lacrimal present; no inter-parietal.**
8. pterygoid bones separate, not forming part of palate (Fig. 64).
9. no extra zygapophyses on vertebrae.

Dental formula: $\frac{0\ 0\ 2\ 3}{0\ 0\ 2\ 3} = 20$

Genus:

Orycteropus (1) - *O. afer* is the aardvark.

Remarks: Reviews of the biology of aardvarks were provided by Kingdon (1971a) and Melton (1976). Morphological features and anatomy were described by Sonntag (1925), Sonntag and Woollard (1925), and Clark and Sonntag (1926).

ORDER LAGOMORPHA

Lagomorphs have long confused taxonomists, so much so that Wood (1957) published an article entitled "What, if anything, is a rabbit?" At one time they were considered to have close affinities to rodents and were classified as a suborder of that group. The current consensus is that rodents and lagomorphs are rather distantly related. In fact, lagomorphs resemble artiodactyls in a number of fundamental characteristics (e.g., limb structure). Known fossil representatives, dating from the Oligocene, do not provide sufficient information to resolve the issue.

Although this order is not particularly diverse, its members are geographically widespread. They are important ecological and economic components of mammalian faunas in many parts of the world.

Coprophagy — the reingestion of fecal material — is a common behavior among species of both families of lagomorphs. Two types of fecal pellets are produced: soft moist pellets which are eaten, and hard fibrous ones which are discarded. This habit allows the animal to extract the maximum nutritional value from fibrous plant foods in the forms of proteins, vitamins, and metabolites; microbes present in the pellets also provide nutrients.

Recognition Characters:

- **two pairs of upper incisors, the second pair small and peg-like and located directly behind the first** (Figs. 65, 66).
1. size small to medium.
2. foot posture digitigrade.
3. **tail indistinct or small.**
4. **soles of feet largely or entirely covered with fur.**
5. maxilla fenestrated.
6. incisors and cheekteeth separated by large gap (diastema).
7. testes anterior to penis during breeding season.

Compare with: Rodentia.

Remarks: Pocock (1925) summarized external characters of lagomorphs. Limb structure was examined by Camp and Borell (1937).

KEY TO FAMILIES OF LAGOMORPHA

1a. Pinna short, rounded; no visible tail; pads on feet exposed; no supraorbital process; five upper cheekteeth . . . . **OCHOTONIDAE** (p. 145)

1b. Pinna long, pointed; tail short but visible; pads on feet covered with fur; fan-shaped supraorbital process usually present; six upper cheekteeth (rarely five) . . . . **LEPORIDAE** (p. 146)

Family OCHOTONIDAE
(Pikas)

These chunky, guinea-pig-like mammals are the smallest lagomorphs. They occur primarily in mountainous regions of the northern hemisphere, and less commonly in forests, plains, and deserts. Ochotonids are distinguished from leporids (p.146) by numerous external, cranial, and dental features (see below).

Pikas are herbivorous. A curious habit related to their diet is the curing and storing of hay. In late summer and fall these animals gather cuttings of preferred plants and cure them in sheltered places exposed to the sun. These "haypiles" are then stored among the rocks and serve as a source of food during winter months.

Generally, members of this family are diurnal and active all year. They are solitary or colonial; some species are territorial. Most nest in rock crevices; others construct burrows. Breeding occurs during spring and summer, during which there may be two or three litters consisting of two to six offspring.

One genus, approximately 14 species; discontinuous distribution in mountains of North America, Europe, and Asia, including Japan.

Recognition Characters:
1. **pinna short, rounded.**
2. **tail very small, indistinct.**
3. limbs short.
4. **digits 5-4.**
5. **pads on digits exposed.**
6. **no supraorbital process** (Fig. 65).
7. **maxilla with single (occasionally two or three) perforations** (Fig. 65).
8. **nasal widest anteriorly** (Fig. 65).
9. jugal projecting conspicuously beyond posterior margin of zygomatic arch (Fig. 65).
10. cutting edge of first upper incisor V-shaped.

Dental formula: $\dfrac{2\ 0\ 3\ 2}{1\ 0\ 2\ 3} = 26$

Compare with: Leporidae.

Genus:

Ochotona (14) - Pikas.

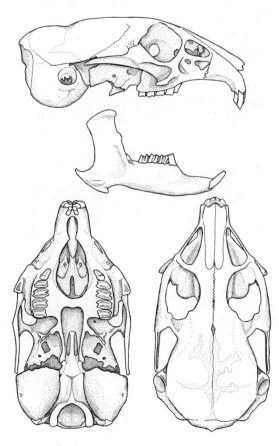

Figure 65. Skull of an ochotonid (*Ochotona*, x 1½).

145

Family LEPORIDAE
(Rabbits, hares)

Because they are distributed widely and are usually numerous and conspicuous, rabbits and hares are almost universally known. Probably the most obvious outward features are the relatively large ears and hindlimbs, small tufted tail, and hopping gait. A few, like Arctic hares (*Lepus arcticus*), can hop bipedally for short distances. Unlike pikas, leporids do not store food.

A distinction is often made between hares (e.g., *Lepus, Pronolagus*) and rabbits (e.g., *Sylvilagus, Oryctolagus*). Hares bear precocial young in the open, whereas rabbits produce altricial young in nests. However, the common names are often used interchangeably (see below).

Hares and rabbits occupy various habitats in boreal, temperate, and tropical areas from sea level to 5000 meters. They take shelter in crevices and hollows or construct burrows or shallow depressions in soil or vegetation. They are mostly nocturnal and herbivorous. Their populations often exhibit large cyclic fluctuations (Keith, 1963).

Whereas in most mammals males are larger than females, the reverse is true in leporids. Most species are solitary (*Oryctolagus* is colonial), and many are territorial. Females are polyestrous. Two to eight (but occasionally a dozen or more) young are produced in a litter.

Rabbits and hares carry a variety of diseases transmissible to humans (e.g., tularemia). Humans value them for food and sport; they are often agricultural pests, especially in places where they have been introduced.

Eight genera, approximately 50 species; worldwide, including introduced forms in Australia, New Zealand, and some oceanic islands.

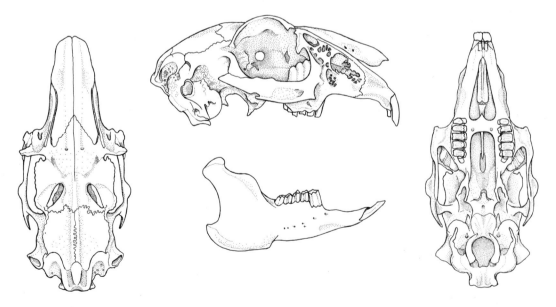

Figure 66. Skull of a leporid (*Lepus*, x 2/3).

Recognition Characters:

1. **pinna long, pointed.**
2. **tail short but distinct.**
3. hindlimbs longer than forelimbs, modified for hopping and running
4. **digits 4-4,** but first digit reduced on forefoot and hindfoot.
5. **pads on digits present but covered with hair.**
6. **supraorbital process present, fan-shaped** (often fused to varying degrees with frontal bone) (Fig. 66).
7. **maxilla with numerous perforations** (Fig. 66).
8. **nasal widest posteriorly** (Fig. 66).
9. jugal contained wholly within zygomatic arch.
10. cutting edge of first upper incisor straight.

Dental formula: $\dfrac{2\ 0\ 3\ 2\text{-}3}{1\ 0\ 2\ \text{-}3} = 26\text{-}28$

Compare with: Ochotonidae.

Representative Genera:

Lepus (25) - Hares, jack-rabbits.
Oryctolagus (1) - *O. cuniculus,* the Old World rabbit or European hare, is the common domesticated species.
Pronolagus (5) - Rock hares.
Sylvilagus (13) - Rabbits, cottontails.

Hare.

ORDER RODENTIA

Rodents constitute the most diverse group of mammals, comprising over 40 percent of the extant species. These mammals are very adaptable — they are worldwide in distribution, occur in virtually all habitats from sea level to high mountains, have varied diets, and are successful commensals of humans.

The most distinctive features of rodents are in the dentition. All species have a single pair of incisors in both upper and lower jaws. Each incisor has enamel only on the front surface. The soft dentine that forms the rest of the tooth wears away rapidly, producing a tooth with a sharp front edge and a characteristic chisel shape. These teeth grow continuously, and the long, open roots extend deep into the rostrum and mandible. These roots are usually traceable on the side of the skull. The cheekteeth vary from simple to complex. They may be firmly rooted in the jaw, or, like the incisors, they may be open-rooted and evergrowing.

The relationships among rodents are perhaps the least understood of those of any of the large orders of mammals. Consequently there is much confusion over the taxonomic arrangement of families. Traditionally, rodents have been divided into three suborders (Sciuromorpha, Hystricomorpha, and Myomorpha) on the basis of the nature of the masseter jaw muscle and associated skull features (Simpson, 1945). This scheme has resulted in difficulties, however, owing to well-recognized instances of evolutionary convergences in such features. The myomorphs appear to be a reasonably cohesive group. Major disagreements arise chiefly over the relationships and classification of families in the other suborders. Wood (1965) proposed a classification which retained the Myomorpha as it was but rearranged other families into two new suborders, one containing the Aplodontidae (Protrogomorpha) and the other the South American "hystricomorphs" (Caviomorpha). He also formed an unnamed group that consisted of nine families of uncertain relationships. This classification has been adopted by Vaughan (1978). I prefer to arrange the families in the traditional groupings, although only on an informal basis. A review of the problems of hystricomorph origins and familial assignments is provided in a series of papers by Wood (1955, 1959a, 1959b, 1965, 1974, 1975) and by Hoffstetter (1972), Landry (1957), Lavocat (1974), and Simpson (1974).

The oldest and most primitive known rodents are sciuromorphs placed in the extinct family Paramyidae, known first from the late Paleocene. They share characteristics of the masseter muscles and associated skull structure with the extant family Aplodontidae (see below). Paramyid-like features of the dentition are found in the family Sciuridae. The presumed evolution of other rodents from paramyids is not traceable at present.

Contrary to popular opinion, most rodents are omnivorous (Landry, 1970). Some carry transmissible diseases (e.g., bubonic plague). Many are valued for their flesh or pelts, and some are agricultural pests.

Recognition Characters:

1. no postmandibular process.

2. **one upper and one lower incisor per side of jaw.**

3. incisors rootless, with enamel restricted to anterior face of tooth.

4. distinct gap (diastema) present between incisors and cheekteeth.

5. no canines.

6. anteroposterior and rotary jaw motion possible.

Compare with: Lagomorpha.

Remarks: Because of the immense number of species, there are few general treatments of rodents. One such review was provided by Hanney (1975). Ellerman (1940, 1941, 1949) treated the taxonomic arrangements of families and genera, and Simpson (1945) reviewed classification and phylogeny. Eibl-Eibesfeldt (1958) and Eisenberg (1967) summarized behavior. Prakash and Ghosh (1975) treated adaptations of desert rodents. The role of rodents in the transmission of disease was summarized by Twigg (1978). Aspects of the biology of hystricomorph rodents were reviewed in a volume edited by Rowlands and Weir (1974). For other information, see references to specific families.

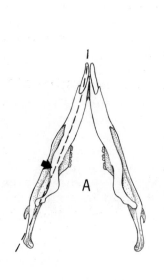
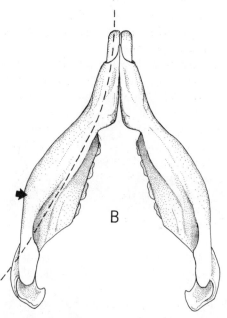

Figure 67. Ventral views of the lower jaw of a sciuromorph (A) and an hystricomorph (B), showing relationship of incisor root (dashed lines) to the angular process (at arrows).

KEY TO FAMILIES OF RODENTIA

1a. Lower jaws ±V-shaped in ventral view—base of angular process located behind (essentially on a straight line posterior to) root of incisor (Fig. 67A) 2

1b. Lower jaws ±U-shaped in ventral view—base of angular process located lateral to root of incisors (Fig. 67B) 17

Figure 68. Anterior and lateral views of the infraorbital canal in a heteromyid.

2a (1a).   External cheek pouches present; infraorbital canal
           opening laterally on and perforating side of rostrum
           (Fig. 68) 3
2b.   No external cheek pouches; infraorbital canal
           opening anteriorly, not perforating side of rostrum
           (Fig. 69) 4

3a (2a).   Body form robust; tail short; infraorbital canal small,
           not perforating entire rostrum; two distinct pits be-
           tween last molars . . . . **GEOMYIDAE** (p.179)
3b.   Body form slender; tail long; infraorbital canal rela-
           tively large, perforating entire rostrum; no pits be-
           tween last molars . . . . **HETEROMYIDAE** (p.177)

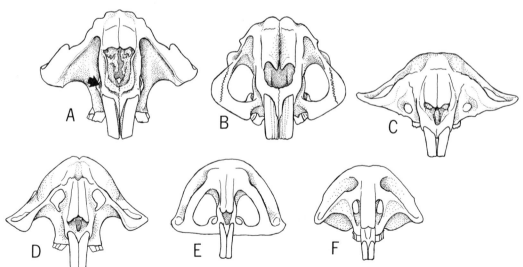

Figure 69. Anterior views of rodent skulls showing infraorbital canal: small slit-like canal compressed against side of rostrum, a castorid (A); very large canal, an erethizontid (B); small round canal, an aplodontid (C); oval canal located in upper half of rostrum, a rhizomyid (D); large oval canal, a zapodid (E); V-shaped canal, a murid (F). Not drawn to scale.

4a (2b).	Infraorbital canal very small, round or slit-like (Fig. 69A); postorbital process present, very small to large	5
4b.	Infraorbital canal medium to large, V-shaped, oval or round (Figs. 69 B-F); no postorbital process (if present, small)	6
5a (4a).	Tail cylindrical, bushy; postorbital process large, pointed; no depression in basioccipital	**SCIURIDAE** (p. 160)
5b.	Tail broad and flat, scaly; postorbital process very small, blunt; distinct depression in basioccipital	**CASTORIDAE** (p. 158)
6a (4b).	Infraorbital canal large—as large as or larger than foramen magnum (Fig. 69B)	7
6b.	Infraorbital canal small—less than diameter of foramen magnum (Fig. 69C)	10
7a (6a).	Gliding membrane present between forelimb and hindlimb; tail with several rows of large scales on underside; crowns of cheekteeth with alternating transverse ridges and depressions	**ANOMALURIDAE** (p. 162)
7b.	No gliding membrane; no large scales on underside of tail; crowns of upper cheekteeth flat, lacking alternating ridges and depressions	8

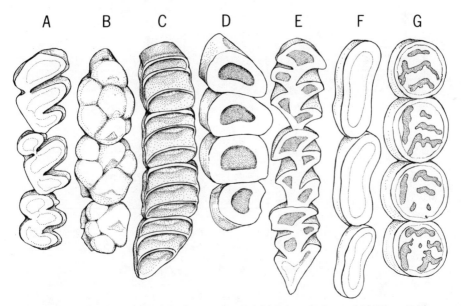

Figure 70. Crown patterns of upper cheekteeth in rodents: folds of enamel, a murid (A); cuspidate, a murid (B); transverse plates, a chinchillid (C); ring-like, a bathyergid (D); prismatic, a murid (E); kidney-shaped, an octodontid (F); islands of dentine rimmed with enamel, an hystricid (G).

8a (7b). Forelimbs and hindlimbs ± equal in size; paroccipital process broad, curving beneath and in contact with auditory bulla; upper cheekteeth simple, eight-shaped or kidney-shaped (Fig. 70F); angular process of lower jaw extremely long and pointed . . . . **CTENODACTYLIDAE** (p.206)

8b. Hindlimbs much longer than forelimbs; paroccipital process small, elongate, often indistinct; cheekteeth simple to complex, but never eight-shaped or kidney-shaped; angular process of lower jaw very reduced or short and blunt 9

9a (8b). Body form and size hare-like; tail very bushy; tragus present in pinna; horizontal segment of jugal broad; lacrimal small; angular process small, not perforated by foramen . . . . **PEDETIDAE** (p.163)

9b. Body form and size mouse- or rat-like; tail not bushy (a terminal tuft may be present); no tragus in pinna; horizontal segment of jugal narrow; lacrimal large; angular process prominent, perforated by a large foramen . . . . **DIPODIDAE** (p.175)

10a (6b). Five functional digits on all feet; auditory bulla flask-shaped; no zygomatic plate; angular process of lower jaw strongly inflected (Fig. 71); occlusal surface of each upper cheektooth ring-shaped, with a small lateral projection . . . . **APLODONTIDAE** (p.156)

10b. Fewer than five functional digits on forefeet and/or hindfeet; auditory bulla not flask-shaped; zygomatic plate present; angular process of lower jaw not strongly inflected; occlusal surface of upper cheek-teeth not ring-shaped, lacking lateral projection 11

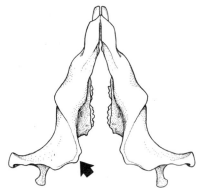

Figure 71. Inflected angular process (at arrow) of the lower jaw in an aplodontid.

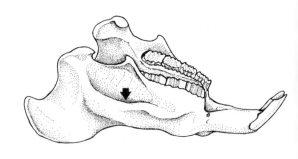

Figure 72. Groove (at arrow) on the lateral surface of the lower jaw, a hydrochoerid.

11a (10b). Cheekteeth 4/4 .... **GLIRIDAE** (p.169)

11b.   Cheekteeth fewer than 4/4—usually 3/3, rarely 4/3........................12

12a (11b). No tail; cranium distinctly angular in profile—occipital bone sloping anteriorly to posterior base of zygomatic arch (see Fig. 85) .... **SPALACIDAE** (p.181)

12b.   Tail present, short to long; cranium rounded or flat in profile—occipital bone ± vertical, not sloping anteriorly to posterior base of zygomatic arch 13

13a (12b). Auditory bulla enormously inflated, constituting nearly one-half length of skull; angular process of lower jaw perforated by a foramen; cheekteeth simple, each having a smooth concave basin .... **SELEVENIIDAE** (p.170)

13b.   Auditory bulla little to moderately inflated, constituting much less than half length of skull; angular process of lower jaw not perforate; cheekteeth relatively simple to complex, but never having a single concave basin 14

14a (13b). **Infraorbital canal oval (Fig. 69D, E)** 15

14b.   Infraorbital canal vertically narrowed, usually V-shaped (Fig. 69F) 16

15a (14a). Body form robust, gopher-like; limbs short; tail short; nasals not extending anteriorly beyond level of upper incisors; infraorbital canal restricted to upper half of rostrum (Fig. 69D) .... **RHIZOMYIDAE** (p.172)

15b.   Body form slender, mouse-like; limbs relatively long; tail long; nasals extending anteriorly well beyond level of upper incisors; infraorbital canal extending into lower half of rostrum (Fig. 69E) .... **ZAPODIDAE** (p.173)

16a (14b). Zygomatic plate very narrow, nearly horizontal; palate with large foramina between first upper cheekteeth .... **PLATACANTHOMYIDAE** (p.170)

16b.   Zygomatic plate broad (rarely narrow), tilted strongly upward (rarely horizontal); no large foramina in palate between first upper cheekteeth .... **MURIDAE** (p.164)

17a (1b). Five functional digits on all feet; infraorbital canal smaller than foramen magnum .... **BATHYERGIDAE** (p. 205)

17b.   Fewer than five functional digits on forefeet and/or hindfeet; infraorbital canal as large as or larger than foramen magnum 18

18a (17b). Lower jaw with prominent groove and ridge on lateral surface (Fig. 72) 19

18b. No prominent groove and ridge on lateral surface of lower jaw 20

19a (18a). Size large; digits partly webbed; paroccipital process extremely long; upper toothrows converging only slightly anteriorly; last upper molar huge, longer than combined length of other cheekteeth ...... **HYDROCHOERIDAE** (p.189)

19b. Size small to medium; digits not webbed; paroccipital process not overly long; upper toothrows highly convergent anteriorly, the premolars nearly in contact medially(see Fig. 88); last upper molar not larger than combined length of other cheekteeth .... **CAVIIDAE** (p.187)

20a (18b). Digits 4-3 (a fourth small digit present on hindfoot in some) 21

20b. Digits not 4-3 22

21a (20a). Tail long; crowns of cheekteeth consisting of a series of transverse plates (Fig. 70C) .... **CHINCHILLIDAE** (p.193)

21b. Tail short or absent; crowns of cheekteeth consisting of enamel folds and/or islands (Fig. 70G) .... **DASYPROCTIDAE** (p.191)

22a (20b). Jugals and maxillae greatly enlarged, forming rough-textured plates housing internal cavities .... **CUNICULIDAE** (p.192)

22b. Jugal and maxilla not enlarged or forming rough-textured plates 23

23a. Lacrimal canal opening at front edge of infraorbital canal on side of rostrum (see Fig. 89) .... **ABROCOMIDAE** (p.199)

23a (22b). Lacrimal canal not opening on side of rostrum 24

24a (23b). Digits 3-4; upper incisor with three grooves on anterior surface .... **THRYONOMYIDAE** (p.202)

24b. Digits 4-4 or 4-5; grooves on upper incisors absent or fewer than three 25

25a (24b). Crowns of cheekteeth terraced—inner cusps of upper teeth and outer cusps of lower teeth elevated over remainder of teeth.......................... **PETROMYIDAE** (p.204)

25b. Crowns of cheekteeth relatively flat, not terraced 26

26a (25b). Crowns of cheekteeth eight-shaped (octodont) or kidney-shaped (Fig. 70F); last upper and lower molar reduced .... **OCTODONTIDAE** (p.197)

26b. Crowns of cheekteeth consisting of enamel folds, enamel islands, or transverse plates (Fig. 70 C, G); last upper and lower molars not reduced 27

Scaly-tailed squirrel.

"SCIUROMORPHA"

Recognition Characters:

1. infraorbital canal very small (Castoridae, Sciuridae) and not transmitting any part of masseter muscle, or very large (Pedetidae, Anomaluridae) and transmitting much of the medial band of masseter muscle.
2. lower jaw relatively unspecialized, without deflected angular process (sometimes inflected) or ridge and groove on lateral surface.
3. cheekteeth usually 4/4 (five upper cheekteeth in Aplodontidae, some Sciuridae).

Family APLODONTIDAE
(Mountain beaver or sewellel)

Primitive conditions of the zygomatic arch and masseter muscle are retained in this family of rodents, in which the origin of the masseter muscle is confined to the zygomatic arch. This feature, along with other cranial features and peculiar cheekteeth (see below) set aplodontids apart from all other rodents.

The name "mountain beaver" is a misnomer, for these rodents are not aquatic and occur commonly also in lowlands. However, they are confined to moist areas, often near streams. Because their kidneys are unable to produce urine which is more concentrated than the blood (Nungesser and Pfeiffer, 1965), they require a plentiful source of water. They frequent dense shrubbery, where their burrowing activity may be quite noticeable.

Mountain beavers are mostly nocturnal. They consume a wide variety of plant materials, including leaves, bark, shoots, and seedling trees. They occasionally climb trees to obtain twigs. Food may be stored in winter.

Aplodontids do not hibernate. Females bear 2 to 6 young.

One genus, 1 species; northwestern United States, extreme southwestern Canada.

Recognition Characters:
- **skull flattened, greatly widened posteriorly** (Fig. 73).
- **infraorbital canal medium-sized, round** (see Fig. 69C).

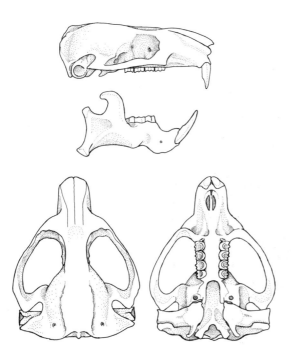

Figure 73. Skull of an aplodontid (*Aplodontia*, x ¾).

- **crowns of cheekteeth ring-like, each with a small projection (located laterally on upper teeth, medially on lower teeth)** (Fig. 73).

1. body form thickset (30-46 cm).
2. **tail vestigial.**
3. digits 5-5, not webbed.
4. pinna very small, without a tragus.
5. no gliding membrane.
6. no postorbital process.
7. **auditory bulla not inflated, flask-shaped.**
8. **no zygomatic plate.**
9. infraorbital canal as above.
10. **angular process of lower jaw sharply inflected** (Fig. 73).
11. crowns of cheekteeth as above.

Dental formula: $\frac{1\ 0\ 2\ 3}{1\ 0\ 1\ 3} = 22$

Compare with: Geomyidae, Bathyergidae, Thryonomyidae, Ctenomyidae, Octodontidae, Rhizomyidae.

Genus:

Aplodontia (1) - *A. rufa* is the mountain beaver or sewellel.

Remarks: Wood (1965) placed this family in a separate suborder (Protrogomorpha).

Taylor (1918) revised the taxonomy of *Aplodontia*. Evolution of the family was explored by Shotwell (1958).

Family CASTORIDAE
(Beavers)

These large, thickset rodents are adapted for aquatic habits. External indications of this are the dense fur, webbed hindfeet, flat tail, and valvular ears and nostrils. The small eyes are protected by a nictitating membrane, a structure generally absent in mammals.

Beavers inhabit streams, rivers, and lakes in areas where preferred plant foods (willow, aspen, birch, alder) are available. Favored parts are twigs, leaves, and bark. Cuttings are either eaten, stored in food caches for later consumption, or are used together with mud to construct lodges and dams. Lodges may each house several families; they are usually constructed only in ponds and lakes. By contrast, beavers excavate dens in banks when they inhabit larger streams and rivers.

Apparently beavers are monogamous. They occur in small groups of related individuals. Beavers communicate by tail-slapping, through vocalizations, and by rubbing scent from paired anal glands on mudpiles. They usually bear three or four offspring in one litter per year in early summer.

Beavers are sometimes considered pests because they dam streams and eat the bark of fruit trees. Their pelts are valued for the quality of the fur.

One genus, 2 species; chiefly north of Mexico in North America, also Europe, northern Asia, Siberia.

Recognition Characters:

- **tail large, broad and flat, mostly naked and scaly.**

- **distinct depression in basioccipital** (Fig. 74).

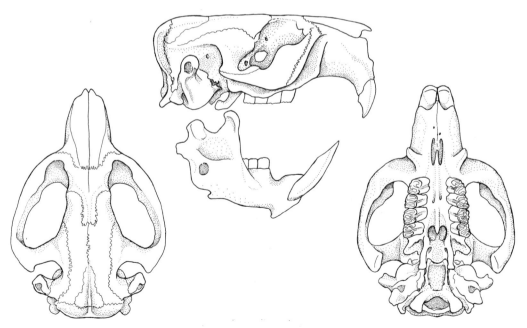

Figure 74. Skull of a castorid (*Castor*, x ¾).

1. body form thickset (95-160 cm).
2. tail as described above.
3. **digits 5-5, webbed on hindfoot.**
4. pinna small, without a tragus.
5. no gliding membrane.
6. postorbital process very small.
7. auditory bulla not inflated, ± flask-shaped.
8. zygomatic plate present.
9. **infraorbital canal very small, slit-like** (Fig. 74).
10. angular process not inflected.
11. crowns of cheekteeth flat, with narrow inner and outer enamel folds.

Dental formula: $\frac{1\ 0\ 1\ 3}{1\ 0\ 1\ 3} = 20$

Compare with: Sciuridae.

Genus:

Castor (2) - C. canadensis and C. fiber are the North American and Eurasian beavers, respectively.

Remark: A summary of beaver natural history is provided by Jenkins and Busher (1979).

RODENTIA

Family SCIURIDAE
(Squirrels, chipmunks, marmots)

Broadly defined, this family consists of three groups: flying squirrels, tree squirrels, and ground squirrels. Flying squirrels (about a dozen genera) are easily recognized by furred gliding membranes which extend between the limbs and by horizontally arranged hairs on the tail. A calcareous rod (calcar) extending from the wrist adds support to the gliding membrane. Flying squirrels are mostly nocturnal. Tree squirrels are chiefly diurnal and lack a gliding membrane. Both tree squirrels and flying squirrels share many arboreal adaptations — they have rounded heads with large eyes, sharp curved claws on the feet, long tails, and ankles with extraordinary rotational capabilities. By contrast, ground squirrels (including marmots and prairie dogs) have relatively flattened heads, straight claws, short tails, and unspecialized ankles. Ground squirrels are diurnal. Still other forms (e.g., chipmunks) are generalized —they occupy a niche seemingly intermediate between those of tree squirrels and ground squirrels, since they spend time both in trees and on the ground. In contrast to those of many other rodents, the cheekteeth of sciurids are rooted; they usually have prominent ridges and cusps.

Color vision is well developed in many diurnal forms. This is evidenced by the presence of many cones in the retina of the eye and by the varied and bright colors of many forms, particularly species of tree squirrels.

Terrestrial species are often gregarious and territorial. Prairie dogs, for example, congregate in "towns." Within such communities, behavior patterns are complex and well defined (King, 1955). In marmots, the degree of development of social systems varies with the nature of the habitat (Barash, 1974). Tree squirrels are usually solitary but occasionally gather in groups to feed when food (e.g., fruits, nuts) is abundant.

Sciurids eat leaves of grasses and other vegetation, nuts, seeds, resin, bark, fruit, fungi, and nectar; several species also eat insects. Temperate ground squirrels hibernate in winter; other species store food against times of shortages. Squirrels build nests of leaves or take shelter in tree holes, among rocks, or in burrows.

Females usually bear several young. The number of litters varies with the length of the breeding period; two or three litters may be produced per year.

Fifty-one genera, approximately 250 species; worldwide except Australian region, Madagascar, and polar regions.

Recognition Characters:

1. body form slender (7-101 cm).
2. **tail relatively short to long, often bushy.**
3. **digits 4-5, not webbed.**
4. pinna small to relatively large, without a tragus.
5. gliding membrane usually absent (present in about a dozen genera); if membrane present, calcar also present, arising from wrist.
6. **postorbital process large (Fig. 75).**
7. auditory bulla moderately inflated, not flask-shaped.
8. zygomatic plate present.
9. **infraorbital canal very small, slit-like (Fig. 75).**
10. angular process of lower jaw usually slightly inflected.
11. **crowns of cheekteeth usually not flat, with distinct cusps or ridges and valleys (Fig. 75).**

160

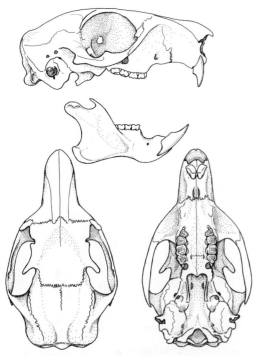

Figure 75. Skull of a sciurid (*Sciurus*, x ¾).

Dental formula: $\dfrac{1\ 0}{1\ 0}\dfrac{1\text{-}2}{1}\dfrac{3}{3} = 20\text{-}22$

Compare with: Castoridae, Anomaluridae.

Representative Genera:

Ammospermophilus (5) - Antelope ground squirrels.

Callosciurus (13) - Beautiful squirrels.

Cynomys (5) - Prairie dogs.

Dremomys (5) - Orange-bellied squirrels, red-cheeked squirrels.

Eutamias (16) - Chipmunks.

Funambulus (5) - Asiatic striped squirrels, African bush squirrels.

Funisciurus (including *Paraxerus*) (20) - African striped squirrels.

Glaucomys (2) - New World flying squirrels.

Heliosciurus (3) - Sun squirrels.

Hylopetes (6) - Arrow-tailed flying squirrels.

Lariscus (2) - Malayan striped squirrels.

Marmota (8) - Marmots, woodchuck.

Microsciurus (8) - Neotropical dwarf squirrels.

Petaurista (5) - Giant flying squirrels.

Petinomys (7) - Dwarf flying squirrels.

Ratufa (4) - Giant squirrels.

Rhinosciurus (1) - *R. laticaudatus* is the long-nosed squirrel.

Sciurus (25) - Tree squirrels.

Spermophilus (30) - Ground squirrels.

Tamias (1) - *T. striatus* is the eastern American chipmunk.

Tamiasciurus (2) - Chickarees.

Tamiops (2) - Asiatic striped squirrels.

Xerus (4) - African ground squirrels.

Remarks: Evolution of fossil and modern squirrels was investigated by Black (1963, 1972) and Bryant (1945). Sciurid taxonomy was treated in papers by Howell (1938), Moore (1959), Moore and Tate (1965), and Pocock (1923). Variation in reproductive traits was described by Moore (1961). MacClintock (1970) provided a general treatment of North American squirrels.

Family ANOMALURIDAE
(Scaly-tailed squirrels)

These gliding squirrels are the African equivalents of flying squirrels (p. 160) in North America and Eurasia and sugar gliders (p. 49) in Australia. The presence of scales on the ventral surface of the tail is unique among rodents. They function as a braking device when the animal alights on the trunk of a tree by being pressed against the bark. The skull is illustrated in Fig. 76.

Few habits of anomalurids have been described. The diet is varied and includes bark, fruit, leaves, flowers, nuts, and insects. Scaly-tailed squirrels den in hollow trees. Most are solitary, but *Idiurus* occurs in groups of as many as 100 individuals. One appears to be the usual number of offspring.

Four genera, perhaps 12 species; western and central Africa.

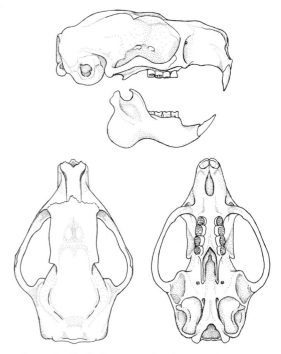

Figure 76. Skull of an anomalurid (*Anomalurus*, x ¾).

Recognition Characters:

- **double row of scales on underside and near base of tail.**
1. body form slender (14-89 cm).
2. **tail long, upper side bushy.**
3. digits 4-5 or 5-5, not webbed.
4. pinna large, without a tragus.
5. **gliding membrane present between wrist and ankle, and between ankle and tail** (except in *Zenkerella*, flightless scaly-tailed squirrels); **calcar present, arising from elbow.**
6. postorbital process small.
7. auditory bulla not inflated, not flask-shaped.
8. **no zygomatic plate.**
9. **infraorbital canal large, oval.**
10. angular process not inflected.
11. crowns of cheekteeth relatively flat, with distinct transverse ridges.

Dental formula: $\frac{1\ 0\ 1\ 3}{1\ 0\ 1\ 3} = 20$

Compare with: Sciuridae.

Representative Genera:

Anomalurus (5) - Scaly-tailed squirrels.
Idiurus (2) - Pygmy scaly-tailed squirrels.

Remarks: Despite their superficial resemblance to true squirrels (Sciuridae), the systematic affinities of anomalurids are uncertain. For a brief review of suggested relationships, see McLaughlin (1967).

Aspects of the biology of several species were treated by Kingdon (1974b).

Family PEDETIDAE
(Springhaas or spring hare)

The most obvious differentiating feature of these rodents is their kangaroo-like appearance — the forelimbs are small and concealed against the chest when folded, and the hindlimbs are large and powerful. The massive tail is brushed at the end and serves as a brace when the animal is resting on the hindlimbs. The large ears contain a tragus-like flap of skin which seals the ear opening when the animal digs.

Spring hares are bipedal. Like that of other similarly adapted rodents (e.g., Dipodidae, some Heteromyidae and Muridae), the gait at high speeds is a series of unstable leaps or "ricochets." Peculiar anatomical specializations for this habit

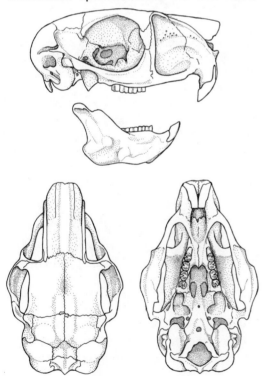

Figure 77. Skull of a pedetid (*Pedetes*, x ½).

were described by Hatt (1932) and references therein.

Pedetes is active chiefly at night. Preferred foods include roots, bulbs, fruit, and shoots. These animals excavate extensive burrows in which one or two individuals reside. They plug all but one entrance to the burrow. One relatively precocial young is usual.

One genus, 1 species; central and southern Africa.

Recognition Characters:

- **hindlimbs much longer than forelimbs.**
- **frontal and nasal bones very broad** (relatively narrow in other "sciuromorphs") (Fig. 77).

1. body hare-like (72-90 cm).
2. tail long, well haired.
3. **digits 5-4, not webbed, bushy at tip.**
4. **pinna large, with a distinct tragus.**
5. no gliding membrane.
6. postorbital process very small or absent.
7. **auditory bulla greatly inflated,** not flask-shaped (Fig. 77).
8. no zygomatic plate.
9. **infraorbital canal extremely large, oval.**
10. angular process not inflected.
11. **cheekteeth flat, simple, bilophodont, each with a single fold of enamel on the side of each tooth** (Fig. 77)

Dental formula: $\frac{1\ 0\ 1\ 3}{1\ 0\ 1\ 3} = 20$

Genus:

Pedetes (1) - The spring hare is *P. capensis.*

Remarks: The systematic position of pedetids is uncertain. For a brief review of the problem, see McLaughlin (1967).

A summary of the habits of these rodents is given by Kingdon (1974b).

"MYOMORPHA"

Recognition Characters:

1. infraorbital canal small to relatively large, accommodating part of the medial band of the masseter muscle or none at all.
2. lower jaw relatively unspecialized, without deflected angular process (sometimes inflected) or ridge and groove on lateral surface.
3. cheekteeth usually 3/3 (no premolars; the latter present in Geomyidae, Heteromyidae, Gliridae).

Family MURIDAE (including CRICETIDAE)
(Rats, mice, voles, muskrats, gerbils, hamsters, and allies)

Murids are ubiquitous mammals, familiar to every housewife and farmer. Members of this family are important elements in the diets of many predators, and they represent major primary consumers in many ecological settings. Many are also important for their role as carriers of disease, as crop pests, or as a source of meat or pelts.

This family constitutes fully one-sixth of all species of mammals. The family Cricetidae of other classifications is here considered a part of the Muridae for reasons cogently stated by Ellerman (1940), Hershkovitz (1962), and Hooper and Musser (1964). As many as eleven subfamilies are sometimes recognized. The unique "maned rat," the only species of the Lophiomyinae, is porcupine-like in appearance and possesses a skull which has peculiar granulated plates completely covering the temporal fossae. The four largest subfamilies are the Old World rats and mice (Murinae), New World rats and mice (Cricetinae), voles (Microtinae), and gerbils (Gerbillinae). Cricetines and murines are usually generalized in form and habits. The upper cheekteeth in both are cuspidate, but differ in having two (cricetines) or three (murines) longitudinally arranged series of cusps. Microtines usually occur in mesic habitats and are distinguished by a chunky body, short tail and legs, small ears, and prismatic cheekteeth. Gerbils are saltatorial, have inflated auditory bullae, and occupy xeric habitats.

Most murids are opportunistic and feed on a variety of foods. However, microtines are strictly herbivorous; a few murids are insectivorous (e.g., *Onychomys, Blarinomys*). Food storage is common in the family. Cheek pouches present in some forms (e.g., *Cricetomys, Cricetus*) aid in storage and transportation of collected seeds and other material. Although most species are terrestrial, some are arboreal (e.g., *Lophiomys, Tylomys, Uromys*), semi-aquatic (e.g., *Hydromys, Nectomys*), or fossorial (e.g., *Ellobius, Myospalax*). Murids occur in diverse habitats from sea level to elevations exceeding 5000 meters.

Some murids, especially microtines, are subject to extraordinary population fluctuations. Spectacular migrations of lemmings (*Lemmus, Dicrostonyx*) have been recorded during periods of high densities.

Reproductive habits and behavior are highly varied. These rodents are solitary to seasonally or permanently gregarious. Many, if not most, species are territorial.

Murids are generally polyestrous. The usual gestation period is three to five weeks. Litter sizes exceeding 20 offspring are known, but the usual number is 2 to 6. The length of the breeding season varies according to food availability, temperature, and other factors. Young develop rapidly—in some microtines, sexual maturity is reached in three weeks.

Because of the diversity of species and morphological variation in the family (including arboreal, fossorial, aquatic, saltatorial, and generalized forms), it is practically impossible to provide an exclusive diagnosis for the group. Murids are best characterized by employing a combination of characters and by eliminating other similar families.

Approximately 195 genera, 1000 species; worldwide in occurrence except extreme north and south (Antarctica) and a few islands, but introduced everywhere as a commensal of man.

Recognition Characters:

1. body mouse- to rat-sized (10-90 cm), unspecialized or adapted for swimming, climbing, digging, or hopping.
2. limbs usually unspecialized (except some that are modified for above habits).
3. tail short to very long, scaly to well haired.
4. eyes relatively large, visible.
5. pinna small to large.
6. cheek pouches, if present, opening internally (at least seven genera).
7. cranium variable in shape, rounded in profile or flat and triangular (e.g., *Ellobius, Myospalax*) (Fig. 78).
8. **infraorbital canal medium-sized, usually V-shaped (wider dorsally than ventrally),** opening anteriorly (Fig. 69F).
9. zygomatic plate broad (rarely narrow), tilted upward.
10. nasals usually extending anteriorly to or beyond level of upper incisors (Fig. 78).
11. auditory bulla usually not greatly inflated (except for 12 or so genera of gerbils).
12. no foramen in angular process of lower jaw.
13. crowns of molars cuspidate or flat, with angular (prismatic) or rounded folds of enamel (see Fig. 70A, B, E).

Dental formula: $\frac{1\ 0\ 0\ 2\text{-}3}{1\ 0\ 0\ 2\text{-}3} = 12\text{-}16$

Compare with: all myomorph families and the hystricomorph families Caviidae, Chinchillidae, Octodontidae, Abrocomidae, Echimyidae, Thryonomyidae, Petromyidae, and Bathyergidae.

Representative Genera:

Cricetinae

Akodon (35) - Grass mice.
Baiomys (3) - Pygmy mice.
Blarinomys (1) - *B. breviceps* is the shrew mouse.
Calomys (4) - Vesper mice.
Chinchillula (1) - *C. sahamae* is the chinchilla mouse.
Cricetulus (7) - Rat-like hamsters.
Cricetus (1) - *C. cricetus* is the common hamster.
Eligmodontia (1) - *E. typus* is the gerbil mouse.
Holochilus (2) - Marsh rats.
Ichthyomys (2) - Fish-eating rats.
Mesocricetus (1) - *M. auratus* is the golden hamster.
Myospalax (5) - Mole rats.
Neotoma (22) - Woodrats, packrats.
Notiomys (6) - Mole mice.
Onychomys (2) - Grasshopper mice.

RODENTIA

Oryzomys (50) - Rice rats.
Oxymycterus (9) - Burrowing mice.
Peromyscus (55) - Deer mice, white-footed mice.
Phyllotis (14) - Leaf-eared mice.
Punomys (1) - *P. lemminus* is the puna mouse.
Reithrodontomys (16) - New World harvest mice.
Rheomys (5) - Water mice.
Rhipidomys (7) - Climbing mice.
Scotinomys (4) - Brown mice.
Sigmodon (13) - Cotton rats.
Thomasomys (25) - Paramo mice.
Tylomys (7) - Climbing rats.

Dendromurinae

Dendromus (4) - African climbing mice.
Steatomys (3) - Fat mice.

Gerbillinae

Gerbillus (40) - Gerbils, sand rats.
Meriones (12) - Jirds.
Tatera (12) - Naked-soled gerbils.

Hydromyinae

Hydromys (3) - Australian water rats.

Lophiomyinae

Lophiomys (1) - *L. imhausi* is the maned rat.

Microtinae

Alticola (5) - Mountain voles.
Arborimus (3) - Red tree mice.
Clethrionomys (5) - Red-backed mice.
Dicrostonyx (3) - Collared lemmings.

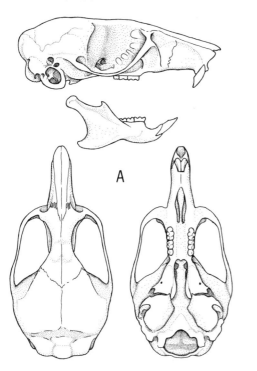
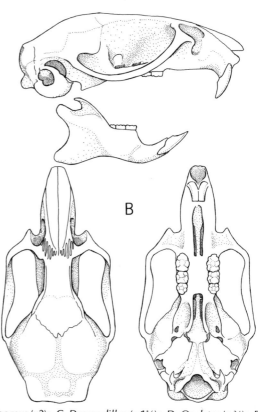

Figure 78. Skulls of murids: A, *Peromyscus* (x2¼); B, *Aethomys* (x2); C, *Desmodillus* (x 1½); D, *Ondatra* (x ¾); E, *Myospalax* (x 1); F, *Echiothrix* (x1).

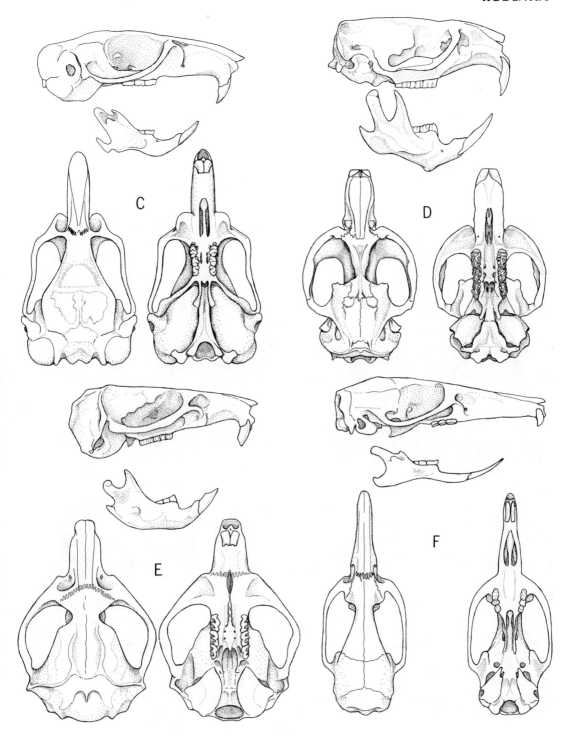

C

D

E

F

Ellobius (2) - Mole voles.

Eothenomys (6) - Asiatic voles.

Lagurus (3) - Sagebrush voles, steppe lemmings.

Lemmus (3) - Lemmings.

Microtus (including *Arvicola* and *Pitymys*) (55) - Common voles.

Ondatra (1) - *O. zibethicus* is the muskrat.

Phenacomys (2) - Heather voles.

Murinae

Acomys (4) - Spiny mice.

Apodemus (7) - Wood mice.

Arvicanthus (4) - Grass mice.

Bandicota (2) - Bandicoot rats.

Cricetomys (2) - Giant pouched rats.

Dasymys (1) - *D. incomtus* is the shaggy swamp rat.

Echiothrix (1) - *E. leucura* is the Celebes shrew rat.

Grammomys (6) - African thicket rats.

Lemmiscomys (4) - Striped mice.

Lophuromys (8) - Brush-furred mice.

Melomys (12) - Mosaic-tailed rats.

Micromys (1) - *M. minutus* is the Old World harvest mouse.

Mus (20) - House mice; *M. musculus* is a common commensal species.

Notomys (9) - Australian hopping mice.

Oenomys (1) - *O. hypoxanthus* is the rusty-nosed rat.

Praomys (8) - African soft-furred rats.

Pseudomys (including *Leggadina*) (20) - Australian native mice.

Rattus (120) - Common rats; the roof or black rat, *R. rattus*, and Norway rat, *R. norvegicus*, are distributed worldwide as commensals of man.

Uromys (5) - Giant naked-tailed rats.

Nesomyinae

Eliurus (2) - Madagascar mice.

Nesomys (3) - Madagascar mice.

Otomyinae

Otomys (6) - Swamp rats.

Phloeomyinae

Chiropodomys (6) - Pencil-tailed tree mice.

Pogonomys (9) - Prehensile-tailed rats.

Rhynchomyinae

Rhynchomys (1) - Shrew-like rats.

Remarks: Ellerman (1941), Hershkovitz (1962), Hooper and Musser (1964), and Misonne (1969) discussed the relationships of murids. Elton (1942) studied the ecology of microtines. Useful studies of individual genera include Ewer (1967) on *Cricetomys*, King (1968) on *Peromyscus*, Barnett (1958) and Calhoun (1963) on *Rattus*, Errington (1963) on *Ondatra*, and Linsdale and Tevis (1951) on *Neotoma*.

Common rat.

Family GLIRIDAE
(Dormice)

Glirids resemble small squirrels or chipmunks—they are scansorial or arboreal and have large eyes, curved claws on the digits, and (usually) a long bushy tail. The cheekteeth have distinctive transverse ridges. A unique trait among mammals is the ability of these animals to regenerate the tail (Mohr, 1941).

These rodents consume fruit, nuts, grain, insects, and small vertebrates. They are nocturnal. Nests are made in tree holes, bushes, buildings, among rocks, or in other animal burrows. Dormice store food in burrows and hibernate in winter. They also add fat to the body prior to dormancy. Hibernation is interrupted by occasional spells of activity.

One to two litters of 2 to 9 young are produced per year.

Seven genera, 12 species; Africa (excluding the Sahara), Europe, Asia Minor, southwestern Asia, Japan.

Recognition Characters:

1. body small, squirrel-like (11-36 cm).
2. limbs unspecialized.
3. **tail moderately long, bushy** (except *Myomimus*).
4. eyes relatively large, visible.
5. pinna moderately large.
6. no cheek pouches.
7. cranium rounded or flattened in profile (Fig. 79).
8. infraorbital canal medium-sized, oval or V-shaped, opening anteriorly.
9. zygomatic plate narrow and below infraorbital canal (*Graphiurus*) or vertical.
10. nasals extending anteriorly beyond level of upper incisors (Fig. 79).
11. auditory bulla relatively large, inflated (Fig. 79).
12. foramen in angular process of lower jaw present (some *Graphiurus*) or absent.
13. **crowns of molars with series of cross-ridges or basin-shaped with indistinct ridges** (*Graphiurus*), **low-crowned** (Fig.79).

Dental formula: $\frac{1\ 0\ 1\ 3}{1\ 0\ 1\ 3} = 20$

Compare with: Muridae, Platacantho-myidae.

Representative Genera:

Dryomys (2) - Forest dormice.
Eliomys (2) - Garden dormice.

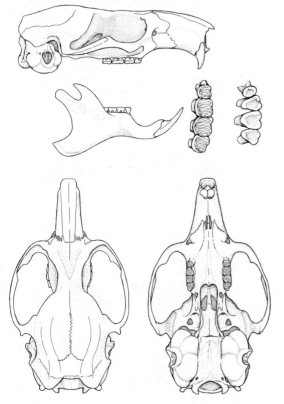

Figure 79. Skull of a glirid (*Glis*, x 1¼). Insert shows different crown patterns of upper cheekteeth in glirids (*Glis* on left, *Graphiurus* on right).

Glirulus (1) - *G. japonicus* is the Japanese dormouse.

Glis (1) - *G. glis* is the common dormouse.

Graphiurus (6) - African dormice.

Myomimus (1) - *M. personatus* is the Asiatic dormouse.

Remark: This family is sometimes called Muscardinidae (e.g., Ellerman, 1940; Kingdon, 1974b) or Myoxidae (e.g., Walker et al., 1975; Winge, 1941).

Family PLATACANTHOMYIDAE
(Spiny dormouse, Chinese dormouse)

These rodents closely resemble glirids. They are distinguishable by characters of the tail and palate, and number of teeth (see below).

The natural history of these dormice is poorly known. Apparently they feed upon fruit, grain, and roots. Nests have been found in tree cavities and among rocks.

Two genera, 2 species; peninsular India and southern China.

Recognition Characters:

- **tail naked and scaly at base, brushed or bushy distally.**

- **large foramina present in palate between upper thoothrows.**

1. body small, mouse-like (17-31 cm).
2. limbs unspecialized.
3. tail as above.
4. eyes relatively large, visible.
5. pinna moderately large.
6. no cheek pouches.
7. cranium rounded in profile.
8. infraorbital canal relatively large, V-shaped (wider dorsally than ventrally), opening anteriorly.

9. zygomatic plate relatively narrow, tilted slightly upward.
10. nasals extending beyond level of upper incisors.
11. auditory bulla small.
12. no foramen in angular process of lower jaw.
13. **crowns of molars with a series of oblique or tranverse ridges.**

Dental formula: $\dfrac{1\ 0\ 0\ 3}{1\ 0\ 0\ 3} = 16$

Compare with: Gliridae.

Genera:

Platacanthomys (1) - *P. lasiurus* is the spiny doormouse.

Typhlomys (1) - *T. cinereus* is the Chinese dormouse.

Remark: Ellerman (1940) placed platacanthomyids with glirids, whereas Wood (1955) considered them close relatives of cricetines.

Family SELEVINIIDAE
(Dzahlman or desert dormouse)

These odd glirid-like rodents inhabit a small arid area in south-central Russia. The plump body form, small cheekteeth, and enormous auditory bullae are distinctive (see below). Two premolars (apparently milk teeth) are present early in life. A curious feature of the molt pattern is that patches of epidermis are shed with the hair (Walker et al., 1975).

Little is known of the natural habits of dzahlmans. They are evidently nocturnal, eat mainly small invertebrates, and become dormant when exposed to low temperatures.

One genus, one species; small area in central Asia.

Recognition Characters:

● **cheekteeth very small.**
1. body small, stocky (14-18 cm).
2. limbs short, unspecialized.
3. tail long, well haired.
4. eyes relatively large, visible.
5. pinna relatively large.
6. no cheek pouches.
7. cranium rounded in profile.
8. **infraorbital canal small, wider than high,** opening anteriorly.
9. zygomatic plate relatively narrow, more or less vertical.
10. nasals extending beyond level of upper incisors.
11. **auditory bulla huge, constituting nearly one-half of length of skull.**
12. **foramen present in angular process of lower jaw.**
13. **crowns of molars simple, each forming a smooth concave basin.**

Dental formula: $\frac{1\ 0\ 0\ 3}{1\ 0\ 0\ 3} = 16$

Compare with: Gliridae.

Genus:

Selevinia (1) - S. betpakdalaensis is the dzahlman.

Family RHIZOMYIDAE
(Bamboo rats, African mole rats)

These fossorial rodents are the Old World equivalents of pocket gophers (Geomyidae, p.179) in both form and habits. The body is thickset, and appendages (ears, legs, tail) are short. The eyes are small but visible. Pelage color is variable. These animals dig with stout, well-clawed forefeet and robust incisors. After soil is loosened and scooped under the body, it is pushed out of the burrow into a surface mound by the combined action of the forelimbs, face, and chest. Mounds are found at irregular intervals above subterranean tunnels. In contrast to gophers, rhizomyids do not have cheek pouches and have a prominent infraorbital canal.

Members of this family inhabit plains and forests. Their preferred foods are roots and tubers, although other plant parts are also eaten. Bamboo shoots are favored by species of *Rhizomys*. Mole rats are sometimes active above ground.

Each burrow system is occupied by one individual. Pairing occurs during the breeding season. Rhizomyids bear one to five offspring.

Three genera, 6 species; tropical east Africa, southeast Asia, Sumatra.

Recognition Characters:

1. body chunky, gopher-like (23-63 cm).
2. **limbs short, stocky, claws nail-like.**
3. tail relatively short, scantily haired, not scaly.
4. eyes small but usually visible.
5. **pinna small.**
6. no cheek pouches.
7. cranium flat in profile (Fig. 80).

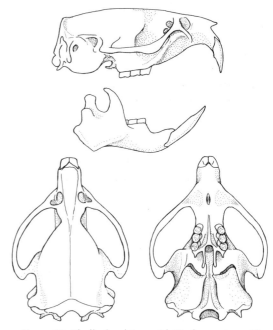

Figure 80. Skull of a rhizomyid (*Tachyoryctes*, x 1).

8. **infraorbital canal medium-sized, oval in shape (Fig. 69D), usually wider than high, opening anteriorly.**
9. zygomatic plate broad, tilted strongly upward.
10. **nasals not extending anteriorly beyond level of upper incisors (Fig. 80).**
11. auditory bulla not enlarged.
12. no foramen in angular process of lower jaw.
13. crowns of molars with folds or islands of enamel (the variability owing to extent of wear).

Dental formula: $\frac{1\ 0\ 0\ 3}{1\ 0\ 0\ 3} = 16$.

Compare with: Muridae (e.g., *Ellobius* and *Myospalax*), Spalacidae, Geomyidae, Bathyergidae, Thryonomyidae, Ctenomyidae, Octodontidae.

Representative Genera:

Rhizomys (3) - Bamboo rats.
Tachyoryctes (2) - African mole rats.

Family ZAPODIDAE
(Birch mice, jumping mice)

Zapodids are the only boreal rodents adapted for a hopping style of locomotion. The hindlimbs are elongate (shorter in *Sicista* than in others), but in contrast to more specialized saltators (e.g., Dipodidae, p.175) there is no reduction in number of digits. The cervical vertebrae are also unfused. Diagnostic characters include the quadritubercular cheekteeth and large, rounded infraorbital foramen (see below). Most species also have a dark band of varied width along the midline of the back.

Members of this family frequent dense vegetation in swamps and moist places in meadows and forests. Activity periods are mainly at night. Their diet consists of seeds, berries, fungi, and small invertebrates. They make grassy nests on the ground surface or in shallow burrows in soil or under debris. Weight is added in the fall prior to a hibernating period lasting up to eight months.

These animals are generally solitary and territorial. Males emerge first in the spring. Females normally bear two to eight young.

Four Genera, 11 species; north temperate areas of North America and Eurasia.

Recognition Characters:

1. body small, mouse-like (12-28 cm).
2. hindlimbs short (*Sicista*) or elongate.
3. **tail very long, sparsely haired.**
4. eyes relatively large, visible.
5. pinna relatively small.
6. no cheek pouches.
7. cranium more or less rounded in profile (Fig. 81).
8. **infraorbital canal large, oval in shape,** opening anteriorly (Fig. 81).
9. **zygomatic plate narrow, horizontal, entirely below infraorbital canal (Fig. 81).**
10. nasals extending anteriorly well beyond level of upper incisors (Fig. 81).
11. auditory bulla not inflated.
12. no foramen in angular process of lower jaw.
13. **crowns of molars with modified quadritubercular pattern.**

Dental formula: $\dfrac{1}{1}\dfrac{0}{0}\dfrac{0\text{-}1}{0}\dfrac{3}{3} = 16\text{-}18$

Compare with: Muridae.

Representative Genera:

Napeozapus (1) - *N. insignis* is the woodland jumping mouse.
Sicista (6) - Birch mice.
Zapus (3) - Jumping mice.

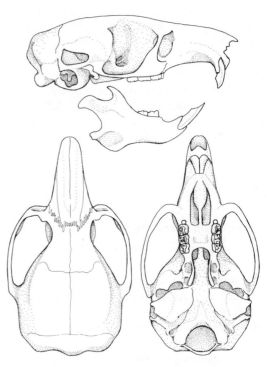

Figure 81. Skull of a zapodid (*Zapus*, x 2½).

RODENTIA

Remarks: The natural history of *Zapus* was studied by Quimby (1951) and Whitaker (1963). Krutzsch (1954) provided a taxonomic review of the genus.

Family DIPODIDAE
(Jerboas)

Jerboas are the most highly specialized saltatorial rodents. They progress chiefly on the hindlimbs, even when walking. The hindlimbs are very elongate (up to four times the length of the forelimbs), and there are only three principal digits in the hindfoot. In most species the metatarsals are fused to form a cannon bone. A long tail serves as a balancing device during locomotion and as a prop when the animal is at rest. Compact neck vertebrae reduce displacement of the head caused by jarring of the body while hopping. In sand-inhabiting species traction is aided by fringes of hairs on the sides of the toes.

Like kangaroo rats (Heteromyidae, p. 177) these rodents are well adapted for

desert living. They conserve water in various ways. They are active only at night. They maintain high humidities in burrows by placing plugs in entrances. The kidneys produce a highly concentrated urine. In addition, delicate sensory structures are protected from the effects of drifting sand or burrowing activities — ear openings are shielded by bristly hairs and the nostrils by a flap of skin, and in some species the eyes are protected by a bony outgrowth located on the anterior border of the orbits. Also, as in some other desert-dwelling rodents, the auditory bullae are huge. This feature enhances the transmission of airborne sounds from eardrum to inner ear by reducing the damping effect of an enclosed air space on vibrations of the ear ossicles.

Food items include seeds, succulent plant parts, and insects. Food is not stored. Dipodids construct extensive burrows and rest in deep chambers during winter dormant periods.

Female jerboas are polyestrous. The litter size ranges from two to six.

Ten genera, 27 species; north Africa, Arabia, and Asia Minor to northeastern China.

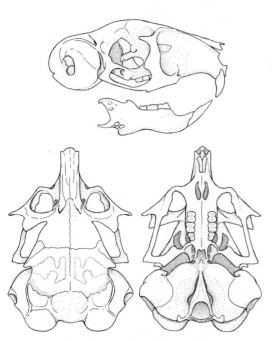

Figure 82. Skull of a dipodid (*Jaculus*, x 1½).

Recognition Characters:

1. size relatively small (11-37 cm).
2. **hindlimbs greatly elongate (cannon bone present in many genera).**
3. **tail very long, well haired, tufted at end.**
4. eyes relatively large, visible.
5. pinna moderate to large in size.
6. no cheek pouches.
7. cranium rounded or flattened in profile (Fig. 82).
8. **infraorbital canal large, oval in shape, opening anteriorly.**

9. **zygomatic plate narrow, horizontal, entirely below infraorbital canal.**
10. **nasals not extending anteriorly beyond level of upper incisors** (Fig. 82)•
11. **auditory bulla greatly inflated** (Fig. 82)•
12. **large foramen (occasionally two) usually present in angular process of lower jaw** (Fig. 82)•
13. **crowns of molars with cusps separated by folds of enamel** (superficially similar in some to the prismatic teeth of microtines).

Dental formula: $\dfrac{1}{1}\ \dfrac{0}{0}\ \dfrac{0\text{-}1}{0}\ \dfrac{3}{3} = 16\text{-}18$

Compare with: Heteromyidae, Muridae (e.g., gerbils).

Representative Genera:

Allactaga (9) - Four- and five-toed jerboas.

Allactagulus (1) - *A. pumilio* is the lesser five-toed jerboa.

Dipus (1) - *D. sagitta* is the hairy-footed jerboa.

Jaculus (including *Scirtopoda*) (5) - Desert jerboas.

Paradipus (1) - *P. ctenodactylus* is the comb-toed jerboa.

Salpingotus (3) - Dwarf jerboas.

Family HETEROMYIDAE
(Pocket mice, kangaroo rats, and allies)

Members of this family are adapted in many ways for life in arid regions. They vary from generalized mouse-like forms to jumping types. In body form, style of locomotion, and habits the saltatorial heteromyids (*Dipodomys, Microdipodops*) closely resemble gerbils (Muridae, p.164) and jerboas (Dipodidae, p.175) but by contrast, heteromyids have external cheekpouches which are used to transport food and nest materials. The fur varies from sparse and spiny to thick and soft. Features of the auditory bullae, infraorbital canals, and nasal bones are distinctive (see below).

Kangaroo rats and mice exhibit specializations common to many desert-adapted rodents. They reduce water losses by restricting activity to nights when conditions are cool and humid; by occupying sealed, humid burrows in the daytime; by producing a highly concentrated urine; and by the ability to subsist entirely on water obtained directly from dry food sources and metabolic water produced during oxidative processes. A counter-current system in the nasal passages further reduces water losses by cooling humid exhaled air, causing water to condense on the nasal mucosa (Schmidt-Nielsen et al., 1970); heat is also conserved in this process.

Heteromyids frequent deserts, plains, and open forests; a few are found in rocky places. All species are burrowers. They feed mainly on seeds, but infrequently take leafy vegetation and insects. *Dipodomys microps* forages almost exclusively on the leaves of saltbush (*Atriplex confertifolia*). The outer salty layer of epidermis is shaved off with the flattened incisors and the fleshy inner tissue is consumed (Kenagy, 1972, 1973).

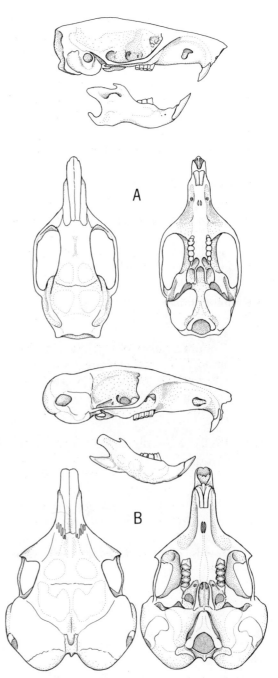

Figure 83. Skulls of heteromyids: A, *Liomys*; B, *Dipodomys* (both x 1½).

Heteromyids combat food shortages by storing food in burrows, by accumulating fat deposits in the tail (*Microdipodops*), or by becoming torpid (*Perognathus*).

These animals are solitary and intolerant of one another. Females are polyestrous and normally bear 3-6 young per litter.

Five genera, perhaps 75 species; southern Canada south to northern South America.

Recognition Characters:

1. body mouse- to rat-like (11-42 cm).
2. **hindlimbs relatively long to very long** (*Dipodomys, Microdipodops*).
3. tail long to very long, well haired, occasionally tufted at end.
4. eyes relatively large, visible.
5. pinna relatively small.
6. **cheek pouches present, opening externally.**
7. **cranium ± rounded in profile** (Fig. 83).
8. **infraorbital canal compressed against and entirely piercing the rostrum, opening laterally** (Fig. 83).
9. zygomatic plate broad, tilted upward.
10. nasals extending anteriorly well beyond level of upper incisors (Fig. 83).
11. **auditory bulla slightly inflated** (*Liomys, Heteromys*) to greatly inflated (*Dipodomys, Microdipodops*) (Fig. 83).
12. no foramen in angular process of lower jaw.
13. **crowns of molars simple, with two lobes.**

Dental formula: $\frac{1}{1}\frac{0}{0}\frac{1}{1}\frac{3}{3} = 20$

Compare with: Dipodidae.

Genera:

Dipodomys (21) - Kangaroo rats.
Heteromys (8) - Spiny pocket mice.
Liomys (11) - Spiny pocket mice.
Microdipodops (2) - Kangaroo mice.
Perognathus (25) - Pocket mice.

Remarks: The heteromyids are here placed in the Myomorpha following Wood (1955, 1965).

Their fossil history and evolution were examined by Wood (1935), and behavior by Eisenberg (1936). The classic studies of water balance in kangaroo rats were summarized in Schmidt-Nielsen (1964) (see also MacMillen, 1972), and rates of metabolism were studied by McNab (1979).

Family GEOMYIDAE
(Pocket gophers)

In habits and superficial appearance, pocket gophers agree closely with other fossorial rodents, particularly rhizomyids (p.172). The robust body, short tail, ears, and limbs, small eyes, and blunt snout are found also in other fossorial mammals. By contrast, gophers are the only group of fossors possessing external cheek pouches; these pockets are used for transporting food. The skull, cheekteeth, and infraorbital canal (see below and Fig. 84) also separate geomyids from other similar forms.

These rodents prefer deep friable soils. The diet consists mostly of roots and tubers, but also includes other plant parts. Burrows contain numerous tunnels, a deep nest

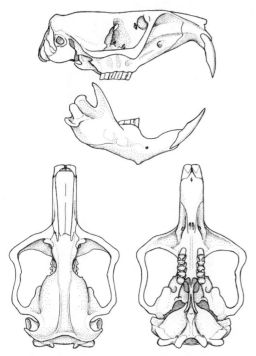

Figure 84. Skull of a geomyid (*Thomomys*, x 1).

chamber, and storerooms for food and excrement. Mounds of dirt, plugged from beneath, identify the underground course taken by the burrow system. Soil is loosened by the forelimbs and incisors and shoveled behind the body. When a sufficient amount has accumulated, the animal turns around and pushes the dirt out of the burrow. A skin fold behind the incisors prevents dirt from entering the mouth as the animal digs. In wintertime, gophers commonly push dirt into tunnels excavated in snow. This habit is revealed after snowmelt by the peculiar "gopher cores" of soil remaining on the surface of the ground.

Generally pocket gophers are solitary, but many individuals may be concentrated in small areas with friable soils. Pairing evidently occurs only during the breeding season. Gophers have a pugnacious disposition and are mutually antagonistic. There are one to several litters per year. A dozen or more young are recorded, but 2-8 young are usual.

Gophers are garden and agricultural pests in many places. Predators include weasels, other mammalian carnivores, snakes, and several owls.

Five genera, perhaps 40 species; temperate North America to northern Colombia.

Recognition Characters:

- **two large pits located in palate between last molars** (Fig. 84).

- **premolar 8-shaped, larger than any molar** (Fig. 84).

1. body chunky, of medium size (15-44 cm).
2. limbs short, forefoot with enlarged claws used in digging.
3. **tail short, scantily haired, not scaly.**
4. eyes relatively small but visible.
5. **pinna very reduced.**

6. **cheek pouches present, opening externally.**
7. cranium robust, flat in profile (Fig. 84).
8. **infraorbital canal compressed against side of rostrum, opening laterally.**
9. zygomatic plate broad, tilted strongly upward.
10. **nasals not extending anteriorly beyond level of upper incisors** (Fig. 84).
11. auditory bulla not greatly inflated.
12. no foramen in angular process of lower jaw.
13. **crowns of molars simple, ring-shaped** (Fig. 84).

Dental formula: $\frac{1\ 0\ 1\ 3}{1\ 0\ 1\ 3} = 20$

Compare with: Muridae (e.g., *Ellobius* and *Myospalax*), Spalacidae, Rhizomyidae, Bathyergidae, Thryonomyidae, Ctenomyidae, Octodontidae.

Representative Genera:

Geomys (7) - Eastern American pocket gophers.

Orthogeomys (including *Heterogeomys* and *Macrogeomys*) (11) - Giant pocket gophers, taltuzas.

Pappogeomys (including *Cratogeomys*) (9) - Mexican pocket gophers.

Thomomys (7) - Western American pocket gophers.

Remarks: The geomyids are here placed in Myomorpha following Wood (1955, 1965). The generic arrangement follows Russell (1968).

Family SPALACIDAE
(Mole rats)

Spalacids are the most highly specialized burrowing rodents. Although mole rats resemble other fossors in general body form, they differ in several ways. They have no visible tail. The eyes are reduced to vestiges under the skin, and the orbits are mostly occupied by enlarged jaw muscles. These muscles power the digging action of the large projecting incisors. The forefeet are not used extensively for burrowing; they are unspecialized and bear small claws. The head is broad and wedge-shaped; the skull is correspondingly angular (Fig. 85).

Mole rats excavate elaborate and extensive burrow systems. Loose dirt in the tunnels is tightly packed against the walls by the bulldozer-like action of the snout and forehead. Males and females are separate except during the breeding season. At this time they throw large quantities of dirt up into breeding mounds, in which chambers for nests, **food, and excrement are fashioned. One litter of 2 to 4 young is produced per year.**

These animals eat bulbs, roots, tubers, and occasional insects. They utter low grunting sounds.

One genus, 3 species; southeastern Europe and eastern Mediterranean region.

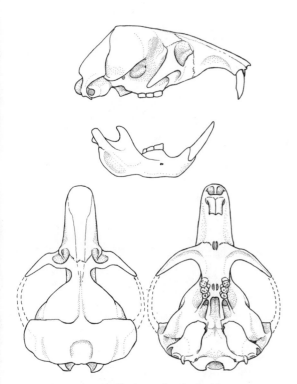

Figure 85. Skull of a spalacid (*Spalax*, x 1).

Recognition Characters:
- **cranium distinctly angular in profile (occipital region sloping far forward) (Fig. 85).**
  1. **body relatively small, mole-like (15-30 cm).**
  2. **limbs short, no enlarged claws.**
  3. **no tail.**
  4. **eyes not visible, completely covered by skin.**
  5. **pinna very small.**
  6. no cheek pouches.
  7. cranium as described above.
  8. infraorbital canal relatively large, oval in shape, opening anteriorly.
  9. zygomatic plate narrow, entirely below infraorbital canal.
  10. nasals extending anteriorly beyond level of upper incisors (Fig. 85).
  11. auditory bulla not enlarged.
  12. no foramen in angular process of lower jaw.
  13. crowns of molars with several folds or islands of enamel (the variation owing to extent of wear).

RODENTIA

Dental formula: $\dfrac{1\ 0\ 0\ 3}{1\ 0\ 0\ 3} = 16$

Compare with: Geomyidae, Muridae (e.g., *Ellobius* and *Myospalax*), Rhizomyidae, Bathyergidae, Thryonomyidae, Ctenomyidae, Octodontidae.

Genus:

Spalax (3) - Mole rats.

"HYSTRICOMORPHA"

Recognition Characters:

1. infraorbital canal very large (small in Bathyergidae), accommodating much of the medial band of the masseter muscle.
2. lower jaw specialized, with angular process deflected or with prominent ridge and groove on lateral surface (Caviidae, Hydrochoeridae) for attachment of medial band of masseter muscle.
3. cheekteeth usually 4/4 (one premolar, three molars).

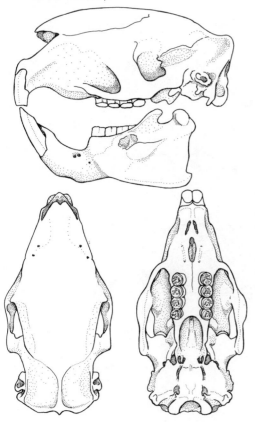

Figure 86. Skull of an hystricid (*Hystrix*, x 1/3).

Family HYSTRICIDAE
(Old World porcupines)

Like their New World counterparts (Erethizontidae, p.185), these large rodents are covered with many spiny hairs. However, they are mostly ground-dwelling and differ in the number of functional digits and other peculiarities of the feet (see below). The skull shape is quite variable in this family.

Hystricids frequent plains, deserts, and forests. They shelter in natural crevices, holes, or caves, in aardvark burrows, or in self-made dens. Several individuals may occupy the same burrow. Temporary dens near food sources may supplement permanent dens. These animals are primarily vegetarians but are known to eat carrion also. Females may reproduce twice yearly and have 1-4 young.

The spines are used for ornamental and medicinal purposes by some people. The flesh is tasty.

Four genera, 12 species; Africa, Italy, southern Asia, Philippines, Borneo, Celebes.

Recognition Characters:

1. **body relatively large, heavy-set (49-95 cm).**
2. **pelage conspicuously spiny, spines often modified into hollow barbless quills.**
3. tail short or moderately long.
4. limbs short.
5. **digits functionally 5-5, not webbed;** claws unspecialized.
6. skull elongate, greatly inflated and smooth (*Hystrix*) (Fig. 86) or not inflated but ridged.

7. infraorbital canal very large, without distinct groove for nerve passage.
8. lacrimal canal not opening on side of rostrum.
9. auditory bulla relatively small.
10. paroccipital process short.
11. jugal variable in extent, but never meeting lacrimal.
12. lower jaw without ridge or groove on lateral surface; angular process not deflected; coronoid process small (*Atherurus*) or prominent.

13. upper toothrows ± parallel (Fig. 86).
14. **crowns of cheekteeth flat, with transverse folds of enamel separating from each other to form islands with wear** (Figs. 70G, 86).

Dental formula: $\dfrac{1\ 0\ 1\ 3}{1\ 0\ 1\ 3} = 20$

Compare with: Erethizontidae.

Representative Genera:

Atherurus (3) - Brush-tailed porcupines.
Hystrix (6) - Old World porcupines.

Old World porcupine.

Family ERETHIZONTIDAE
(New World porcupines)

These robust rodents have a pelage consisting of stiff bristles or spines mixed with soft hairs. Despite their clumsy-looking build they are agile and better adapted for climbing than Old World porcupines — the feet are broad, and the four functional digits bear well-developed curved claws. In *Coendou* most of the tail is naked and prehensile. The vision of erethizontids is mediocre, but their senses of hearing and smell are acute.

Erethizontids occur in forested areas where they eat bark, fruit, roots, leaves, and other plant parts. They rest in crude tree nests or in natural cavities, logs, rock crevices, brush, and among roots of trees. Alternate den sites are often used. Porcupines are mostly nocturnal. Erethizontids are very timid and generally flee when encountered. If cornered, they roll up into a ball (e.g., *Coendou*) or strike with the tail (e.g., *Erethizon*).

New World porcupines usually have one young bearing a partial complement of soft quills. There is one litter per year.

The quills of porcupines are often used as decorations by people.

Four genera, 8 species; disjunct distribution including North America as far south as northern Mexico, and southern Mexico to northern Argentina.

Recognition Characters:

1. **body moderately large, heavy-set (50-115 cm).**
2. **pelage conspicuously spiny, spines not modified into hollow quills, each spine with** (*Erethizon*) **or without proximally directed barbs.**
3. tail short (*Erethizon*, *Echinoprocta*) to long (*Coendou* , *Chaetomys*).
4. limbs relatively short.
5. **digits functionally 4-4 (pollex and hallux reduced) or 4-5 not webbed; claws long, curved.**
6. skull usually blocky, moderately ridged (Fig. 87).
7. infraorbital canal very large (Fig. 87), without distinct groove for nerve passage.
8. lacrimal canal not opening on side of rostrum.
9. auditory bulla relatively large.
10. paroccipital process short.
11. jugal not approaching lacrimal.

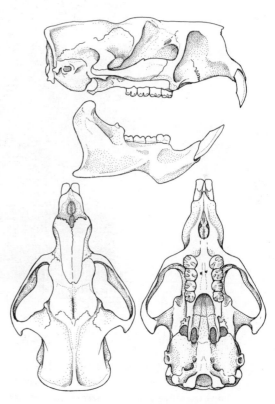

Figure 87. Skull of an erethizontid (*Erethizon*, x ½).

Prehensile-tailed porcupine.

12. lower jaw without ridge or groove on lateral surface; angular process not deflected; coronoid process prominent.
13. upper toothrows slightly convergent anteriorly.
14. **crowns of cheekteeth flat, with narrow** *(Chaetomys)* **or wide enamel folds not usually separating from each other to form islands with wear** (Fig. 87).

Dental formula: $\frac{1}{1}\frac{0}{0}\frac{1}{1}\frac{3}{3} = 20$

Compare with: Hystricidae.

Representative Genera:

Coendou (5) - Prehensile-tailed porcupines.

Erethizon (1) - *E. dorsatum* is the North American porcupine.

186

Family CAVIIDAE
(Guinea pigs or cavies, Patagonian hares)

At first glance, guinea pigs and the rabbit-like Patagonian hares seem like odd bedfellows. Closer scrutiny, particularly of the evergrowing prismatic cheekteeth, convergent toothrows, and peculiar groove on the side of each dentary bone suggests close affinity. Pronounced cursorial adaptations are found in *Dolichotus*. These include a vestigial clavicle and a reduced number of digits in the feet. The nails vary from claw-like (e.g., *Cavia*) to hoof-like (*Dolichotus*).

Caviids are social animals, occurring in pairs or groups. They frequent open areas in wet and dry grasslands, savannahs, and rocky areas where they occupy self-excavated dens or other animal burrows.

Although chiefly nocturnal, they often are active in the daytime. The diet consists primarily of leaves. There are two or more breeding efforts per year. One to five precocial young are produced.

These rodents are valued for their meat and are used as pets and laboratory animals.

Five genera, 12 species; South America excepting much of Brazil and Chile.

Recognition Characters:

1. body hare-like (*Dolichotus*) or small and stocky (15-80 cm).
2. pelage short to long; hairs soft or stiff, not spiny.
3. **tail very short.**
4. limbs long (*Dolichotus*) or short.
5. **digits 4-3,** not webbed; claws unspecialized or hoof-like (*Dolichotus*).
6. skull elongate (*Dolichotus*) or relatively short and broad, with moderate to no ridging (Fig. 88).
7. infraorbital canal very large, without distinct groove for nerve passage.
8. **lacrimal canal with small opening on side of rostrum at front edge of infraorbital canal** (no opening in *Dolichotus*).
9. auditory bulla relatively large (Fig. 88).
10. paroccipital process prominent, slightly curved (Fig. 88).
11. jugal not approaching lacrimal.
12. **lower jaw with prominent ridge and groove on lateral surface** (Figs. 72, 88); **angular process not deflected;** coronoid process prominent.
13. **upper toothrows strongly convergent anteriorly** (Fig. 88).
14. crowns of cheekteeth flat and prismatic, with sharp angular folds of enamel (Fig. 88).

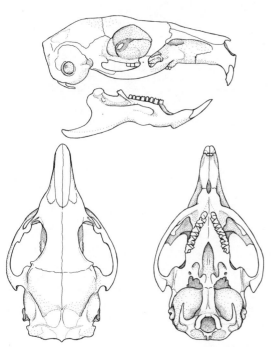

Figure 88. Skull of a caviid (*Galea*, x 1).

RODENTIA

Dental formula: $\dfrac{1}{1}\dfrac{0}{0}\dfrac{1}{1}\dfrac{3}{3} = 20$

Compare with: Dinomyidae, Chinchillidae.

Representative Genera:

Cavia (3) - Guinea pigs, cavies; *C. porcellus* is the domesticated guinea pig.
Dolichotus (2) - Patagonian hares.
Galea (3) - Cuis.

Microcavia (3) - Desert cavies.

Remarks: Behavior and ecology of desert cavies were described by Rood (1970). A history of the origin of domestic guinea pigs was given by Weir (1974).

Family HYDROCHOERIDAE
(Capybara)

This robust tropical mammal is the largest living rodent. Its semi-aquatic habits are evidenced by several structural adaptations—the digits are partially webbed, and the eyes, ears, and nostrils are shifted to a dorsal position on the head. Other features such as the convergent toothrows, prismatic cheekteeth, grooved dentary bone, number of digits, and vestigial tail are reminiscent of the Caviidae. The pig-like appearance is accentuated by the blunt snout and sparse hair covering.

Capybaras are diurnal inhabitants of densely vegetated habitats near watercourses, and they are excellent swimmers. They eat aquatic vegetation, grasses, and other plant materials.

Capybaras are social animals, occurring in bands of up to twenty individuals. Reproduction is aseasonal, but apparently individual females breed only once each year. Three or four young are usual.

Since capybaras compete with domestic livestock for forage, they have been exterminated from a wide portion of their former range.

One genus, 1 species; Panama and northeastern South America south to Uruguay.

Recognition Characters:

- **third upper and lower molars huge, the third upper molar longer than other three cheekteeth combined** (Fig. 89).

1. **body large (up to 125 cm), pig-like.**
2. pelage long, coarse, sparse.
3. **tail very short.**
4. limbs relatively short.

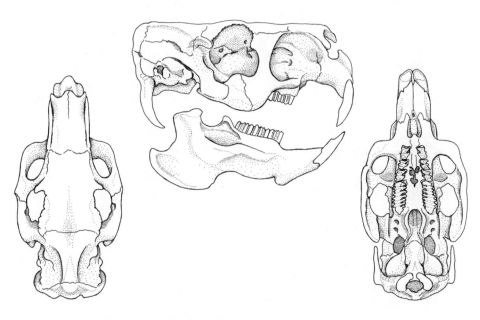

Figure 89. Skull of a hydrochoerid (*Hydrochoerus*, x ¼).

5. **digits 4-3, partially webbed;** claws unspecialized.
6. **skull massive, elongate, not ridged** (Fig. 89).
7. infraorbital canal very large, without distinct groove for nerve passage.
8. **lacrimal canal with small opening on side of rostrum at front edge of infraorbital canal** (Fig. 89).
9. auditory bulla relatively large.
10. **paroccipital process very long (longest of all rodents),** curved anteriorly (Fig. 89).
11. jugal not approaching lacrimal.
12. **lower jaw with prominent ridge and groove on lateral surface** (Figs. 72, 89); **angular process not deflected;** coronoid process prominent.
13. **upper toothrows slightly convergent anteriorly** (Fig. 89).
14. **crowns of cheekteeth flat and prismatic, with sharp angular folds of enamel, the latter forming numerous transverse ridges on the large third molars** (Fig. 89).

Dental formula: $\frac{1\ 0\ 1\ 3}{1\ 0\ 1\ 3} = 20$

Genus:

   Hydrochoerus (1) - *H. hydrochaeris* is the capybara.

Remark: The family Hydrochoeridae is considered a subfamily of Caviidae by Ellerman (1940) and Landry (1957).

Family DINOMYIDAE
(Pacarana)

This South American family contains only one species. It is distinguishable by relatively large size, unusual pelage, and features of the lower jaw and cheekteeth (see below).

The habits of pacaranas are poorly known. They frequent the lower reaches of the Andes Mountains. Apparently they are timid and docile (Walker et al., 1975). Fruit, leaves, and stems compose the diet. Two young are normally produced.

One genus, 1 species; northwestern South America.

Recognition Characters:

1. body relatively large, heavy-set (93-99 cm).
2. pelage thick, soft, with a pair of white stripes or series of white spots along back.
3. tail short, well haired.
4. limbs short.
5. **digits 4-4,** not webbed; claws large, strong.
6. skull blocky, not heavily ridged.
7. infraorbital canal very large, without distinct groove for nerve passage.
8. lacrimal canal not opening on side of rostrum.
9. auditory bulla moderately large.
10. paroccipital process short.
11. jugal not approaching lacrimal.
12. lower jaw without ridge or groove on lateral surface; **angular process strongly deflected; coronoid process very small or absent.**
13. upper toothrows strongly convergent anteriorly.
14. **crowns of cheekteeth flat, consisting of a series of four transverse plates.**

Dental formula: $\frac{1\ 0\ 1\ 3}{1\ 0\ 1\ 3} = 20$

Compare with: Chinchillidae, Caviidae, Dasyproctidae, Cuniculidae.

Genus:

   Dinomys (1) - *D. branickii* is the pacarana.

Family DASYPROCTIDAE
(Agoutis, acouchis)

In some ways these tropical forest rodents are the ecological and·structural equivalents of small forest-dwelling antelopes (Bovidae, p.294, and chevrotains (Tragulidae p.287) of the Old World. The body is compact and essentially tailless, but the limbs exhibit cursorial adaptations—they are slender, and the digits are reduced in number and bear broad thick claws. The clavicle is vestigial.

Dasyproctids are diurnal. They subsist primarily on fruit, but other plant foods are also taken. Seeds of fruit are often hoarded. These animals take refuge in burrows among rocks, roots of trees, under logs, or in creek banks. Sleeping shelters are also maintained.

Members of this family occur singly or in pairs. Permanent pair bonds are formed. Small territories are established, but the extent to which an area is defended varies with the abundance and distribution of the seasonal fruit fall. Flight behavior is unique—as a predator approaches, dasyproctids remain crouched in a sitting position until the last moment and then bolt away, often emitting shrill screams. Females bear 2-6 offspring, which are extremely precocial.

Dasyproctid flesh is tasty and they are widely hunted.

Two genera, 9 species; tropical America, southern Mexico to central South America, and the lesser Antilles.

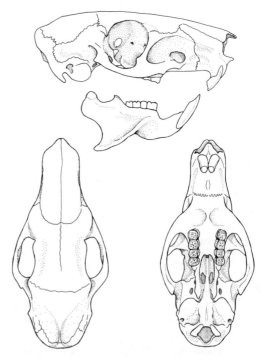

Figure 90. Skull of a dasproctid (*Dasyprocta*, x ½).

Recognition Characters:

1. body relatively large (37-62 cm).
2. pelage moderately long, coarse.
3. tail short (*Myoprocta*) or absent.

4. limbs, especially hindlimbs, relatively long, slender.
5. digits 4-3, not webbed; claws hoof-like.
6. **skull elongate, not heavily ridged** (Fig. 90).
7. infraorbital canal very large, without a distinct groove for nerve passage.
8. **lacrimal canal with large opening on side of rostrum at front edge of infraorbital canal (Fig. 90).**
9. auditory bulla relatively large.
10. paroccipital process relatively short.
11. jugal not approaching lacrimal.
12. lower jaw without ridge or groove on lateral surface; angular process deflected; coronoid process prominent.
13. upper toothrows ± parallel.

14. crowns of cheekteeth flat, consisting of transverse folds of enamel separating from each other to form islands in adults (Fig. 90).

Dental formula: $\dfrac{1\ 0\ 1\ 3}{1\ 0\ 1\ 3} = 20$

Compare with: Cuniculidae.

Genera:

Dasyprocta (7)- Agoutis.
Myoprocta (2) - Acouchis.

Remark: Aspects of the natural history of agoutis and acouchis were treated by Smythe (1978) and Morris (1962), respectively.

Family CUNICULIDAE
(Pacas)

Only two species make up this family. In each the body is thick and has a blunt head and short legs. Pacas differ from dasyproctids (p.191) in having five digits on the hindfoot, a conspicuously spotted pelage, and curiously constructed skull (see below). Pouches formed by the peculiar zygomatic arches serve as resonating chambers which modify vocalizations into low rumbling sounds (Hershkovitz, 1955).

Pacas are solitary and nocturnal. Like dasyproctids, they are reminiscent of small antelopes in habits. The diet consists of fruit, roots, leaves, and other plant matter. These animals take shelter in self-made burrows in places like those frequented by dasyproctids. They take to water readily. Normally one young is produced.

One genus, 2 species; central Mexico to southern Brazil.

Recognition Characters:

● **skull robust, with rough-textured plates over jugals and maxillae.**

1. body relatively large (62-83 cm).
2. pelage moderately long and coarse, **with a series of conspicuous white spots along side.**
3. tail absent.
4. **limbs relatively short.**
5. **digits 4-5,** not webbed; claws hoof-like.
6. skull as described above.
7. **infraorbital canal very large, with a distinct groove for nerve passage at inner base of infraorbital canal.**
8. lacrimal canal not opening on side of rostrum.
9. auditory bulla relatively small.
10. paroccipital process relatively long.
11. jugal not approaching lacrimal.
12. lower jaw without ridge or groove on lateral surface; angular process deflected; coronoid process prominent.
13. upper toothrows ± parallel.
14. crowns of cheekteeth flat, consisting of transverse folds of enamel separating from each other to form islands in adults.

Dental formula: $\dfrac{1\ 0\ 1\ 3}{1\ 0\ 1\ 3} = 20$

Compare with: Dasyproctidae.

Genus:

Agouti (=Cuniculus) (2) - Pacas.

Remark: Some authors (e.g., Starrett, 1967) included pacas in the family Dasyproctidae.

Family CHINCHILLIDAE
(Chinchillas, viscachas)

Members of this family resemble long-tailed rabbits. Their fur is long (generally thick and soft), the eyes and ears are prominent, and the hindlimbs are elongate. They progress by running and leaping (often bipedally).

These colonial animals are diurnal or nocturnal inhabitants of plains, rocky slopes, and cliffs. A colony (or viscachera) may be composed of many individuals. Burrows of the plains viscacha (*Lagostomus*) are gradually enlarged over a period of decades into enormous excavations having numerous tunnels and entrances.

For most of the year chinchillids are tolerant of one another. In *Lagostomus*, males become antagonistic at the onset of the breeding season. The males are much larger than females in *Lagostomus*, but females are larger in *Chinchilla*. One to five young are produced. Young are nursed from lateral abdominal nipples while the female is in a sitting position (Weir, 1974a). Females of the plains viscacha ovulate 200-800 eggs at a time, the largest number known among mammals (Weir, 1971).

Because of exploitation of chinchillas (*C. laniger*) for their hides, wild populations have been virtually exterminated.

Three genera, 5 species; lowlands of Argentina and in Andes.

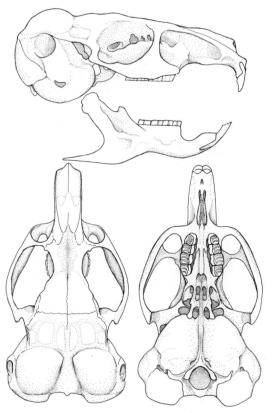

Figure 91. Skull of a chinchillid (*Chinchilla*, x 1).

Recognition Characters:

1. body relatively slender (30-85 cm).
2. **pelage long, soft, dense.**
3. tail long, well haired.
4. forelimbs short, hindlimbs long.
5. digits 4-3 or 4-4, not webbed; claws unspecialized.
6. skull elongate and ridged (*Lagostomus*), or relatively broad and with little or no ridging (Fig. 91).
7. infraorbital canal very large, with (*Lagostomus*) or without distinct groove for nerve passage.
8. **lacrimal canal with large opening on side of rostrum at front edge of infraorbital canal(Fig. 91).**
9. auditory bulla small (*Lagostomus*) to very large (Fig. 91).
10. paroccipital process long (*Lagostomus*) or short and bound to bulla.

11. **jugal approaching** (*Chinchilla*) **or in contact with lacrimal.**
12. **lower jaw without ridge or groove on lateral surface; angular process elongate** (Fig. 91) **and not deflected;** coronoid process prominent.
13. upper toothrows convergent anteriorly.
14. **crowns of cheekteeth flat, consisting of a series of transverse plates** (Figs. 70C, 91).

Dental formula: $\dfrac{1\ 0\ 1\ 3}{1\ 0\ 1\ 3} = 20$

Compare with: Caviidae, Octodontidae, Abrocomidae.

Genera:

Chinchilla (1) - *C. laniger* is the chinchilla.
Lagidium (3) - Mountain viscachas.
Lagostomus (1) - *L. maximus* is the plains viscacha.

Remark: Selected references on the biology of chinchillids include Pearson (1948, 1949), Llanos and Crespo (1952), and Arata (1967).

Family CAPROMYIDAE
(Hutias, nutria)

This poorly-known family consists of a dozen recent species (four of which are recently extinct) with a very limited distribution. All are stout-bodied and have small eyes and ears and a relatively naked rat-like tail. The highest chromosome number in mammals (2n = 88) is recorded in the Jamaican hutia, *Geocapromys brownii* (George and Weir, 1972).

Hutias are ground-dwelling or arboreal; they have a diet of bark, fruit, nuts, leaves, and lizards. Nutrias are amphibious and feed upon aquatic vegetation and shellfish. Capromyids are diurnal or nocturnal, burrowing in banks (*Myocastor*), under rocks, logs, or the roots of trees.

Breeding is aseasonal, and two litters of 2-6 young are common.

Four genera, 12 species; southern South America and the Lesser and Greater Antilles.

Recognition Characters:

1. body small to large, robust (37-80 cm).
2. pelage soft or coarse, not spiny.
3. tail variable, very short to long and prehensile (*Capromys*), well haired or naked.
4. limbs short.
5. digits 4-5, webbed only in *Myocastor*; claws unspecialized.
6. skull blocky, ridged (Fig. 92).
7. infraorbital canal very large, without distinct groove for nerve passage.
8. lacrimal canal not opening on side of rostrum.
9. auditory bulla medium to relatively large.
10. **paroccipital process relatively long, usually standing apart from bulla** (Fig. 92).
11. jugal not approaching lacrimal.
12. lower jaw without ridge or groove on lateral surface; angular process deflected (strongly so in *Myocastor*); coronoid process very small(*Myocastor*) or prominent.
13. upper toothrows convergent anteriorly.
14. crowns of cheekteeth flat, with large inner and outer enamel folds separating from each other to form islands with age (Fig. 92).

Dental formula: $\dfrac{1\ 0\ 1\ 3}{1\ 0\ 1\ 3}$ = 20

Compare with: Echimyidae.

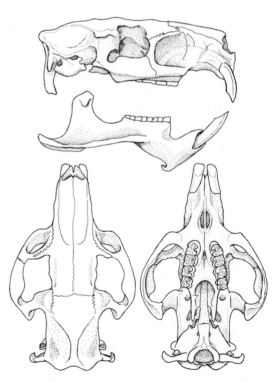

Figure 92. Skull of a capromyid (*Myocastor*, x ½).

RODENTIA

Representative Genera:

Capromys (4) Cuban hutias.
Myocastor (1) - Nutria or coypu.

Remark: *Myocastor* is placed in a separate family by some authors (e.g., Packard, (1967).

Family OCTODONTIDAE
(Octodonts, degu, tuco tucos)

Members of this family are readily identified by the simple but peculiar configuration of the cheekteeth (Figs. 70F, 93). Body form is variable—the family contains rather generalized forms resembling woodrats or chinchillas and two fossorial genera (*Ctenomys*, *Spalacopus*) which bear a remarkable similarity to gophers (Geomyidae, p.179).

The habits of octodontids are varied. They are diurnal or nocturnal and are most frequent in open rocky or grassy areas. A variety of plant foods is consumed. Fossorial forms feed on roots and tubers; *Spalacopus* caches food. Burrows are elaborate in *Ctenomys* and *Spalacopus*; soil is loosened largely by use of the incisors. Other species nest in shallow burrows, rock crevices, or in thickets.

Octodonts occur singly or in colonies. Breeding is seasonal, but more than one litter may be produced, each containing one to five young.

Six genera, perhaps 35 species; chiefly in Andes of west-central South America from southern Peru to central Chile.

Recognition Characters:

1. body relatively small, rat- or gopher-like (17-37 cm).
2. pelage generally long, soft or relatively coarse.
3. tail short or long, well haired (bushy in some).
4. limbs short.
5. digits functionally 4-4 or 4-5 (fifth digit of hindfoot often reduced), not webbed, **with row of bristles extending beyond claw on each;** claws medium-sized to large, curved, sharp.

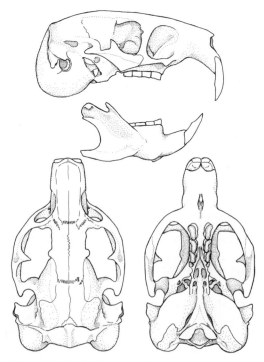

Figure 93. Skull of an octodontid (*Ctenomys*, x 1).

6. skull blocky or elongate, little to strongly ridged (Fig. 93).
7. infraorbital canal very large, with or without (*Spalacopus*) distinct groove for nerve passage at inner base of infraorbital canal.
8. lacrimal canal not opening on side of rostrum.
9. auditory bulla relatively small (*Spalacopus*) to large and inflated (*Octomys*, viscacha rats) (Fig. 93).
10. **paroccipital process short**, bound to bulla.
11. jugal not approaching lacrimal.
12. lower jaw without ridge or groove on lateral surface; angular process deflected; coronoid process prominent.

13. upper toothrows slightly convergent anteriorly.

14. **crowns of cheekteeth simple, eight-shaped or kidney-shaped** (Figs. 70F, 93).

Dental formula: $\dfrac{1\ 0\ 1\ 3}{1\ 0\ 1\ 3}$ =20

Compare with: Abrocomidae, Echimyidae, Chinchillidae, Thryonomyidae, Bathyergidae.

Representative Genera:

Ctenomys (25) - Tuco tucos.
Octodon (3) - Degu.
Spalacopus (1) - *S. cyanus* is the coruro.

Remarks: Some authors (e.g., Walker et al., 1975; Packard, 1967) put *Ctenomys* in a distinct family (Ctenomyidae).

Pearson (1960) studied the natural history of tuco tucos.

Family ABROCOMIDAE
(Chinchilla rats)

In external characters, these rodents, like certain octodontids (p.197), resemble hybrids between rats and chinchillas. They are best identified by pecularities of the cranial and dental anatomy (see below).

The natural history of abrocomids is poorly known. They dwell in rocky habitats, are vegetarians, and may be colonial. Two young are recorded per birth.

One genus, 2 species; in Andes of west-central South America from southern Peru to central Chile.

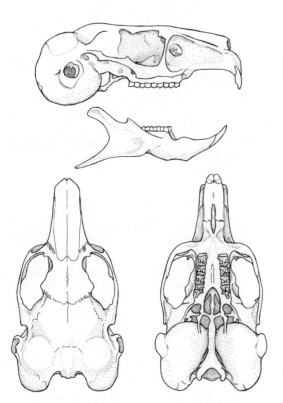

Figure 94. Skull of an abrocomid (*Abrocoma*, x 1).

Recognition Characters:

1. **body medium-sized, rat-like** (21-35 cm).
2. pelage long, soft.
3. tail short to moderately long, covered with short hairs.
4. limbs short.
5. digits functionally 4-4 (fifth digit on hindfoot is small), not webbed, **with bristles extending over unspecialized claws.**
6. **skull elongate, not ridged** (Fig. 94).
7. infraorbital canal very large, without distinct groove for nerve passage.
8. **lacrimal canal with large opening on side of rostrum at front edge of infraorbital canal**(Fig. 94).
9. **auditory bulla large** (Fig. 94).
10. paroccipital process short, curved under and bound to bulla.
11. **jugal widely separated from lacrimal.**
12. lower jaw without ridge or groove on lateral surface; **angular process very elongate and only slightly deflected** (Fig. 94); **coronoid process small.**
13. upper toothrows ± parallel.
14. **crowns of cheekteeth flat, upper teeth with one inner and one outer angular enamel fold** (Fig. 94), **lower teeth with two inner and one outer fold.**

Dental formula: $\frac{1\ 0\ 1\ 3}{1\ 0\ 1\ 3} = 20$

Compare with: Echimyidae, Petromyidae, Octodontidae, Chinchillidae, Muridae.

Genus:

Abrocoma (2) - Chinchilla rats.

Family ECHIMYIDAE
(Spiny rats)

Despite the diversity and abundance of the members of this family, echimyids are among the poorest-known rodents. Combined characteristics of rat-like body, infraorbital canal, and paroccipital processes set this family apart from other hystricomorphs. In most species, the fur consists of stiff or spiny hairs, giving the animals a coarse appearance.

There are two subfamilies. One, the Dactylomyinae, contains three genera (e.g., *Thrinacodus*) with arboreal proclivities. The medial two toes of the feet are set opposite the lateral ones. The remaining genera are mostly terrestrial (*Euryzygomatomys* apparently is fossorial).

Spiny rats are primarily nocturnal and are herbivorous. They take refuge in hollow logs or trees and in burrows. Females bear one to six young.

Fourteen genera, approximately 40 species; Central America from Nicaragua south to central South America, and the island of Martinique.

Recognition Characters:

1. **body small to medium-sized, rat-like (16-76 cm).**
2. **pelage usually coarse or spiny.**
3. tail short (*Euryzygomatomys*) to long, sparsely or well haired.
4. limbs moderately long.
5. digits 4-5, not webbed; claws unspecialized.
6. **skull elongate, little to heavily ridged** (Fig. 95).
7. infraorbital canal very large, with or without distinct groove for nerve passage.
8. **lacrimal canal not opening on side of rostrum.**
9. auditory bulla moderately large.
10. **paroccipital process elongate, curving under bulla.** (Fig. 95).
11. jugal not approaching lacrimal.
12. lower jaw without ridge or groove on lateral surface; angular process slender and deflected; coronoid process relatively small to moderately large.
13. upper toothrows ± parallel.
14. crowns of cheekteeth flat, variable in pattern, having rounded enamel folds separating from each other to form islands with wear, sharply angular enamel folds forming prisms, or transverse plates (Fig. 95).

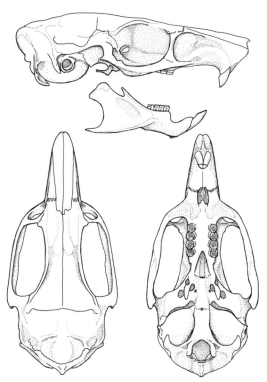

Figure 95. Skull of an echimyid (*Proechimys*, x 1).

Dental formula: $\dfrac{1\ 0\ 1\ 3}{1\ 0\ 1\ 3} = 20$

Compare with: Abrocomidae, Petromyidae, Muridae.

Representative Genera:

Cercomys (2) - Punarés.
Diplomys (3) - Soft-furred spiny rats.
Echimys (12) - Spiny rats.
Euryzygomatomys (1) - *E. spinosus* is the guira.
Proechimys (12) - Spiny rats.
Thrinacodus (2) - Spiny bamboo rats.

Family THRYONOMYIDAE
(Cane rats or grasscutters)

These blunt-nosed, sturdy rodents are common in many parts of Africa. The pelage is bristly and the tail and ears are short. The grooved incisors are the most distinctive cranial features.

Grasscutters are chiefly nocturnal, sheltering among rocks or dense vegetatve growth during the day. Shallow burrows may also be used. Their diet consists of bark, fruit, nuts, and grass. Feeding locations are connected to resting spots by grass corridors. Although their natural habitat is in marshy areas and moist grasslands, these animals often invade agricultural areas where they become pests. Apparently they are not colonial, but they become densely concentrated in suitable areas. Breeding is seasonal or aseasonal; the usual number of young is two to five.

Thryonomyids are an important source of protein for people in many places. In Ghana they are collected by communal hunting parties (Asibey, 1974).

One genus, 6 species; Africa south of the Sahara.

Recognition Characters:

- **upper incisors with three deep grooves** (Fig. 96).

1. body medium, heavy-set (42-85 cm).
2. **pelage coarse, bristly.**
3. tail short, well haired.
4. limbs short.
5. **digits functionally 3-4, not webbed, with large, thick claws.**
6. **skull massive, strongly ridged** (Fig. 96).
7. **infraorbital canal very large, with distinct groove for nerve passage at inner base of canal.**
8. lacrimal canal not opening on side of rostrum.
9. **auditory bulla relatively small.**
10. **paroccipital process relatively large, ± straight** (Fig. 96).
11. **jugal nearly in contact with lacrimal.**
12. lower jaw without ridge or groove on lateral surface; angular process elongate and deflected; coronoid process prominent.
13. upper toothrows ± parallel.
14. **crowns of cheekteeth with thick enamel folds not separating from each other to form islands with wear** (Fig. 96).

Dental formula: $\frac{1\ 0\ 1\ 3}{1\ 0\ 1\ 3} = 20$

Compare with: Ctenomyidae, Bathyergidae, Octodontidae.

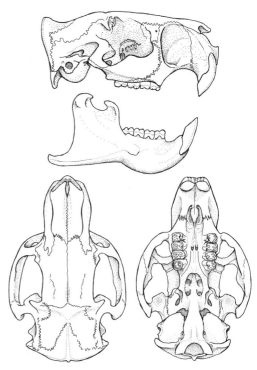

Figure 96. Skull of a thryonomyid (*Thryonomys*, x ½).

Genus:

Thryonomys (6) - Cane rats or grasscutters.

Family PETROMYIDAE
(Dassie rat or rock rat)

This family consists of a single species inhabiting rocky areas of southwest Africa. The general body form, well-haired tail, and flattened skull are reminiscent of those of ground squirrels, and like many squirrels, these rodents are diurnal and utter whistling warning calls. The terraced cheekteeth (see below) are unique.

These animals consume green vegetation, berries, and seeds. They occur singly or in pairs. Breeding is seasonal; one or two young are produced. One pair of mammae is located over each shoulder blade.

One genus, 1 species; southwest Africa.

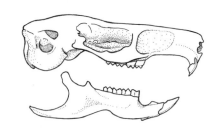

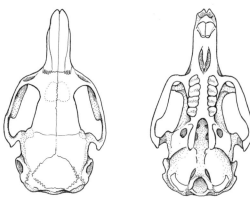

Figure 97. Skull of a petromyid (*Petromus*, x 1).

Recognition Characters:

1. **body relatively small, squirrel-like (27-38 cm).**
2. **pelage very soft, silky.**
3. **tail moderately long, bushy.**
4. limbs moderately long.
5. digits 4-4, not webbed; claws unspecialized.
6. skull relatively broad, only slightly ridged (Fig. 97).
7. **infraorbital canal very large, with distinct groove for nerve passage at inner base of canal.**
8. lacrimal canal not opening on side of rostrum.
9. **auditory bulla large.**
10. paroccipital process elongate, curved under bulla (Fig. 97).
11. jugal not approaching lacrimal.
12. lower jaw without ridge or groove on lateral surface; angular process slightly deflected; coronoid process relatively small.

13. upper toothrows ± parallel.
14. **crowns of cheekteeth terraced, the inner side of the upper teeth and outer side of the lower teeth elevated over rest of tooth surfaces; pattern simple, with one outer and inner enamel fold per tooth (Fig. 97).**

Dental formula: $\frac{1}{1} \frac{0}{0} \frac{1}{1} \frac{3}{3} = 20$

Compare with: Echimyidae, Abrocomidae.

Genus:

Petromus (1) - *P. typicus* is the dassie rat.

204

Family BATHYERGIDAE
(Mole rats, blesmols)

Members of this family have pronounced fossorial specializations. The body is stocky. The tail is small and the eyes and pinnae are minute. The limbs and digits are sturdily constructed and are well clawed, but only *Bathyergus* uses the limbs extensively in digging. Large procumbent incisors are the primary digging tools. The lips close behind the incisors, preventing dirt from entering the mouth. *Heterocephalus* is virtually hairless; the pelage is thick and velvety in other forms.

Cranial features of blesmols are distinctive. The cheekteeth are high-crowned, peculiarly shaped, and variable in number (see below). Unlike those of other hystricomorphs, the infraorbital canal is small and does not transmit any of the masseter muscle. The medial portion of the muscle originates instead from inside the orbit, which is largely taken over by this muscle. A large masseteric fossa and strongly deflected angular process provide a large surface area for insertion of the masseter.

Bathyergids occupy friable soils in deserts and savannahs. They live singly or in colonies and eat roots, tubers, and invertebrates. Burrows are generally shallow; mounds mark locations of tunneling activity. Loosened soil is usually pushed backwards out of the burrow by the hindlimbs. Burrow systems of social species are often very complex. Communal digging (involving relays of individuals digging and pushing dirt) takes place in *Heterocephalus* (Jarvis and Sale, 1971). Directional movement of blesmols in burrows may be determined by sensitivity of the cornea of the eye to air currents (Eloff, 1958). Construction of mounds and tunnels is reduced during cold periods. As might be expected, the naked mole rat (*Heterocephalus*) is a poor thermoregulator (McNab, 1966) and consequently tends to occupy soils where the average burrow temperature is quite high.

The breeding period varies geographically. One to five offspring are produced.

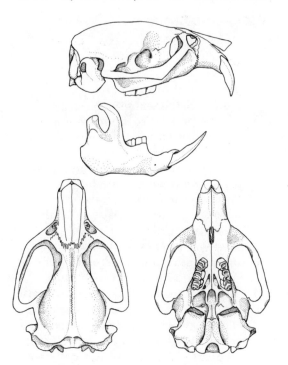

Figure 98. Skull of a bathyergid (*Cryptomys*, x 1).

Five genera, about 20 species; Africa south of the Sahara.

Recognition Characters:

1. **body relatively small to medium-sized, robust, gopher-like (9-40 cm).**
2. pelage short, soft, or reduced to a few scattered hairs (*Heterocephalus*).

3. tail virtually absent (*Heliophobius*) or short and scantily haired.
4. limbs short.
5. **digits 5-5, not webbed; claws medium or large.**
6. skull blocky, usually heavily ridged.
7. **infraorbital canal small (transmitting little or no muscle (Fig. 98), without distinct groove for nerve passage.**
8. lacrimal canal not opening on side of rostrum.
9. **auditory bulla relatively large, flattened.**
10. paroccipital process short (Fig. 98).
11. **jugal widely separated from lacrimal.**
12. lower jaw without ridge lateral and ventral to cheekteeth; **angular process strongly deflected;** coronoid process small to large.
13. upper toothrows ± parallel.
14. **crowns of cheekteeth simple, ring-like.** (Figs. 70D, 98).

Dental formula: $\dfrac{1}{1}\dfrac{0}{0}\dfrac{2\text{-}3}{2\text{-}3}\dfrac{0\text{-}3}{0\text{-}3} = 12\text{-}28$

Compare: Ctenomyidae, Thryonomyidae, Octodontidae.

Representative Genera:

Bathyergus (1) - *B. suillus* is the Cape sand mole.
Cryptomys (15) - Blesmols, common mole rats.
Heliophobius (3) - Sand rats.
Heterocephalus (1) - Naked mole rat.

Remark: For a review of bathyergid habits and additional references, see Kingdon (1974b).

Family CTENODACTYLIDAE
(Gundis)

Gundis are compact, soft-furred rodents superficially resembling guinea pigs (p.187). Structural details of the cheekteeth, mandible, and cranium are diagnostic, however (see below).

Ctenodactylids prefer rocky places, where they find shelter in crevices; they do not burrow. They eat green vegetation, seeds, and flowers. Most of their activity occurs in early morning. They are gregarious and emit squeaks and whistling sounds.

The breeding habits of gundis are little known. Two or three offspring appear usual.

Four genera, 6 species; northern Africa, from Somaliland to Senegal and Morocco.

Recognition Characters:

1. body medium-sized, compact, guinea-pig-like (17-28 cm).
2. pelage soft.
3. tail short, bushy.
4. limbs relatively short.
5. digits 4-4, not webbed; claws unspecialized.
6. skull broad, swollen, not ridged.
7. infraorbital canal very large, without distinct groove for nerve passage.
8. lacrimal canal not opening on side of rostrum (an oblique canal is, however, present in maxilla).
9. auditory bulla large, inflated.
10. **paroccipital process broad, curving under and in contact with bulla.**
11. **jugal in broad contact with lacrimal bone.**
12. **lower jaw with small ridge lateral and ventral to cheekteeth; angular process elongate but not deflected; no coronoid process.**

13. upper toothrows ± parallel.
14. crowns of cheekteeth relatively simple, upper teeth kidney- or eight-shaped, lower teeth with one or two (*Pectinator*) inner enamel folds.

Dental formula: $\dfrac{1\ 0\ 1\text{-}2\ 3}{1\ 0\ 1\text{-}2\ 3} = 20\text{-}24$

Compare with: Caviidae.

Representative Genera:

Ctenodactylus (2) - Gundis.
Pectinator (1) - *P. spekei* is the bushy-tailed rat.

Remark: George (1974) investigated the habits of ctenodactylids.

ORDER CARNIVORA

Carnivores are specialized predaceous mammals. Obvious indications of a carnivorous habit include modifications of the teeth, particularly of the canines and cheekteeth (see below). Carnivores also have a keen sense of smell—olfactory lobes of the brain are large, and the turbinal bones are elaborate and provide a large surface area for support of the nasal mucosa. They are worldwide in distribution, although the only Australian representative, the dingo, was probably introduced there by primitive humans.

Although many members of this order are indeed carnivorous, others are second-arily adapted to eat a wide variety of foods, including insects and other invertebrates and fruit. Bears and raccoons are omnivorous, and even the more specialized carnivorous species (e.g., cats) regularly consume vegetative matter.

The taxonomic arrangement of the carnivores and a closely related group, the pinnipeds, is disputed. I follow the convention of assigning the two groups to separate orders (Ewer, 1973; Scheffer, 1958; Stains, 1967; Walker et al., 1975), although others (e.g., Tedford, 1976; Vaughan, 1978) include them in the Carnivora (see discussion below, p.230).

The earliest members of this order (the extinct family Miacidae) appear in the Paleocene. Another carnivorous order (Creodonta) existed simultaneously throughout the early Tertiary. The Carnivora and Pinnipedia remain as the principal orders of broadly-adapted predators.

Recognition Characters:

1. size small to large.
2. body form variable, well haired.
3. **limbs variable, well clawed, not modified into flippers.**
4. eyes variable in position, usually well separated.
5. pinna prominent.
6. lacrimal foramen present.
7. incisors 3/3 (3/2 in *Enhydra*, a mustelid).
8. **canines large, pointed, curved.**
9. cheekteeth secodont or bunodont; **carnassial teeth present** (weakly developed in Ursidae and Procyonidae); molars usually with crushing surfaces (except lower first molar in most).

Compare with: Pinnipedia, Insectivora.

Remarks: A recent and excellent general reference to carnivores is Ewer (1973). In addition, the classification and phylo-genetic relationships of the families are examined by Simpson (1945), among others. The periodical *Carnivora* is devoted entirely to studies of this group.

KEY TO FAMILIES OF CARNIVORA

1a.   Auditory bulla constricted in middle .... **VIVERRIDAE** (p.221)

1b.   Auditory bulla not constricted in middle 2

2a (1b). Last (and only) upper molar very small and simple (Fig. 99C) or absent 3

2b.   Last (and not necessarily the only) upper molar relatively large, complex (Fig. 99A, B) 4

3a (2a). Forelimbs and hindlimbs ± equal in size; four digits on hindfoot; cranium globular; rostrum very short, blunt .... **FELIDAE** (p.227)

3b.   Forelimbs distinctly larger than hindlimbs; five digits on hindfoot; cranium gently rounded or flattened; rostrum relatively long, pointed .... **HYAENIDAE** (p.224)

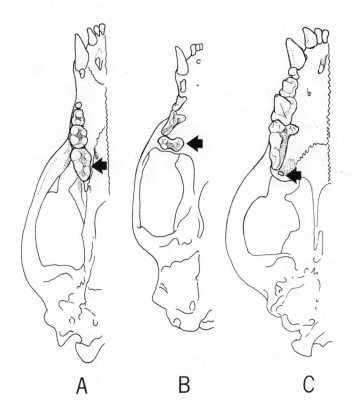

A   B   C

Figure 99. Upper cheekteeth of an ursid (A), a mustelid (B), and a hyaenid (C). Note size and shape of last molar.

4a (2b). Cranium usually squarish and flat in profile; rostrum relatively short; jaw articulation usually firm—post-mandibular process encircling mandibular fossa and condyle of lower jaw (Fig. 100A); only one upper molar—usually dumbbell-shaped or squarish (Fig. 99B). . . . . **MUSTELIDAE** (p.218)

4b. Cranium rounded in profile; rostrum usually elongate; jaw articulation relatively loose—postmandibular process not encircling condyle of lower jaw (Fig. 100B); more than one upper molar—last one usually elongate, never dumbbell-shaped (Fig. 98A) 5

5a (4b). Foot posture digitigrade; four digits on hindfoot; mastoid process smaller than paroccipital process (Fig. 101A); carnassials usually well developed . . . . **CANIDAE** (p.211)

5b. Foot posture plantigrade; five digits on hindfoot; mastoid process ± equal in size to paroccipital process (Fig. 101B); carnassials weakly developed or absent 6

6a (5b). Size large (skull greater than 13 cm in length); tail short; alisphenoid canal present (Fig. 102); last upper molar elongate (Fig. 99A) . . . . **URSIDAE** (p.214)

6b. Size medium (skull less than 13 cm in length); tail long; no alisphenoid canal (rarely present); last upper molar rounded or squarish . . . .**PROCYONIDAE** (p.216)

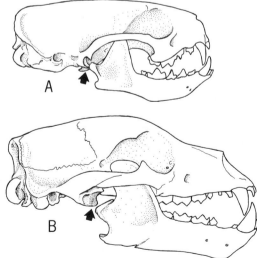

Figure 100. Mandibular fossae (at arrows) of a mustelid (A) and an ursid (B).

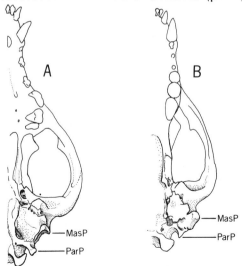

Figure 101. Mastoid and paroccipital processes of a canid (A) and an ursid (B). MasP, mastoid process; ParP, paroccipital process.

Family CANIDAE
(Dogs, wolves, foxes, jackals)

As a result of a long symbiotic relationship between humans and domestic dogs, members of this family are widely known. Canids are well haired and have a bushy tail, long limbs, and a lithe body. The ears are large, pointed, and erect. A long muzzle encloses complex turbinal bones. Carnassial teeth are well developed; post-carnassial teeth have crushing surfaces.

Canids are alert and intelligent, and rely on acutely-developed senses of smell and hearing to detect and locate prey. They are opportunistic feeders, hunting singly or in packs. Prey are captured by ambush (small rodents) or by chase (larger mammals). Coyotes (*Canis latrans*) often run down prey in relays. Many species have exceptional endurance. In addition to vertebrate prey, canids commonly feed on molluscs, insects, and other invertebrates, fruit, and carrion. The mostly insectivorous

big-eared fox has an unusually large number of teeth (50) for a placental mammal. Canids occupy all terrestrial habitats from the Arctic to the tropics.

These mammals are among the best thermoregulators. The fur of some cold-adapted species (e.g., Arctic fox) is extremely dense in winter and protects animals exposed to temperatures as low as -70°C. Canids also possess remarkable adaptations for coping with warm temperatures. Heat is released primarily by panting. This process, though not unique to canids, is well developed in them. It involves a series of extremely rapid, shallow breaths of air (up to 400 per minute), which flows unidirectionally in through the nose and out through the mouth (Schmidt-Nielsen et al., 1970). Heat is lost by evaporation of water from secretions of nasal glands and from saliva (Blatt et al., 1972).

Social behavior has been described for several species (see references in **Remarks**). Visual communication is important—the predominant behavioral cues are facial expressions and the carriage of the ears, head, body, and tail. Territoriality is commonplace. Foxes are generally solitary except during the mating season. Others (e.g., coyotes, wolves, hunting dogs) are social. The latter species often establish permanent pair bonds between sexes.

Canids are monoestrous. Breeding is seasonal in temperate species, but aseasonal in others (e.g., African hunting dog). Litters contain 2-12 pups. Vacant or self-made burrows are used during the pup-rearing period.

Humans value canids as pets and for their fur, the quality of which is determined by the length and density of guard hairs. Different color phases are

Figure 102. Alisphenoid canal (at arrow), a canid.

211

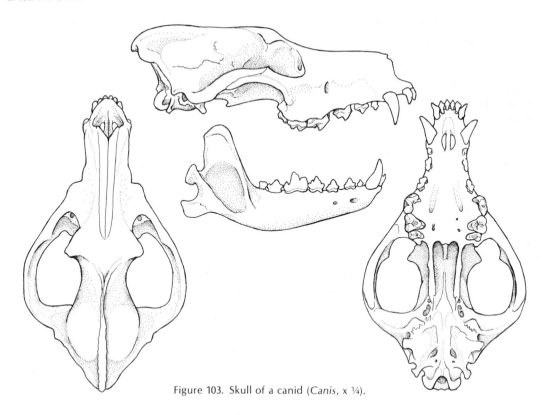

Figure 103. Skull of a canid (*Canis*, x ¼).

common in foxes. Some species (e.g., coyotes) are pests to the livestock industry.

Fourteen genera, approximately 35 species; worldwide except Antarctica and most oceanic islands.

Recognition Characters:

1. size medium (53-193 cm).
2. **tail long, bushy.**
3. foot posture digitigrade.
4. digits usually 5-4 (four on forefoot in *Lycaon*).
5. claws well developed, relatively straight, non-retractile.
6. **skull elongate; rostrum relatively long, narrow** (Fig. 103).
7. mastoid process smaller than paroccipital process (Figs. 101A, 103).
8. alisphenoid canal present.
9. carnassials well developed.
10. **last upper molar relatively large, transversely elongate** (Fig. 103).

Dental formula: $\dfrac{3\ 1\ 4\ 1\text{-}4}{3\ 1\ 4\ 2\text{-}5} = 38\text{-}50$

(usually $\dfrac{3\ 1\ 4\ 2}{3\ 1\ 4\ 3} = 42$)

Compare with: Ursidae, Viverridae.

Representative Genera:

Canis (including *Fennicus, Dusicyon, Alopex,* and *Vulpes;* see **Remarks**) (27)- Familiar species include: domestic dog (*C. familiaris*); coyote (*C. latrans*); wolf(*C. lupus*); golden and black-backed jackals (*C. aureus* and *C. mesomelas*); red fox (*C. vulpes*); Arctic fox (*C. lagopus*); and fennec (*C. zerda*).

Chrysocyon (1) - *C. brachyurus* is the maned wolf.

Lycaon (1) - *L. pictus* is the African hunting dog.

Nyctereutes (1) - *N. procyonoides* is the raccoon dog.

Otocyon (1) - *O. megalotis* is the big-eared fox.

Speothos (1) - *S. venaticus* is the bush dog.

Urocyon (1) - *U. cinereoargenteus* is the gray fox.

Remarks: The inclusion of the fennec and most foxes in the genus *Canis* follows changes proposed by Van Gelder (1977, 1978).

Bueler (1973) and Fox (1971, 1975) provided general reviews of biology and behavior of canids. See also Ewer (1973) and references therein. Recent taxonomic reviews were provided by Clutton-Brock et al. (1976) and Van Gelder (1978). Useful papers on anatomy and behavior include Hildebrand (1964), Kleiman (1966, 1967), and Kleiman and Eisenberg (1973). General accounts of African species are provided by Kingdon (1977) and Rosevear (1974). Selected references for individual species are: coyotes (Bekoff, 1978; Young and Jackson, 1951); jackals (Golani, 1969); African hunting dogs (Estes and Goddard, 1967; Kuhme, 1965); wolves (Mech, 1970; Murie, 1944; Young and Goldman, 1964).

Various aspects of the origin, history, and biology of domestic dogs are provided by Beck (1973), Fiennes and Fiennes (1968), Fox (1978), Scott (1968), and Scott and Fuller (1965).

Family URSIDAE
(Bears)

Bears are large-bodied, powerfully built carnivores with a stubby tail and short stout limbs. Like those of procyonids, the feet have broad soles and five digits, and the foot posture is plantigrade. The canines are large, and except for several vestigial premolars the cheekteeth are adapted for crushing (Fig. 104). Smell is the best-developed sense.

The diet comprises a wide variety of plant and animal matter, including carrion. A few ursids have restricted diets. The giant panda, for example, feeds chiefly on bamboo shoots. Sloth bears eat insects which are sucked into the mouth by a peculiar pump-like action of the lips and mouth. Bears may move about at any time of day, although most restrict activity to night. They seek out temporary shelters in brush or hollows during times of inactivity.

Generally solitary, bears commonly travel in pairs during the mating period. Despite their massive proportions, some species are good climbers. One to four young (usually two) are produced in alternate years. Development is relatively slow and sexual maturity is not attained until the third year.

In winter, temperate species typically retreat to dens and hibernate. Recent studies (reviewed in Folk et al., 1976) indicate that although dormant animals show no appreciable decrease in body temperature, metabolic and heart rates drop to 50 percent of normal. In contrast to

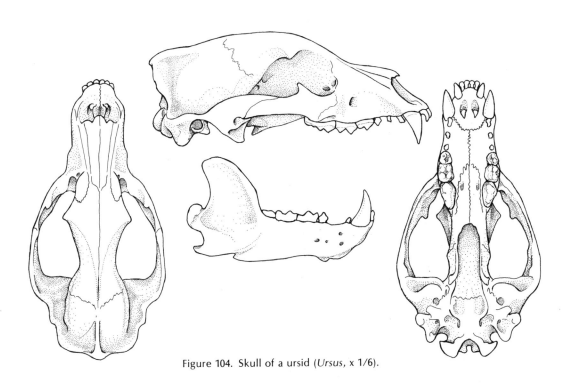

Figure 104. Skull of a ursid (*Ursus*, x 1/6).

other hibernators, bears do not frequently interrupt the dormant period for feeding and excretory activities. Cubs are born shortly before bears emerge from the den in the spring.

Four genera, 8 species; worldwide except Australia and Antarctica, occurring in Africa only in Atlas Mountains (but probably now extinct there) and in South America only in the Andes.

Recognition Characters:

1. **size large** (110-260 cm).
2. **tail short.**
3. **foot posture plantigrade.**
4. digits 5-5.
5. **claws large, curved,** non-retractile.
6. skull elongate; rostrum relatively long, narrow (Fig. 104).
7. **mastoid process ± equal in size to paroccipital process** (Figs. 101B, 104).
8. alisphenoid canal present.
9. **carnassials poorly developed; molars with flat, broad crowns** (Fig. 104).
10. **last upper molar very large, elongate anteroposteriorly** (Fig. 104).

Dental formula: $\dfrac{3\ 1\ 4\ 2}{3\ 1\ 4\ 3} = 42$

(first three premolars vestigial, often absent.)

Compare with: Canidae, Procyonidae.

Genera:

Ailuropoda (1) - *A. melanoleuca* is the giant panda.

Melursus (including *Helarctos*; see **Remarks**) (2) - *M. ursinus* is the sloth bear; *M. malayanus* is the Malayan sun bear.

Tremarctos (1) - *T. ornatus* is the spectacled bear.

Ursus (including *Thalarctos* and *Selenarctos*; see **Remarks**) (4) - *U arctos, U. americanus, U. thibetanus,* and *U. maritimus* and the grizzly or brown bear, American black bear, Asiatic black bear, and polar bear, respectively.

Remarks: Well-documented crosses between several species of bears indicate that no more than four genera should be recognized (Gray, 1972; Van Gelder, 1977).

Selected references to bears are Couturier (1954), Herrero (1972), and Pelton et al. (1976). A useful older reference is Pocock (1914). Papers dealing with the special taxonomic problem of the giant panda include Davis (1964), Sarich (1973), and Simpson (1945), and references therein.

Family PROCYONIDAE
(Raccoons and allies)

This group of mostly New World species is adapted to terrestrial and arboreal habitats. The limbs are relatively elongate. The foot posture is plantigrade, and each foot has five long, separate, and flexible digits. A distinguishing feature in most species is the alternate light and dark banding on the tail. Prominent facial markings are also often present.

With few exceptions, procyonids have omnivorous feeding habits, as evidenced by the rather sharp-cusped but crushing cheekteeth. All species are excellent climbers, and dens are usually located in trees. These mammals are mostly nocturnal.

Procyonids usually occur singly or in family groups. Female coatis (*Nasua*) travel in bands; the normally solitary males join the females only during the breeding period (Kaufman, 1962). Procyonids usually bear one litter of 1 to 6 young annually.

Seven genera, perhaps 18 species; exclusively North and South America except for *Ailurus* of southeast Asia.

Recognition Characters:

1. size medium (61-135 cm).
2. **tail long, usually ringed with alternating black- and light-colored bands.**
3. **foot posture plantigrade or semi-plantigrade.**
4. digits 5-5.
5. claws prominent, non-retractile.
6. skull robust, usually elongate; rostrum not particularly narrow (Fig. 105).

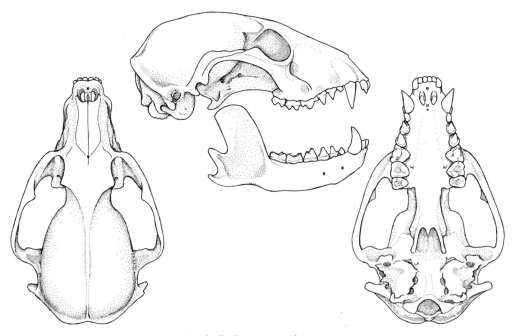

Figure 105. Skull of a procyonid (*Procyon*, x ½).

7. **mastoid process equal to or larger in size than paroccipital process** (Fig. 105).
8. no alisphenoid canal (except in *Ailurus*).
9. **carnassials poorly developed, molars broad** (Fig. 105).
10. **last upper molar relatively large, rounded** (Fig. 105).

Dental formula: $\dfrac{3\ 1\ 3\text{-}4\ \ 2}{3\ 1\ 3\text{-}4\ 2\text{-}4} = 36\text{-}40$

Compare with: Ursidae, Mustelidae.

Representative Genera:

Ailurus (1) - *A. fulgens* is the lesser panda.
Bassaricyon (3) - Olingos.
Bassariscus (2) - Ringed-tailed cats.
Nasua (3) - Coatis.
Potos (1) - *P. flavus* is the kinkajou.
Procyon (6) - Raccoons; *P. lotor* is the familiar North American species.

Remarks: The taxonomic position of several genera (e.g., *Bassariscus, Ailurus*) is open to question. For a discussion of taxonomic problems in this family, see Simpson (1945). Other important references include Ewer (1973) and Pocock (1921a).

Behavior and ecology of coatis was studied by Kaufmann (1962). *Procyon* biology and taxonomy was summarized by Goldman (1950) and by Lotze and Anderson (1979).

Family MUSTELIDAE
(Weasels, otters, skunks, badgers)

Members of this family have a reputation for being highly specialized killers with pugnacious dispositions. They are well endowed for predaceous habits. The dentition comprises sharp, elongate canines and well-developed shearing and crushing cheekteeth. The face is short and blunt, and the braincase is flattened and disproportionately large, providing a broad surface area for attachment of enlarged temporal muscles. A large flange surrounding the mandibular condyle prevents disarticulation of the lower jaw during struggles with oversized prey.

The body form in mustelids is long and slender (e.g., *Mustela*, *Lutra*), stout (e.g., *Taxidea*, *Gulo*), or generalized. Slender-bodies forms have high rates of metabolism for their size, requiring increased food consumption (Brown and Lasiewski, 1972; Moors, 1977). Color and pattern vary with species. Temperate weasels have whitish winter coats; the degree of seasonal change varies geographically.

Anal glands are developed to various degrees in all mustelids. The habit of using secretions of these glands for defense is best known in skunks, but all mustelids have a characteristic musky odor.

Mustelids frequent many habitats; they are ground-dwelling or are variously suited for arboreal (e.g., *Eira*, *Martes*), semi-fossorial (e.g., *Meles*, *Taxidea*, *Mellivora*), aquatic (e.g., *Lutra*, *Pteronura*), and marine (*Enhydra*) ways of life. Mustelids are ambulatory or progress by bounding or scampering. They take refuge in burrows, cavities in trees or logs, rock crevices, or kelp (*Enhydra*), and are nocturnal or diurnal. The diet consists largely of vertebrate prey, but may also include insects and other invertebrates, honey, fruit, nuts, fungi, and carrion.

Because of their solitary and secretive customs, few mustelids have been extensively studied in the wild. Two cases of peculiar habits are noteworthy. Sea otters are tool-users. They break open shellfish by holding them with the forefeet and smashing them vigorously against a flat rock which is cradled on their chest as they bob belly-up in water. For a thorough description of this behavior see Hall and Schaller (1964). Honey badgers are curious in having a remarkable symbiotic association with the African honeyguide (appropriately named *Indicator indicator*). The bird, perhaps in a modified form of mobbing behavior (Ewer, 1973; Friedman, 1955), seeks out a badger and leads it to honey by uttering excited calls which cease when the badger discovers a beehive. The honeyguide benefits from this activity by consuming remnants left by the badger after it opens the nest.

Mustelids generally breed once a year. Females bear 1-12 young, and many species exhibit delayed implantation. The offspring of sea otters are more precocial than those of other species. Sexual dimorphism in size is often marked.

Twenty-five genera, 70 species; worldwide except Australia, Antarctica, and most oceanic islands.

Recognition Characters:

- **postmandibular process often prominent and curved around mandibular fossa, often locking lower jaw into place** (Figs. 100A, 106).

1. size small to medium (17-155 cm).
2. tail variable, but usually long.
3. foot posture plantigrade (badgers) or digitigrade.

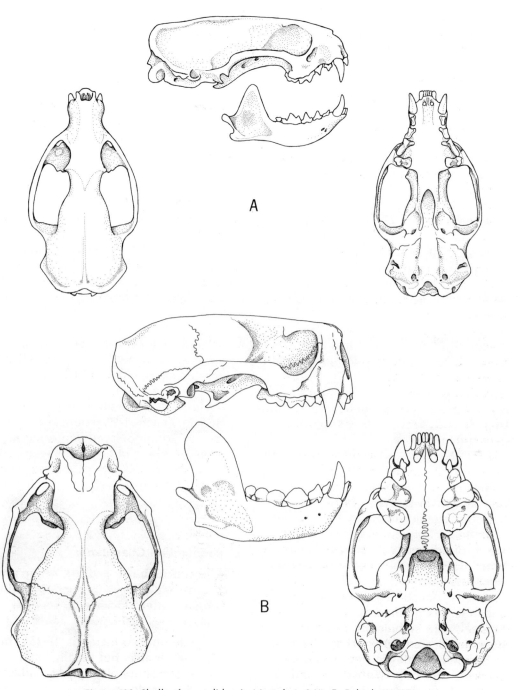

Figure 106. Skulls of mustelids: A, *Mustela* (x 3/4); B, *Enhydra* (x 1/2).

4. digits 5-5.
5. claws well developed, semi-retractile.
6. **skull blocky, robust, often flattened; rostrum short** (Fig. 106).
7. mastoid process absent or smaller than paroccipital process (Fig. 106).
8. no alisphenoid canal.
9. carnassials usually well developed. (Fig. 106).
10. **upper molar relatively large, usually dumbbell-shaped or squarish** (Figs. 99B, 106).

Dental formula: $\dfrac{3}{2\text{-}3}\ \dfrac{1}{1}\ \dfrac{2\text{-}4}{2\text{-}4}\ \dfrac{1}{1\text{-}2} = 30\text{-}38$

(usually $\dfrac{3}{3}\ \dfrac{1}{1}\ \dfrac{3}{3}\ \dfrac{1}{2} = 34$)

Compare with: Viverridae, Procyonidae, Felidae.

Representative Genera:

Aonyx (1) - *A. capensis* is the African clawless otter.

Conepatus (6) - Hog-nosed skunks.

Eira (1) - *E. barbara* is the tayra.

Enhydra (1) *E. lutra* is the sea otter.

Galictis (2) - Grisons.

Gulo(1) - *G. luscus* is the wolverine.

Ictonyx (1) - *I. striatus* is the striped polecat.

Lutra (12) - River otters. The common North American species is *L. canadensis.*

Martes (8) - Martens, fishers, sables.

Meles (1) - *M. meles* is the European badger.

Mellivora (1) - *M. capensis* is the honey badger or ratel.

Melogale (3) - Ferret badgers.

Mephitis (2) - Striped skunks.

Mustela (15) - Weasels, ermines, stoats.

Pteronura (1) - *P. brasiliensis* is the giant otter.

Spilogale (2) - Spotted skunks.

Taxidea (1) - *T. taxus* is the North American badger.

Vormela (1) - *V. peregusna* is the marbeled polecat.

Remarks: The most recent syntheses of mustelid classification are by Pocock (1921b) and Simpson (1945). Mustelid biology and behavior were reviewed by Ewer (1973) and Goethe (1964). Major works on individual species include Fisher (1942), Harris (1968), Jacobi (1938), and Kenyon (1969) on sea otters; Krott (1959) on wolverines; Anderson (1970) on martens and fishers; Hall (1951) on weasels; and Neal (1977) on the European badger. Kingdon (1977) and Rosevear (1974) reviewed the natural history of African species.

Ratel.

Family VIVERRIDAE
(Mongooses, civets, genets, and allies)

Although quite diverse, this family is poorly known. There is extraordinary variety in habits and physical characteristics among members of the family. Viverrids are variously ground-dwelling generalists or semi-aquatic, arboreal, or cursorial. In general form, many resemble other carnivores: dogs (*Bdeogale*); weasels (*Herpestes*); cats (*Cryptoprocta*, *Genetta*); raccoons (*Atilax*); and kinkajous (*Nandinia*, *Arcticus*). Despite these specializations, viverrids are less removed from ancestral carnivores (miacids) than other carnivore familes are. The limbs, for instance, are short in relation to the overall size of the body.

Viverrids frequent many habitats and are nocturnal or diurnal. They are mainly solitary, but some travel in pairs or bands. Groups of dwarf mongooses (*Helogale*) are extended families and are matriarchal, with one female dominating other members in each band (Rasa, 1977). Some viverrids form colonies similar to those of ground squirrels among rocks or in grasslands (e.g., *Suricata*, *Cynictis*), a habit unique among carnivores. Dens are located in rock crevices, caves, trees, brush, natural holes, or self-constructed burrows. Viverrids are carnivorous, omnivorous, or frugivorous; some scavenge on carrion.

Like mustelids (p.218), most viverrids have well-developed anal scent glands which are used for marking and for defense. Kingdon (1977) describes a curious behavior pattern in the banded mongoose, *Mungos mungos*, in which individuals gather in writhing clumps. When exposed to unfamiliar situations they engage in frenzied scent-pasting of strange objects and one another. This clumping behavior becomes aggressive when directed at other animals (including predators), the effect of which is described by Kingdon as "a menacing monster relentlessly advancing as it rears its many heads."

Some species of mongooses (e.g., *Helogale*, *Herpestes*, *Mungos*) have the curious habit of breaking eggs and hard-bodied arthropods by throwing them against rocks or other hard surfaces. This behavior is discussed by Ewer (1973) and is described and illustrated in detail by Eisner and Davis (1967).

Information on reproductive biology and behavior of viverrids in the wild is scanty. The breeding period is seasonal or aseasonal. One or two litters of 1 to 6 offspring are produced annually.

Thirty-six genera, approximately 75 species; widely distributed in Old World except Australia.

Recognition Characters:

- **auditory bulla constricted in middle (Fig. 107) and divided by a septum.**
1. size small to medium (32-185 cm).
2. tail usually long, bushy.
3. foot posture semi-plantigrade to digitigrade.
4. digits usually 5-5 (four on hindfoot in *Cynictis*, four on all feet in *Suricata*).
5. claws well developed, semi-retractile.
6. **skull elongate**; rostrum moderately long (Fig. 107).
7. mastoid process absent or smaller than paroccipital process.
8. alisphenoid canal usually present.
9. **carnassials moderately developed, the upper usually without an anterior cusp and the lower with a**

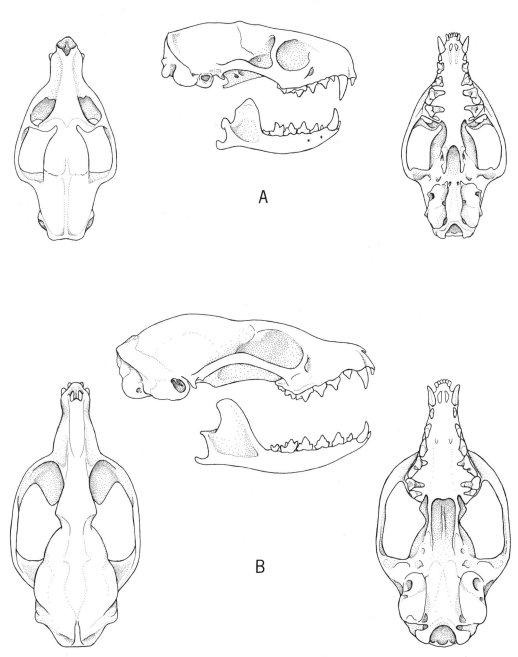

Figure 107. Skulls of viverrids: A, *Herpestes*; B, *Genetta* (both x 3/4).

disproportionately large posterior crushing surface (talonid) (Fig. 107).

10. last upper molar relatively large, transversely elongate or squarish (Fig. 107).

Dental formula: $\dfrac{3}{3}\ \dfrac{1}{1}\ \dfrac{3\text{-}4}{3\text{-}4}\ \dfrac{1\text{-}2}{1\text{-}2}$ = 32-40

Compare with: Mustelidae, Canidae.

Representative Genera:

Arctictis (1) - *A. binturong* is the binturong.

Atilax (1) - *A. paludinosus* is the marsh mongoose.

Bdeogale (4) - Dog mongooses.

Civettictis(1) - *C. civetta* is the African civet.

Crossarchus (3) - Cusimanses.

Cryptoprocta (1) - *C. ferox* is the fossa.

Cynictis (1) - *C. penicillata* is the yellow mongoose.

Fossa (1) - *F. fossa* is the fanaloka.

Genetta (5) - Genets. The most widespread species is the common genet, *G. genetta*.

Helogale (6) - Dwarf mongooses.

Herpestes (13) - Mongooses.

Ichneumia (1) - *I. albicauda* is the white-tailed mongoose.

Mungos (1) - *M. mungos* is the banded mongoose.

Nandinia (1) - *N. binotata* is the African palm civet.

Paradoxurus (3) - Palm civets.

Prionodon (2) - Linsangs

Suricata (1) - *S. suricatta* is the meerkat.

Viverra (3) - Oriental civets.

Viverricula (1) - *V. indica* is the Indian civet.

Remarks: The most recent taxonomic review of the Viverridae is by Gregory and Hellman (1939). Pocock (1915a, 1915b, 1916) examined external characters. The natural history of African forms was reviewed by Kingdon (1977) and Rosevear (1974). Mongoose biology was discussed by Hinton and Dunn (1967). Useful studies of individual species include Ewer (1963), Rasa (1977), and Wemmer (1977).

Genet.

Family HYAENIDAE
(Hyaenas, aardwolf)

The popular notion that hyaenas are scavengers is a half-truth, since spotted hyaenas are now recognized as important predators in their own right. Actually, there are two adaptive types among hyaenids. One type comprises hyaenas (*Crocuta*, *Hyaena*), which have powerful foreparts and a massive skull and dentition (Fig. 108B)—adaptations for capturing large mammals and for obtaining nourishment from virtually all body parts including bones of the prey or carrion. The other (the aardwolf, *Proteles*), is specialized for an insectivorous diet and has a delicate body and skull and reduced dentition (Fig. 108A). Together the incisors and anterior portion of the lower jaw of aardwolves form a spade which evidently assists in digging for insects (Kindon, 1977). All hyaenids have a posteriorly sloping silhouette due to the disproportionately large size of the forelimbs and shoulder region. Vocalizations include laugh-like whoops and howls.

Hyaenids are mostly nocturnal and crepuscular. Natural cavities or abandoned aardvark holes are used as dens. *Crocuta* may share dens with warthogs (Kruuk, 1972). They are carnivorous (*Crocuta*), omnivorous (*Hyaena*), or insectivorous (*Proteles*), and are most common in open plains and savannahs.

Social patterns are flexible. *Proteles* and *Hyaena* usually occur singly or in pairs. *Crocuta* often occurs in "clans"; the degree of gregariousness is positively correlated with prey abundance. Hyaenids maintain individual or group territories. Female hyaenas are dominant to males. The two genera of hyaenas compose one of the few groups of mammals in which the size of females exceeds that of males (Ralls, 1976). In addition, the clitoris of females is male-like—it is enlarged and equipped with a foreskin, and is erectile. Organ mimicry is further perfected by paired swellings of fibrous tissue resembling male testicles. These sexual similarities are discussed by Kruuk (1972) in relation to use of genital displays as social appeasement gestures. The aardwolf does not exhibit these peculiarities.

Hyaenids are polyestrous. Short-term pair bonds develop during the breeding period. Two to four young are usual.

The peculiar habits and vocalizations of hyaenas have prompted people in close contact with them to associate them with sorcery and witchcraft.

Three genera, 4 species; Africa, Asia, India.

Recognition Characters:

1. size medium to large (75-195 cm).
2. tail relatively long, bushy.
3. foot posture digitigrade, **hindlimbs shorter than forelimbs.**
4. digits 4-5 (*Crocuta* and *Hyaena*) or 5-5 (*Proteles*).
5. claws blunt, non-retractile.
6. **skull massive** (hyaenas) **or delicate** (aardwolf); rostrum relatively long, narrow (Fig. 108).
7. mastoid process absent or smaller than paroccipital process (Fig. 108).
8. no alisphenoid canal.
9. carnassials well developed (except in *Proteles*) (Fig. 108).
10. **upper molar, if present, very small, round or elongate** (Fig. 108).

Dental formula: $\frac{3\ 1\ 3\text{-}4\ 0\text{-}1}{3\ 1\ 1\text{-}3\ 1\text{-}2} = 26\text{-}34$
(variation occurring mostly in *Proteles*; hyaenas normally $\frac{3\ 1\ 4\ 1}{3\ 1\ 3\ 1} = 34$).

Compare with: Felidae.

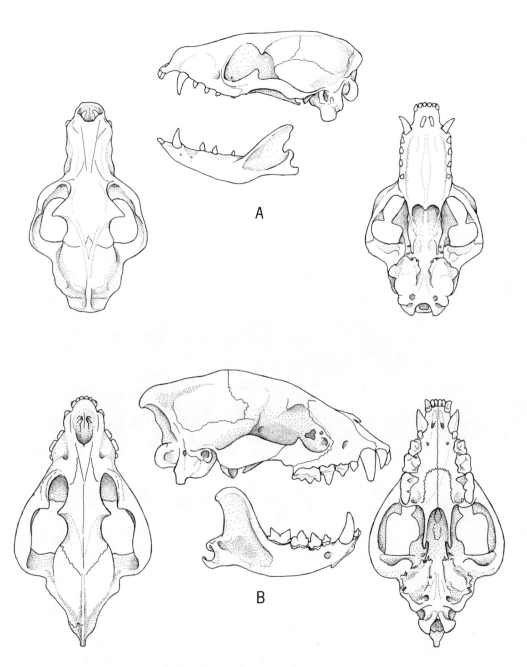

Figure 108. Skulls of hyaenids: A, *Proteles* (x⅜); B, *Hyaena* (x ¼).

Genera:

Crocuta (1) - *C. crocuta* is the spotted hyaena.

Hyaena (2) - *H. brunnei* and *H. hyaena* are the brown and striped hyaenas, respectively.

Proteles (1) - *P. cristatus* is the aardwolf.

Remark: Excellent summaries of the natural history of hyaenid species were provided by Kingdon (1977), Kruuk (1972, 1975), and Kruuk and Sands (1972).

Striped hyaena.

Family FELIDAE
(Cats)

Cats are superbly adapted predators. Virtually all characteristics of their structure and behavior are fashioned for killing. The dentition consists of long, narrow, and sharp stabbing canines and cheekteeth shaped only for shearing (Fig. 109). Enlarged temporal and masseter muscles enable cats to inflict a powerful bite. Sharp curved claws serve as meat-hooks for capturing and manipulating prey. The claws retract neatly into sheaths when not in use. Binocular vision, made possible by an evolutionary shift of the eyes anteriorly and medially and by a reduction in the size of the muzzle, assists in the location of prey and in the delivery of an accurate pounce and bite.

The appearance and abundance of large cats in the fossil record coincides with the ascent of modern ungulates. There are several groups of extinct felids. The familiar sabre-toothed cats differed considerably from modern felids in their manner of killing. The stabbing bite of extant cats involves both the upper and lower jaws. In contrast, the stab of sabre-tooths was inflicted by a downward thrust of enormous upper canines, and the masseter muscles were relatively very small.

Felids are comparatively uniform in physical characteristics, suggesting similar degrees of specialization for a predaceous habit. Variation occurs primarily in size and color pattern. Coexisting species of cats probably avoid competition by exploiting prey species of different sizes.

Most cats are solitary and often fiercely intolerant of one another except at mating. Even in the more gregarious species (e.g., lions, cheetahs), the group is usually merely an extension of the family. Home ranges overlap, but individuals practice mutual avoidance. Their ferocity has resulted in the evolution of elaborate appeasement and threat behavior. Cats typically engage in threat displays by enlarging their apparent size—they stand straight-legged, arch the back, erect ruffs of hair, bare the canines, and snarl.

Virtually all cats prey upon terrestrial vertebrates, though fruit, fish, molluscs, and insects may fortify the diet. They are primarily nocturnal. They are stealthy hunters, making use of their keen vision to locate prey. Prey animals are pounced upon from ambush or after a short chase. An exception is the cheetah, which relies on speed and relatively long chases to run down its prey. The soles of the feet of cheetahs resemble tire treads, enabling them to change directions quickly (Ewer, 1973). Most species of cats can also climb well. In addition to serving as sources of prey, trees also are used as shelters, places of ambush, and as sites for storing food. Other refuges include caves, burrows of other animals, other available holes or cavities, and undergrowth.

Frequency of breeding varies from one to two litters per year in small species to one breeding effort every two or three years in large ones. Females are seasonally polyestrous. The litter size is usually two or three, and the maximum is six (domestic cats commonly have more).

Two genera, perhaps 35 species; worldwide except Australia, Antarctica, and some islands.

Recognition Characters:

1. size medium (75-370 cm).
2. tail short or long, not bushy.
3. foot posture digitigrade.
4. **digits 5-4.**

5. **claws sharp, strongly curved, retractile** (only partly retractile in *Acinonyx*).
6. **skull short, rounded dorsally; rostrum very short, blunt** (Fig. 109).
7. mastoid process ± equal in size to paroccipital process (Fig. 109).
8. no alisphenoid canal.
9. **carnassials very well developed** (Fig. 109).
10. last upper molar tiny, round (Figs. 99C, 109).

Dental formula: $\dfrac{3}{3}\dfrac{1}{1}\dfrac{2\text{-}3}{2}\dfrac{1}{1} = 28\text{-}30$

Compare with: Hyaenidae

Genera:

Acinonyx (1) - *A. jubatus* is the cheetah.
Felis (including *Leo, Lynx,* and *Neofelis;* see **Remarks**) (34) - Some familiar species are: house cat (*F. catus*), bobcat (*F. rufus*), African lion (*F. leo*), tiger (*F. tigris*), jaguar (*F. onca*), leopard (*F. pardalis*), caracal (*F. caracal*), mountain lion (*F. concolor*), serval (*F. serval*), and Canadian and European lynx (*F. canadensis* and *F. lynx*).

Remarks: There is little agreement on felid taxonomy. Contrary to usual custom, I recognize only two genera of felids. The assignment of all but the cheetah to *Felis* is supported by studies of Gray (1972) and Van Gelder (1977), who reported hybrids between members of the genera *Leo, Lynx,* and *Felis.* Simpson (1945) also reviewed taxonomic arguments in favor of such changes.

Other interesting works on felids include Dominis and Edey (1968), Ewer (1973), Guggisberg (1975), Kleiman and

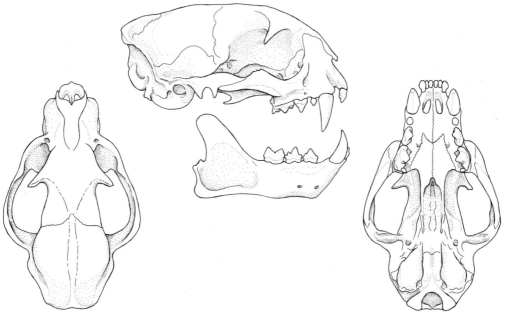

Figure 109. Skull of felid (*Felis,* x 3/8).

Eisenberg (1973), Leyhausen (196), Pocock (1917, 1951), Simpson (1941), and volumes edited by Eaton (1973, 1974, 1976-1977). Papers on individual species include Rudnai (1973) and Schaller (1972) on African lions, Eaton (1973) on cheetahs, Schaller (1967) on tigers, Young (1958) on bobcats, and Hornocker (1970) and Young and Goldman (1946) on mountain lions. Kingdon (1977) and Rosevear (1974) reviewed African species.

Leopard.

ORDER PINNIPEDIA

Pinnipeds, or "fin-foots", differ most obviously from other groups of aquatic specialists (Sirenia, Mysticeti, Odontoceti) in having flipper-like forelimbs and hindlimbs and in lacking a fluke-like tail. They also spend at least a portion of their life on land or ice. Members of this order can be separated into two groups on the basis of their means of locomotion: "walkers" (sea lions, fur seals, walruses) and "wrigglers" (true seals). Their diet consists primarily of fish, crustaceans, and molluscs.

Pinnipeds possess many physiological and anatomical adaptations that aid survival in sea water. Heat conservation is maximized by the presence of insulating layers of blubber and fur and by vasomotor control of blood flow to the extremities. In addition, special arrangements of small blood vessels in the flippers (retia mirabilia) shunt heat from the outgoing arterial circulation to the cool venous blood returning to the body. Dives are sustained by the high oxygen stores in muscle myoglobin, slowed heart rate (bradycardia), and channeling of blood to metabolically active tissues.

It has long been recognized that pinnipeds have close affinities to terrestrial carnivores, yet there is little consensus about the taxonomic assignment of pinnipeds. They have been given ordinal rank (Scheffer, 1958) or subordinal status in the order Carnivora (Simpson, 1945), although some recent authors (Mitchell and Tedford, 1973; Repenning and Tedford, 1977; Tedford, 1976) accord them no more than superfamily status in the Carnivora. Taxonomic questions center around whether the pinnipeds arose from one or two carnivore ancestors (McLaren, 1960; Mitchell, 1967, 1975). Pending further clarification, the pinnipeds are here assigned to a separate order.

Recognition Characters:

1. size medium to large.
2. **body streamlined, torpedo-shaped; hair very short.**
3. **forelimbs and hindlimbs modified into flippers.**
4. eyes positioned forward on face, close together.
5. pinna reduced or absent.
6. no lacrimal foramen.
7. incisors 1-3/0-2.
8. no carnassials.
9. cheekteeth relatively simple, conical or multi-cusped, without crushing surfaces.

Compare with: Carnivora.

Remarks: Good general references on pinniped biology include King (1964), Ridgeway (1972), Ronald and Mansfield (1975), and Scheffer (1958). Behavior and physiology were treated by Harrison et al. (1968). For the most part, generic and species numbers in family accounts are taken from Rice (1977).

KEY TO FAMILIES OF PINNIPEDIA

1a.   Hind limb permanently extended posteriorly, not capable of being turned forward and used in terrestrial locomotion; body usually spotted or banded; no alisphenoid canal; cheekteeth usually multi-cusped .... **PHOCIDAE** (p.236)

1b.   Hind limb capable of being turned forward and used in terrestrial locomotion; body ± uniform in color, without spots or bands; alisphenoid canal present (see Fig. 102); cheekteeth simple, usually one-cusped or peg-like...2

2a (1b).   Pinna present; supraorbital process well developed; lower incisors present; upper canine prominent but not tusk-like .... **OTARIIDAE** (p.232)

2b.   No pinna; no supraorbital process; no lower incisors; upper canine large, tusk-like .... **ODOBENIDAE** (p.234)

Sea lion.

Family OTARIIDAE
(Eared seals, sea lions)

Members of this group of pinnipeds are not as specialized for an aquatic existence as their counterparts, the phocids (p.236) Unlike true seals, when on land otariids retain the ability to rotate the hindlimbs to a forward position under the rear of the body. Pinnae are small but present, and the testes are scrotal. Propulsion in water is achieved mostly by undulations of the body and by movements of the oar-like foreflippers.

These animals are gregarious, congregating on sandy beaches, rocks, or reefs. They feed chiefly on fishes and squid. Vocalizations include barks and roars.

Otariids assemble in large herds to breed. Males are much larger than females. Harems, which include one bull and up to several dozen females, are established in the spring. Females are zealously guarded by the bull. After giving birth to a single pup conceived during the previous year's breeding activities, each female is courted by the male. Copulations take place within the confines of the harem group. Bulls generally do not feed during the breeding period. During the non-breeding season, animals often migrate considerable distances to preferred feeding sites.

The California sea lion is displayed as the "trained seal" in zoos and circuses. Fur seals are valued for their pelts.

Five genera, 14 species; coastlines of Pacific, South Atlantic, and Indian oceans.

Recognition Characters:

- **pinna present** (absent in other two pinniped families)
- **supraorbital process well developed** (absent or rudimentary in other two families) (Fig. 110).
1. body relatively uniform in color, never spotted.
2. **hindlimbs capable of being turned forward.**
3. nails prominent on middle three digits of hindfoot, absent or vestigial on forefoot; skin of flipper extending distally beyond nails.
4. testes scrotal.
5. **mastoid process separate from auditory bulla** (Fig. 110).
6. **medial two upper incisors with transverse groove** (Fig. 110).
7. cheekteeth simple, usually with one large cusp (Fig. 110).

Dental formula: $\frac{3}{2}\frac{1}{1}\frac{4}{4}\frac{1\text{-}3}{1} = 34\text{-}38$

Compare with: Odobenidae, Phocidae.

Representative Genera:

Arctocephalus (including *Zalophus;* see **Remarks**) (9) - Southern fur seals, California sea lion. *A. pusillus*, the giant fur seal, and *A. californianus*, the california sea lion, are common species.

Callorhinus (1) - *C. ursinus* is the northern fur seal.

Eumetopias (1) - *E. jubata* is Steller's sea lion.

Otaria (1) - *O. flavescens* is the South American sea lion.

Remarks: *Zalophus* is placed in *Arctocephalus* following Van Gelder (1977). Treatments of natural history of individual species include Hamilton (1934, 1939), Marlow (1967, 1975), Peterson (1968), and Peterson and Bartholomew (1967).

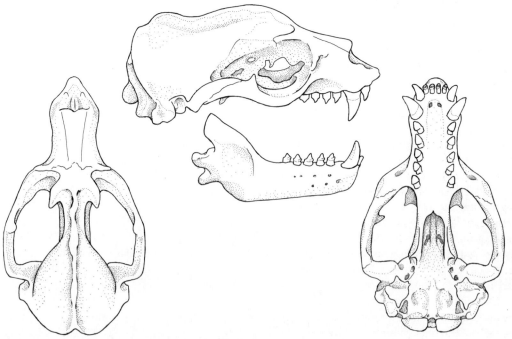

Figure 110. Skull of an otariid (*Arctocephalus*, x 1/4).

Family ODOBENIDAE
(Walrus)

The single species in this family is the largest living pinniped. The most obvious feature is the large tusk-like upper canine (Fig. 111) found in both sexes. Odobenids most closely resemble otariids (p.232) in superficial appearance, behavior, and cranial morphology.

These pinnipeds inhabit shallow waters, rocky shores, and ice in north polar regions, following pack ice during seasonal migrations to and from breeding areas. They associate in herds of mixed sexes and ages. Mating takes place during the northward migration in spring. Breeding is probably polygynous, but little information is known of mating behavior. Pharyngeal pouches in males produce a spectacular "bell-sound" used in courtship displays (Ray et al., 1975; Schevill et al., 1966). A single pup is produced.

Walruses feed mostly on molluscs and other invertebrates. Feeding behavior is not precisely known, but they probably use their fleshy upper lips and sensory vibrissae on the snout to locate shellfish on the sea floor, and then dislodge the prey with the tusks.

One genus, 1 species; Atlantic and Pacific Oceans in Arctic regions.

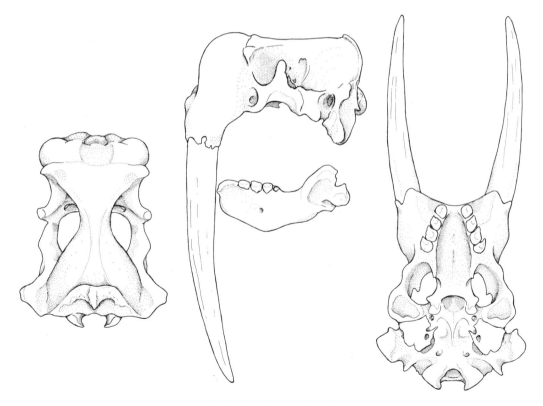

Figure 111. Skull of an odobenid (*Odobenus*, x ⅛).

Recognition Characters:

- **upper canine enormous, tusk-like** (Fig. 111).

- **no lower incisors** (present in other pinniped families) (Fig. 111).

1. body uniform in color, never spotted.
2. hindlimbs capable of being turned forward.
3. nails present on all digits of forefoot and hindfoot; skin of flipper not extending distally beyond nails.
4. testes abdominal.
5. **mastoid process enormous, bound to auditory bulla** (Fig. 111).
6. upper incisors small, conical (Fig. 111).
7. **cheekteeth simple, peg-like** (Fig. 110).

Dental formula: $\dfrac{1\text{-}2}{0}\ \dfrac{1}{1}\ \dfrac{3\text{-}4}{3\text{-}4}\ \dfrac{0}{0} = 18\text{-}24$

Compare with: Otariidae.

Genus:

Odobenus (1) - *O. rosmarus* is the walrus.

Remark: Ecology and behavior of walruses were treated by Brooks (1954) and Mansfield (1958).

Family PHOCIDAE
(True seals or earless seals)

Representatives of this family are the most aquatically-adapted pinnipeds. Appendages such as pinnae and genitals are absent or located internally. The hindlimbs are functionally modified into a tail which provides the major propulsive force in water. They move by waving the hindflippers from side to side (whales move the tail in an up-and-down fashion). Movements on land or ice are awkward— the forelimbs propel the seal forward while the hindlimbs are generally dragged along behind. For this reason, these pinnipeds are commonly referred to as "wrigglers". They do not adopt an upright stance like that of sea lions and walruses.

Phocids are also the only pinnipeds that commonly exhibit spots or bands. Pups are uniformly colored and have a dense woolly underfur that is generally lacking in adults. Adult ribbon and harp seals are sexually dimorphic for banding pattern; the patterns are more prominent in males. Spotted species (e.g., harbor seals) are quite variable in color and spot pattern.

Retreats are located on ice flows and on rocky, muddy, or sandy beaches and flats. Most species are gregarious, but a few are solitary. The diet consists primarily of crustaceans, molluscs, and small fishes. Complexly-cusped cheekteeth in crab-eater seals and leopard seals are used for filtering krill and capturing penguins, respectively.

These animals usually form large associations during the breeding season. Since copulation usually takes place in

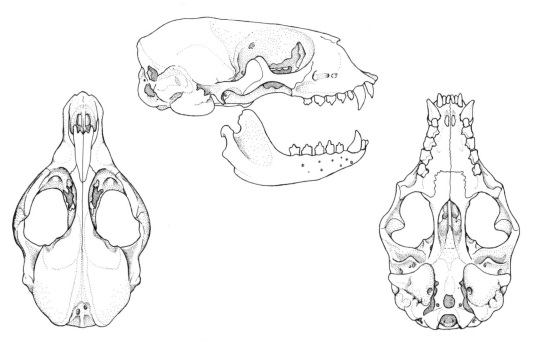

Figure 112. Skull of a phocid (*Phoca*, x 1/4).

water, mating behavior is poorly known even for common species. A single pup is produced.

Ten genera, 19 species; coastlines north of 30° north latitude and south of 50° south latitude, Lake Baikal, Caspian Sea, and scattered locations elsewhere.

Recognition Characters:

- **no alisphenoid canal** (present in other two pinniped families).

1. **body usually spotted or banded** (uniformly colored in some).
2. **hindlimbs extended posteriorly, incapable of forward rotation.**
3. claws present on digits of forefoot and usually on hindfoot; skin on flipper not extending beyond nails.
4. testes abdominal.
5. mastoid process bound to auditory bulla, the latter inflated (Fig. 112).
6. upper incisors not grooved (Fig. 112).
7. **cheekteeth usually multi-cusped** (elaborately so in *Lobodon*) (Fig. 112).

Dental formula: $\frac{2\text{-}3}{1\text{-}2} \frac{1}{1} \frac{4}{4} \frac{0\text{-}2}{0\text{-}2} = 26\text{-}36$

Compare with: Otariidae.

Representative Genera:

Hydrurga (1) - *H. leptonyx* is the leopard seal.
Leptonychotes (1) - *L. weddelli* is the Weddell seal.
Lobodon (1) - *L. carcinophagus* is the crabeater seal.
Monachus(3) - Monk seals.
Mirounga(2) - Elephant seals.
Phoca (including *Pusa* and *Pagophilus*) (7) - Harbor, ringed, spotted, harp, and ribbon seals and allies.

Remarks: Useful references on phocid species include Bertram (1940), Hewer (1974), King (1956), LeBoeuf and Briggs (1977), McLaren (1958), and Sivertsen (1941).

CETACEANS:
ORDERS MYSTICETI and ODONTOCETI

Cetaceans are strictly aquatic mammals characterized by a fish-like (fusiform) and essentially hairless body, a horizontally flattened tail with terminal flukes, a thick layer of blubber, telescoped skull (see below), paddle-shaped forelimbs (flippers) and no hindlimbs (but vestiges of the pelvic girdles are usually present). Absent also are pinnae, oil glands (and in large part sweat glands) in the skin, and clavicles. The nostrils are located on the dorsal surface of the head forming a single or double blowhole. The diploid chromosome number is typically 44 (Kulu, 1972).

The history of cetaceans is poorly known, but they are clearly derived from early land-dwelling eutherians. This ancestry is evidenced by the presence of typical mammalian limb buds in young embryos and by skeletal similarities between early cetaceans and generalized terrestrial mammals. Cetaceans appeared first in the Eocene. They diverged rapidly into three distinct groups: baleen whales (Mysticeti, p.240), toothed whales (Odontoceti, p.247), and the extinct zeuglodonts (Archaeoceti). Some recent authors (e.g., Rice, 1967, 1977; Vaughan, 1978) have treated the three groups as separate orders, and that procedure is followed here.

The skulls of the two groups of modern cetaceans are unlike those of any other mammal. Alteration of the position of bones has resulted in a massive remodeling of the cranium, a condition called "telescoping". For example, the maxillae and premaxillae are lengthened and enlarged posteriorly (especially in odontocetes) and the supraoccipital is expanded anteriorly (especially in mysticetes). This rearrangement is due largely to an evolutionary shift in location of the nostrils to the top of the head. Intervening bones (frontals, parietals, nasals) have been compressed or obscured by the expansions of these bones. The skull is often asymmetrical, particularly in odontocetes (e.g., Physeteridae, p.252). The function of this asymmetry is unknown.

Propulsion is accomplished almost entirely by vertical movements of the flukes. These have no special bony supports—they are fortified by fibrous connective tissue. The high speeds attained by smaller species of whales are due to a reduction in friction produced by the torpedo-like shape, a smooth flexible skin, and reduced external appendages (e.g., pinnae), and to the efficient use of the crescent-shaped flukes.

Numerous anatomical and physiological features aid in diving and temperature regulation. Prolonged dives to great depths are made possible by several adaptations. Air in the lungs of cetaceans can be expelled more completely at each breath than in those of terrestrial mammals. The blood and other tissues of whales have high oxygen-storage capacities. In fact, the muscles of these animals are almost black from high concentrations of myoglobin. In addition, whales are tolerant of large buildups of metabolic products such as carbon dioxide and lactic acid. Apparently whales do not suffer from "the bends," a debilitating and potentially fatal condition produced by nitrogen (which is forced into solution during a dive by high pressure) coming out of solution to form bubbles that can block circulation. "The bends" occurs in humans if they experience a rapid decrease in pressure as they ascend to the surface. By contrast, deep-diving whales avoid the problem—in these species the lungs are disproportionately small in relation to their overall body size, and air is not continually replenished at high pressures during dives as it is in humans. The amount of nitrogen dissolved in the blood stream is probably too low to cause the bends. Whales combat pressure extremes because the body consists largely of compression-resistant materials (e.g., bone, fluids). Only the thorax becomes compressed appreciably. The ribcage, which is loosely attached to the sternum and vertebral column, partially collapses around the lungs, which are protected by being located high in the thoracic cavity. Rigid-walled air passages prevent compression of gases still remaining in the lung passages.

As in pinnipeds (p.230), a reduced heart rate (bradycardia) and the use of circulatory shunts and retia mirabilia accompany long dives. These adaptations conserve heat and provide for more effective use of available oxygen. Since cetaceans are virtually hairless, they depend more upon blubber for heat conservation than do pinnipeds.

Hearing is the best-developed sense in whales, and echolocation is the principal means of orientation. Vision also is relatively well developed in most species. Although they lack vocal cords, whales emit a wide variety of low- to high-pitched sounds, including squeaks, screams, whistles, clicks, groans, wails, and barks. Probably these sounds are produced by the muscular larynx or valvular nostrils. Mysticetes are less vocal than odontocetes. Vocalizations serve to locate food and provide a means of communication.

Copulation takes place in either a horizontal or vertical position while the animals clasp each other with the pectoral flippers. Unlike terrestrial mammals of different sizes, all whales have a gestation period of roughly the same length—about a year (Kihlstrom, 1972). However, large species of whales have faster fetal growth rates than small species and therefore give birth to larger young (Huggett and Widdas, 1951). Females produce an unusually rich milk which is force-fed to the calves through the teats. The calves grow exceptionally fast.

Remarks: Rice (1967) provided a concise summary of the biology of whales. Howell (1930) summarized morphological adaptations. Other detailed treatments of cetaceans are by Andersen (1969), Gaskin (1972, 1976), Harrison (1972, 1974, 1977), Harrison and King (1965), Hershkovitz (1966), Kellogg (1928), Miller (1923), Mitchell (1975), Norris (1966), Ridgeway (1972), Slijper (1936, 1962, 1976), and Winn and Ollo (1979).

Unless otherwise noted, the classification and names of families, genera, and species within the two orders of whales follows Rice (1977).

ORDER MYSTICETI

This order contains the largest cetaceans, many of which have been the mainstay of the whaling industry for centuries. They differ from odontocetes in many respects (see below and p.247) Teeth, which are present as buds in the gums of embryos, degenerate and are replaced in adult mysticetes by baleen—a series of 100-400 transverse plates of hardened oral tissue of the palate that are suspended from each side of the upper jaw along the outer margins of the mouth. The plates are frayed on the inner surfaces, forming a filter. Water is taken into the mouth and forced out through the baleen as the mouth is closed, trapping planktonic organisms on the inside of the filter. The strained food is scraped from the baleen by the tongue with each closure of the mouth and is swallowed.

Many adaptations of baleen whales to an aquatic environment are shared with odontocetes (see above, p.238).

Recognition Characters:

1. **no teeth** (except in embryos).
2. **baleen present.**
3. two external nasal openings (blowholes) present, slit-like.
4. **skull ± symmetrical.**
5. nasals roofing part of nasal passage.
6. **maxilla extending posteriorly as a long, narrow process, interlocking with frontal, not spreading outward over supraorbital process.**
7. lower jaws loosely joined by ligaments at symphysis.

Compare with: Odontoceti, Sirenia.

Remark: References to baleen whales are included with those listed above for cetaceans (p.239).

KEY TO FAMILIES OF MYSTICETI

1a.   Body chunky; no longitudinal grooves in skin of throat; rostrum highly arched; posterior margins of nasal and premaxilla not extending backward be-beyond level of anterior margin of supraorbital process of frontal (see Fig. 113); maxilla without nasal process .... **BALAENIDAE** (p.241)

1b.   Body slender; longitudinal grooves present in skin of throat; posterior margins of nasal and premaxilla extending backward beyond level of anterior margin of supraorbital process of frontal (see Figs. 114, 115); maxilla with nasal process 2

2a (1b).   Dorsal fin present; throat grooves numerous; supraoccipital extending anteriorly beyond zygomatic process of squamosal (see Fig. 115); lower jaws conspicuously bowed outward.................. **BALAENOPTERIDAE** (p.245)

2b.   No dorsal fin; throat grooves few (2 to 4); supraocci-not extending anteriorly beyond zygomatic processes of squamosal (see Fig. 114); lower jaws ± straight .... **ESCHRICHTIIDAE** (p.243)

Family BALAENIDAE
(Right whales)

Early whalers coined the common name applied to this family because these whales (especially *Balaena glacialis*) were "right" for commercial harvesting: they are slow-moving and are very buoyant (an important consideration for early whalers since techniques for inflating carcasses were developed only recently), and they contain large quantities of oil and baleen (valued for many products, including lubricants and corsets, respectively).

These whales have a chunky body. The head constitutes roughly one-third of the body length. The mouth is huge. The baleen measures up to four meters long in the bowhead whale. The cleft of the mouth is long and curved.

Right whales prefer cooler temperate and subtropical seas. They occur singly or in small groups. Their diet consists of planktonic crustaceans (krill) and molluscs. Females probably breed in alternate years; they bear a single calf.

All three species of balaenids are rare. The right whale (*B. glacialis*) is now strictly protected by international agreement.

Two genera, 3 species; all oceans except tropical seas.

Recognition Characters:

- **head huge, making up about one-third of total length.**

1. **color dark gray to black** (white patches on chin of *Balaena mysticetus*).
2. **body chunky, robust** (6-18.5 m)·
3. dorsal fin absent (*Balaena*, right whales) or sickle-shaped (*Caperea*, pygmy right whale).

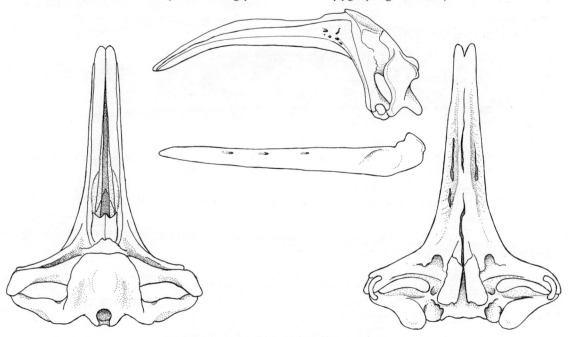

Figure 113. Skull of a balaenid (*Balaena*, x 1/50).

241

3. dorsal fin absent (*Balaena*, right whales) or sickle-shaped (*Caperea*, pygmy right whale).
4. **no longitudinal grooves in skin of throat.**
5. **baleen plates long, narrow.**
6. **rostrum long, narrow, highly arched** (Fig. 113).
7. nasal small.
8. **posterior margins of nasal and premaxilla not extending beyond level of anterior margin of supraorbital process of frontal** (Fig. 113).
9. frontal scarcely visible at crest of skull (Fig. 113).

10. **maxilla without elongate process extending posteriorly** (Fig. 113).
11. anterior margin of parietal behind posterior margins of premaxilla, maxilla, and nasal (Fig. 113).
12. supraoccipital extending anteriorly beyond zygomatic process of squamosal (Fig. 113).

Dental formula: no teeth

Compare with: Balaenopteridae, Eschrichtiidae.

Representative Genus:

Balaena (2) - *B. glacialis* and *B. mysticetus* are the right and bowhead whales, respectively.

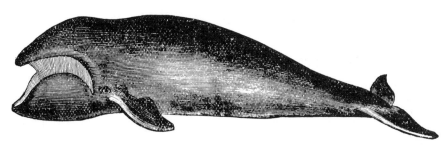

Right whale.

Family ESCHRICHTIIDAE
(Gray whale)

The single species in this family is characterized externally by the absence of a dorsal fin and by a mottled appearance due to light blotches (skin discolorations or patches of barnacles) on a dark background. Gray whales have the least telescoped skull of all mysticetes (Fig. 114).

Members of this family are divided into two isolated stocks, one on each side of the North Pacific. They migrate from northern feeding areas to southern breeding grounds (confined to a few lagoons in Baja California and Korea) and back each year, a round trip of about 20,000 km (12,400 miles), the largest known annual migration of any mammal. They eat mostly amphipods which they dredge from the mud of the sea floor.

Whalers nearly exterminated these animals from coastal waters of the eastern Pacific (North America) in the nineteenth century; the western Pacific stock has probably become extinct. Now strictly protected, the eastern stock probably exceeds 10,000.

One genus, 1 species; North Pacific, Chukchi Sea.

Recognition Characters:

1. body slender (11-15 m).
2. **color gray to black with white mottling.**
3. **dorsal fin absent** (small bumps present).

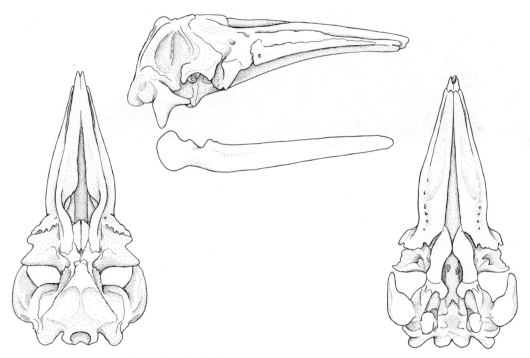

Figure 114. Skull of an eschrichtiid (*Eschrichtius*), x 1/20).

4. **throat with two (occasionally three or four) longitudinal grooves in skin.**
5. **baleen plates short, narrow.**
6. rostrum relatively narrow, slightly arched (Fig. 114).
7. **nasal large.**
8. nasal and premaxilla extending posteriorly beyond level of anterior margin of supraorbital process of frontal (Fig. 113).
9. **frontal broadly exposed at crest of skull** (Fig. 114).
10. maxilla with elongate posterior process (Fig. 114).
11. anterior margin of parietal behind posterior margins of premaxilla, maxilla, and nasal (Fig. 114).
12. **supraoccipital not extending anteriorly beyond zygomatic process of squamosal** (Fig. 114).

Dental formula: no teeth.

Compare with: Balaenopteridae, Balaenidae.

Genus:

Eschrichtius (1) - *E. robustus* is the gray whale.

Remark: The life history of the gray whale was described by Rice and Wolman (1971).

Family BALAENOPTERIDAE
(Rorquals)

Balaenopterids are readily distinguished externally from balaenids (p.241) by the long slender body, relatively small head, and numerous throat grooves. From eschrichtiids (p.243) they differ most obviously by the presence of a dorsal fin. There are also several cranial differences (see below).

In summer rorquals inhabit high latitudes of both hemispheres where they consume swarms of planktonic copepod and euphausid crustaceans and small fish. They capture plankton either by skimming them from the water surface or by gulping them in large masses. During this feeding period these whales store up large amounts of blubber. This food store sustains them during the winter breeding period when adults are not known to feed.

Winter is spent at lower latitudes, but since this period is out of phase in northern and southern hemispheres the two stocks rarely, if ever, mix.

Small species of balaenopterids breed annually; the large species breed in alternate years. Each female gives birth to a single calf.

Because of commercial exploitation by whalers, some species of rorquals (e.g., blue whales, humpbacks) are exceedingly rare. Others (e.g., fin whales) have also declined in numbers. The numbers of blue whales may be so low that their perpetuation is in jeopardy.

Two genera, 6 species; all oceans.

Recognition Characters:
- **rows of baleen continuous anteriorly** (separated at anterior end of mouth in other mysticetes).

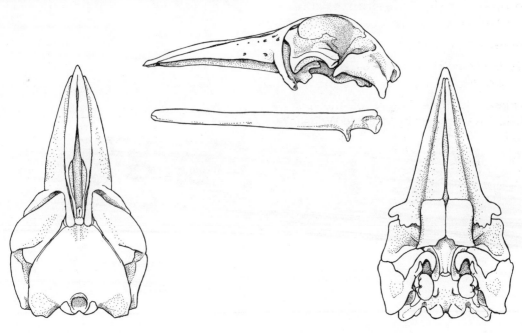

Figure 115. Skull of a balaenopterid (*Balaenoptera*, x 1/18).

● **lower jaw conspicuously bowed outward** (± straight in other mysticetes).

1. body slender (7-31 m).
2. **color gray or black above, with varying amounts of white below.**
3. dorsal fin present, sickle-shaped (*Balaenoptera*) or small (*Megaptera*).
4. **numerous longitudinal grooves in skin of throat.**
5. **baleen plates short, broad.**
6. rostrum relatively broad and flat (Fig. 115).
7. nasal small.
8. nasal and premaxilla extending posteriorly beyond level of anterior margin of supraorbital process of frontal (Fig. 115).
9. frontals scarcely or not at all visible at crest of skull (Fig. 115).
10. maxilla with elongate posterior process (Fig. 115).
11. **parietal extending anteriorly beyond posterior margins of premaxilla, maxilla, and nasal** (Fig. 115).
12. supraoccipital extending anteriorly beyond zygomatic process of squamosal (Fig. 115).

Dental formula: no teeth.

Compare with: Balaenidae, Eschrichtiidae.

Genera:

Balaenoptera (5) - Familiar examples are the fin whale(*B. physalis*), sei whale (*B. borealis*), and blue whale (*B. musculus*).

Megaptera (1) - *M. novaeangliae* is the humpback whale.

Remark: Small (1971) treated the natural history of blue whales and provided a review of the history of whaling.

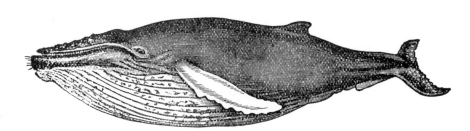

Humpback whale.

ORDER ODONTOCETI

More numerous and diverse than baleen whales (Mysticeti), this order contains dolphins, porpoises, and other toothed whales. Generally the skull of odontocetes is more highly asymmetrical and telescoped than that of mysticetes. Toothed whales have from one to more than 100 teeth. Most forms have a conspicuously rounded forehead containing a swelling called the "melon." This structure, which consists largely of fatty tissue, serves to beam sounds emitted form the blowhole. It is housed on the concave dorsal surface of the skull. The respiratory passages connecting the blowhole and trachea form a system of air chambers. The repiratory tract is separated from the digestive tract by a tube-like extension of the epiglottis.

Odontocetes eat primarily cephalopod molluscs (e.g., squid, octopi) and fishes. Probably all toothed whales use echolocation to capture prey.

Many other characteristics of toothed whales are described above for cetaceans in general (p.238).

Recognition Characters:
1. **teeth present, simple, homodont.**
2. **no baleen.**
3. one nasal opening (blowhole) present, crescent-shaped.
4. **skull usually asymmetrical.**
5. nasals reduced to nubbins, not roofing any part of nasal passage.
6. **maxilla extending posteriorly as a large broad process, not interlocking with frontal, instead spreading outward over portion of supraorbital process.**
7. lower jaws firmly fused at symphysis.

Compare with: Mysticeti, Sirenia.

Remark: For references on odontocetes see above (p.239).

KEY TO FAMILIES OF ODONTOCETI

1a.	Longitudinal grooves usually present in skin of throat; cranium usually strongly asymmetrical—left nasal opening much larger than right one; occipital crest very prominent; pterygoid and palatine not forming parallel shelves	2
1b.	Throat grooves absent; cranium usually only slightly symmetrical—left and right nasal openings ± equal in size; occipital crest not prominent; pterygoid and palatine forming parallel shelves	3
2a (1a).	Snout broad, blunt; rostrum relatively short, broad; first one or two teeth of lower jaw not larger than remaining teeth	**PHYSETERIDAE** (p.250)
2b.	Snout pointed; rostrum long, narrow; first one or two teeth of lower jaw larger than remaining teeth (the latter are sometimes absent)........................	**ZIPHIIDAE** (p.249)

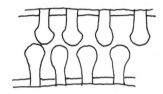

Figure 116. Spade-like cheekteeth of a phocoenid.

Killer whale.

Family ZIPHIIDAE
(Beaked whales)

These medium-sized odontocetes are identified externally by a prominent beak-like snout supported internally by a long rostrum (Fig. 117). The forehead varies, bulging prominently (e.g., *Hyperoodon*) or forming a smooth profile between the beak and head (e.g., *Mesoplodon*).

Because they are oceanic, often inconspicuous or rare, and generally of little commercial value, ziphiids are poorly known. Most species appear to be solitary, but a few aggregate in groups of a few to more than a dozen individuals. They eat squid and deep-sea fishes. At least one species is migratory.

Beaked whales exhibit considerable sexual dimorphism. Males are larger than females in some species, but the females are larger in others. In *Mesoplodon*, the single pair of teeth (in the lower jaw) are larger in males (Fig. 117), occasionally attaining tusk-like proportions. The size and location of the teeth also vary among males of different species of this genus. Beaked whales probably breed annually; a single calf is produced.

Six genera, 18 species; all oceans.

Recognition Characters:

- **posterior margin of fluke without deep notch** (notch present in other families of odontocetes).

1. body slender to moderately robust (length 4-12.5 m).
2. dorsal fin present, small.
3. **one or two pairs of longitudinal grooves in skin of throat.**
4. snout long and narrow, sharply differentiated from bulging forehead (*Hyperoodon* and *Berardius*) or forming a continuous profile with cranium.

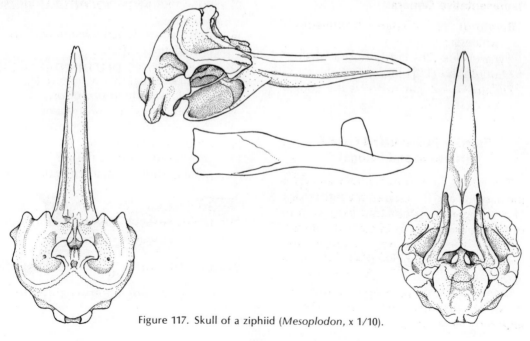

Figure 117. Skull of a ziphiid (*Mesoplodon*, x 1/10).

5. two to seven of cervical vertebrae fused.
6. skull slightly to strongly asymmetrical (Fig. 117).
7. maxilla expanded posteriorly (Fig. 117).
8. occipital crest prominent (Fig. 117).
9. **rostrum very narrow, deep, with open groove** (closed in older animals by dorsal intrusion of vomer) (Fig. 117).
10. no boss on premaxilla.
11. pterygoid and palatine not forming parallel shelves.
12. symphysis of lower jaw short.
13. teeth simple, conical or compressed (Fig. 117).

Dental formula: usually $\frac{0}{1}$ (exceptions are

Beradius, $\frac{0}{2}$, and *Tasmacetus*, $\frac{19}{27}$)

(identity of individual teeth uncertain)

Compare with: Physeteridae.

Representative Genera:

Berardius (2) - Giant bottle-nosed whales.
Hyperoodon (2) - Bottle-nosed whales.
Mesoplodon (11) - Beaked whales.
Ziphius (1) - *Z. cavirostris* is the goose-beaked whale.

Family MONODONTIDAE
(Narwhal and beluga)

This family comprises but two species— the narwhal and the beluga or white whale. They have many delphinid-like features but lack a dorsal fin. As in many delphinids (p.258), the prominent melon and inconspicuous snout give the head a blunt appearance.

One of the two upper teeth of the male narwhal (usually the left) extends anteriorly as a straight, spirally grooved tusk. The tooth of the opposite side is usually rudimentary. Females ordinarily lack tusks but, when present, they are often paired.

These gregarious odontocetes are characteristic of northern seas. Belugas migrate with the ebb and flow of pack ice. In summer they are frequent occupants of Arctic rivers. Narwhals are more pelagic than belugas. All species feed largely upon fishes, squid, and annelid worms. Females bear one calf every two or three years.

The flesh and blubber of belugas are an important source of food for Eskimos. Commerical products include oil and leather.

Two genera, 2 species; Arctic Ocean, Bering and Okhotsk seas, and rivers of Siberia, Alaska, and Canada.

Recognition Characters:

1. body slender (length 3-6 m).
2. **no dorsal fin.**
3. no longitudinal grooves in skin of throat.
4. **snout short, broad** (*Delphinapterus*), **or indistinct** (*Monodon*).
5. cervical vertebrae separate.
6. skull only slightly asymmetrical.
7. maxilla expanded posteriorly.
8. occipital crest not prominent.
9. rostrum broad, with narrow groove.
10. no boss on premaxilla.
11. pterygoid and palatine forming parallel shelves adjacent to nasal passage.
12. symphysis of lower jaw short.
13. teeth (except tusk in *Monodon*) simple, conical.

Dental formula: $\frac{1}{0}$ (*Monodon*) or about $\frac{9}{9}$ (*Delphinapterus*) (identity of individual teeth uncertain).

Genera:

Delphinapterus (1) - *D. leucas* is the beluga or white whale.

Monodon (1) - *M. monoceros* is the narwhal.

Remark: Kleinenberg et al. (1969) studied the natural history of *Delphinapterus*.

White whale.

Family PHYSETERIDAE
(Sperm whales)

Members of this family include the sperm whale, immortalized as "Moby Dick" by Melville, and two poorly known smaller species. The blunt head, constituting one-third or more of the body length, is diagnostic. The snout projects considerably beyond the opening of the mouth and has a single blowhole located on the left side near the end. The skull in physeterids (Fig. 118) is more asymmetrical than in any other odontocetes, and, as in ziphiids (p.249), the occipital region is highly crested.

Sperm whales (*Physeter*) are highly social—they aggregate in groups of a few individuals to many hundreds. Breeding (or harem) schools consist of one large male, females with calves, and subadult males and females. Adult male sperm whales are about twice the size of females. In summer many males migrate to polar seas, while females remain in tropical and temperate waters. The habits of pygmy sperm whales are little known but they also appear to be gregarious. Females of *Physeter* bear a calf once every several years.

The diet of physeterids consists of deep-water squid and fishes (*Physeter*), or shrimp and small cephalopods (*Kogia*). *Physeter* emits clicking and grating sounds.

Many commercial products are obtained from sperm whales (*Physeter*). The head consists largely of an enormous "spermaceti organ" (equivalent to the melon in other odontocetes) which contains large quantities of oil and spermaceti. The latter substance, which smells like sperm (hence the common name for these whales) is liquid wax that is used for making ointments and candles. Oil from the snout and blubber produces a high-quality lubricant and is a base for antibiotics. The teeth of *Physeter* are coveted for ivory.

Two genera, 3 species; all oceans.

Recognition Characters:

- **snout relatively very large, broad, blunt, undifferentiated from rest of head.**

1. **body robust** (length 2-20 m).
2. dorsal fin present, sickle-shaped (*Kogia*) or reduced (*Physeter*).
3. **throat with numerous short longitudinal grooves** (*Physeter*) **or instinct or absent** (*Kogia*).
4. snout as above.
5. six to seven of cervical vertebrae fused.
6. **skull strongly asymmetrical; left nasal passage much larger than right one; right premaxilla enlarged** (Fig. 118).
7. **maxilla expanded posteriorly** (Fig. 118).
8. **occipital crest prominent** (Fig. 118).
9. rostrum short or long, broad (Fig. 118).
10. no boss on premaxilla.
11. pterygoid and palatine not forming parallel shelves.
12. symphysis of lower jaws long (comprising one-third of length of jaws in *Physeter*) or relatively short (*Kogia*).
13. teeth simple, conical (Fig. 118).

Dental formula: $\frac{0}{9\text{-}30}$ (identity of individual teeth uncertain).

Compare with: Ziphiidae.

Genera:

Kogia (2) - Pygmy sperm whales.
Physeter (1) - *P. catodon* is the sperm whale.

Remark: Berzin (1972) provided a comprehensive treatment of morphology and natural history, and Best (1979) reviewed social behavior of *Physeter*.

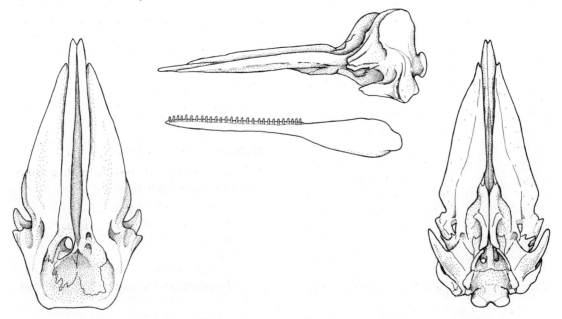

Figure 118. Skull of a physeterid (*Physeter*, x 1/40).

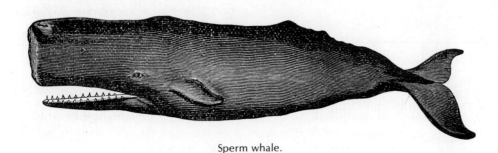

Sperm whale.

Family PLATANISTIDAE
(River dolphins)

These small long-beaked dolphins constitute the only family of cetaceans largely confined to fresh water. The prominent slender snout is sharply differentiated from the truncate melon of the forehead. In contrast to delphinids (p.258) and phocoenids (p.256), the maxilla and frontal bones are not broad posteriorly. Instead, the lateral margin of each maxilla is turned upward to form a longitudinal crest.

Because they inhabit waters clouded with sediment, river dolphins are blind (*Platanista*) or have small eyes. They orient almost entirely by echolocation. At least one species, the susu (*Platanista gangetica*), swims on its side. In so doing, it sweeps the head in a yes-motion, scanning its environment with a narrow beam of sound. These sounds are beamed by the melon, which in the susu contains lattice-like outgrowths of the maxillae that act like an acoustical baffle (Herald et al., 1969).

River dolphins occur in small groups. They eat many kinds of fresh-water invertebrates and mud-dwelling and open-water fishes which they obtain either by pursuit or by probing river bottoms. Other aspects of their biology are not well known.

Four genera, 4 species; river systems of India and China, and rivers and coastal areas of south America.

Recognition Characters:

- **lateral margin of maxilla with prominent longitudinal crest.**

1. body slender (length 1.5-3 m).
2. dorsal fin present, low, obtuse.
3. no longitudinal grooves in skin of throat.
4. **snout long, slender, sharply differentiated from bulging forehead.**

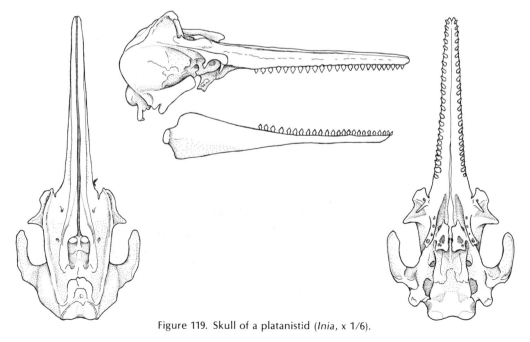

Figure 119. Skull of a platanistid (*Inia*, x 1/6).

5. cervical vertebrae separate.
6. skull only slightly asymmetrical (except in *Platanista*) (Fig. 119).
7. **maxilla narrow, not greatly expanded posteriorly** (Fig. 119).
8. occipital crest poorly developed.
9. **rostrum very narrow, long** (Fig. 119).
10. **premaxilla with prominent swelling (boss) anterior to nasal opening** (Fig. 119).
11. pterygoid and palatine forming parallel shelves adjacent to nasal passage.
12. **symphysis of lower jaw long (comprising one-half of length of jaws).**
13. teeth simple, conical with (prominent ridge around teeth in *Inia*) (Fig. 119).

Dental formula: $\frac{26}{26}$ to $\frac{55}{55}$ (identity of individual teeth uncertain)

Compare with: Delphinidae, Phocoenidae.

Representative Genera:

Inia (1) - *I. geoffrensis* is the Amazon river dolphin.

Platanista (2) - Indus and Ganges river dolphins.

Remark: Numerous articles on these dolphins are published in volumes by Pilleri (1969-1978).

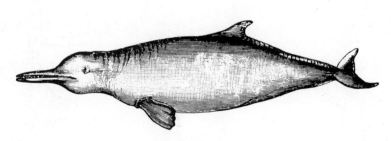

River dolphin.

Family PHOCOENIDAE
(Porpoises)

Although they are in other respects very similar to delphinids (p.258), phocoenids may be distinguished by the presence of a conspicuous bump on each premaxilla in front of the nasal openings and by the peculiar spade-like teeth (Figs. 116, 120). The color of the dorsum varies from gray to black. They are usually lighter underneath; the sides and venter of *Phocoenoides* are white.

Porpoises inhabit bays, estuaries, and shorelines (e.g., *Phocoena*) or oceanic waters (*Phocoenoides*). They eat chiefly shrimp, squid, and fishes. Phocoenids occur singly, in pairs, or in small (rarely large) groups. Females produce one calf annually.

Three genera, 7 species; Northern Hemisphere in all oceans, temperate coastal waters of South America.

Recognition Characters:

1. body slender to relatively robust (length 1.2-1.4 m).
2. dorsal fin usually present (absent in *Neophocaena*, finless porpoise).
3. no longitudinal grooves in skin of throat.
4. **snout without distinct beak.**
5. three to seven of cervical vertebrae fused.
6. skull only slightly asymmetrical (Fig. 120).
7. maxilla expanded posteriorly (Fig. 120).
8. occipital crest not particularly prominent (Fig. 120).
9. rostrum relatively short and broad (Fig. 120).
10. **premaxilla with prominent swelling (boss) anterior to nasal opening** (Fig. 120).
11. pterygoid and palatine forming parallel shelves adjacent to nasal passage.

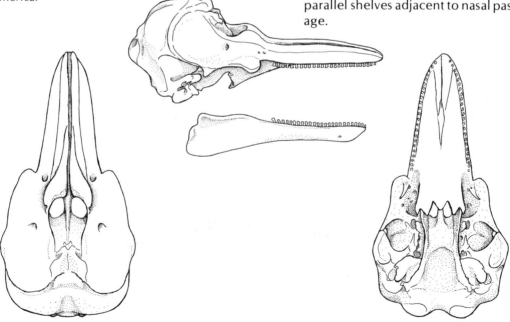

Figure 120. Skull of a phocoenid (*Phocoena*, x 1/4).

12. symphysis of lower jaw short.
13. **teeth usually spade-like, with two to three poorly defined cusps arranged longitudinally** (Figs. 116, 120).

Dental formula: $\frac{15}{15}\text{-}\frac{30}{30}$ (identity of indi-

vidual teeth uncertain).

Compare with: Platanistidae, Delphinidae, Monodontidae.

Representataive Genera:

Phocoena (4) - Common porpoises and the harbor porpoise (*P. phocoena*).
Phocoenoides (1) - *P. dallii* is the Dall porpoise.

Remark: I follow Rice (1967) in recognizing the porpoises as a family separate from the Delphinidae.

257

Family DELPHINIDAE
(Ocean dolphins)

By far the most diverse family of whales, dolphins are small to medium-sized cetaceans of worldwide distribution. Among the most conspicuous of whales, delphinids are well known for their agility, speed, and synchronous group movements. Their structure and habits are varied. The body is usually unicolored, spotted, or striped; some (e.g., *Orcinus*) have striking patterns of black and white. Most have a prominent beak, but others (e.g., *Orcinus, Globicephala*) have a blunt snout. The number of teeth is highly variable.

Delphinids are very gregarious; some species form groups of many thousands of individuals. A well-defined social organization is found in some forms. Males are normally larger than females, which bear one calf at one- to three-year intervals.

Dolphins eat mostly fishes and cephalopods. An exception is the killer whale, which consumes a greater variety of vertebrate prey, including birds, sea otters, and seals. Delphinids are generally active near the surface of the water, for their dives are relatively shallow and are of short duration. They produce many sounds, such as clicks, squeals, and whistles.

Fifteen genera, about 30 species; all oceans, certain rivers and estuaries of South America and southeast Asia.

Recognition Characters:

1. body slender (length 1.5-9.5 m).
2. dorsal fin usually present (absent in *Lissodelphis*).
3. no longitudinal grooves in skin of throat.
4. snout variable: with a distinct beak sharply differentiated from forehead; or with a bulging forehead and no beak; or with a long snout merging continuously with forehead.
5. two to six of cervical vertebrae usually fused.
6. **skull only slightly asymmetrical (Fig. 121).**
7. maxilla expanded posteriorly (Fig. 121).
8. occipital crest not particularly prominent (Fig. 121).
9. rostrum variable (short or long, narrow or broad).
10. **no boss on premaxilla.**
11. pterygoid and palatine forming parallel shelves on each side of nasal passage.
12. symphysis of lower jaw short to moderately long.
13. teeth simple, conical (Fig. 121).

Dental formula: $\frac{0}{2}$ to $\frac{65}{58}$ (identity of individual teeth uncertain)

Compare with: Phocoenidae, Platanistidae, Monodontidae.

Representative Genera:

Delphinus (1) - *D. delphis* is the common or saddlebacked dolphin.
Globicephala (2) - Pilot whales.
Grampus (1) - *G. griseus* is Risso's dolphin or gray grampus.
Lagenorhynchus (6) - Whitesided dolphins and allies.
Lissodelphis (2) - Rightwhale dolphins.
Orcinus (1) - *O. orca* is the killer whale.
Sousa (2) - White dolphins.
Stenella (4) - Spotted dolphins.
Tursiops (1) - *T. truncatus* is the bottlenosed dolphin.

Remarks: A separate family (Stenidae) is recognized by some authors (e.g., Rice, 1967; Fraser, 1966) for the genera *Sousa, Steno,* and *Sotalia.* However, a recent report (Dohl et al., 1974) of a hybrid born to a female *Steno bredanensis* and male *Tursiops truncatus* raises questions about the distinctness of the family. Members of the family Stenidae are therefore placed here with the Delphinidae.

Books of general interest on dolphins include Alpers (1961) and Kellogg (1961).

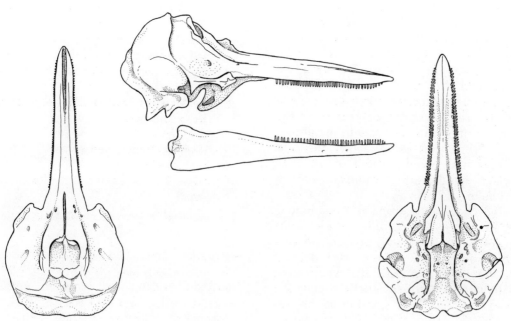

Figure 121. Skull of a delphinid (*Delphinus*, x 1/6).

ORDER SIRENIA

These strictly aquatic mammals occur in coastal waters, estuaries, and rivers in warm, tropical areas. Sirenians are suspected of being the basis for legends concerning mermaids, but although they move slowly and gracefully, their chunky body and homely facial features do not bring to mind an image of a beautiful woman. Their external features are similar in many respects to those of whales, but are indicative of convergence, not close evolutionary relationship. The mouth is small and the margins of the lips bear conspicuous tactile vibrissae. These animals remain under water most of the time, surfacing usually only to breathe. A dense, heavy skeleton allows them to remain submerged without effort. They swim by gentle vertical undulations of the tail fluke.

The cheekteeth erupt in a continuous series as in hyraxes (p.266) and elephants (p.264), with whom they probably share a common ancestry. In the family Trichechidae (p.262) the teeth are indefinite in number. Strictly vegetarian, sirenians crush and grind food by the combined action of the teeth and horny plates on the palate. Sirenians are hunted by humans as a source of meat.

Recognition Characters:

1. **body large (2.5-4.5 m), massive, fusiform (torpedo-shaped), virtually hairless.**
2. no hind limbs (remnants of pelvic girdle may be present internally), forelimbs modified into flippers.
3. **tail modified into a fluke.**
4. nostrils located dorsally at end of snout.
5. **neck short, not visibly separating head and body.**
6. no pinna.
7. skeleton heavy, dense.
8. no clavicle.
9. nasal bones absent or, if present, small.

Compare with: Mysticeti, Odontoceti.

Remarks: Important studies of this order include those of Kaiser (1974), Mohr (1957), Reinhart (1959), and Simpson (1932). Several works cited for cetaceans (p.239) also include information about sirenians.

KEY TO FAMILIES OF SIRENIA

1a. Upper lip deeply cleft; tail rounded; jugal broadened behind orbit, not in contact with premaxilla; supraorbital process large, broadly expanded over orbit; cheekteeth numerous, variable in number . . . . . . **TRICHECHIDAE** (p.262)

1b. Upper lip only slightly cleft; tail cleft; jugal broadened below orbit, in contact with premaxilla; supraorbital process not enlarged or broadly expanded over orbit; cheekteeth at most 3/3 . . . . **DUGONGIDAE** (p.261)

Family DUGONGIDAE
(Dugongs)

Dugongs are readily distinguished from manatees (p.262) by several external and cranial features (see below). The most obvious external difference is the shape of the tail fluke.

These animals frequent sheltered and shallow waters of coastal bays and shorelines where vegetation (chiefly aquatic grasses but also some algae) is abundant. Dugongs are usually found in small groups. The fleshy snout and tusk-like incisors are used to root up aquatic plants, and the interlacing bristles on the lips help grasp the vegetation. The skin is occasionally infested with barnacles. They rarely invade rivers except perhaps to breed. There appears to be no well-defined breeding period. Females normally bear one young.

Two genera, 2 species (a third, *Hydrodamalis gigas*, Steller's sea cow, is evidently extinct); coastal waters of Indo-pacific region (*Hydrodamalis* formerly occurred in Bering Sea).

Recognition Characters:

1. **tail fluke dolphin-like, with pointed lateral projections; posterior margin deeply notched.**
2. **upper lip only slightly cleft.**
3. no nails on flippers.
4. **supraorbital process not enlarged or broadly expanded over orbit.**
5. no nasal bones.
6. premaxilla large, bent sharply downward.
7. **jugal broadened below orbit, in contact with premaxilla.**
8. **palate narrow, distinctly elevated above toothrow, with small median ridge.**
9. **lower jaw with coronoid process projecting upward.**
10. upper incisor tusk-like in males, small and often not protruding through gum in females.
11. **cheekteeth simple, columnar.**

Dental formula: $\dfrac{1\ 0\ 2\text{-}3}{1\ 0\ 2\text{-}3}$ (identity of cheekteeth uncertain)

Compare with: Trichechidae.

Genus:

Dugong (1) - *D. dugon* is the dugong.

Remark: Husar (1978a) and Kingdon (1971) examined the natural history of dugongs.

Family TRICHECHIDAE
(Manatees)

Found in rivers, estuaries, and shallow coastal areas, these mammals graze on a wide variety of aquatic plants. Manatees have thickly bristled upper lips which are partially separated and prehensile. They pull food into the mouth by everting the lips over the food and retracting them as they grasp the food. Trichechids have an indefinite number of cheekteeth which are continually replaced from the rear (five to seven of these are functional at one time) and only six cervical vertebrae. The body of manatees is often covered with algae which themselves harbor a rich community of crustaceans and molluscs. Diatoms and barnacles are also common residents on the skin of manatees.

Trichechids are solitary to mildly social. They breed throughout the year. Females usually produce one calf. During cold periods manatees commonly migrate to warmer areas (usually up rivers) where they may congregate in groups of 40 or more individuals.

One genus, 3 species; coastal waters and rivers of tropical and subtropical Atlantic.

Recognition Characters:

1. **tail fluke evenly rounded; posterior margin not notched.**
2. **upper lip deeply cleft.**
3. small nails usually present on flippers (absent in *Trichechus inunguis*).
4. **supraorbital process large, broadly expanded over orbit** (Fig. 122).
5. nasal bones present, small.
6. premaxilla small, only slightly bent downward.
7. **jugal broadened behind orbit, not in contact with premaxilla.**
8. **palate relatively broad, not elevated above toothrow, with distinct median ridge.**

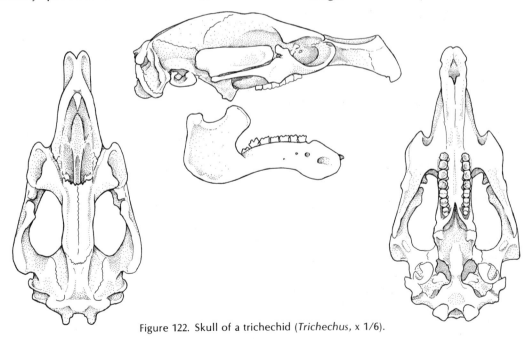

Figure 122. Skull of a trichechid (*Trichechus*, x 1/6).

9. **lower jaw with coronoid process projecting forward** (Fig. 122).
10. **no upper incisors** (Fig. 122).
11. **cheekteeth each with two transverse ridges** (Fig. 122).

Dental formula: $\dfrac{0}{0}\dfrac{0}{0}\dfrac{\text{indefinite}}{\text{indefinite}} = $?

(identity of individual cheekteeth unknown).

Compare with: Dugongidae.

Genus:

Trichechus (3) - Manatees.

Remark: Husar (1977, 1978b, 1978c) reviewed the biology of the three species of manatees.

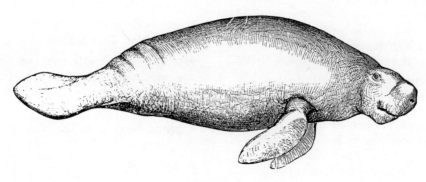

Manatee.

ORDER PROBOSCIDEA

Family ELEPHANTIDAE
(Elephants)

Proboscideans are the largest living terrestrial mammals. Only two species remain of this once widespread and relatively diverse order (five other extinct families are known). The most conspicuous recognition features of elephants are the long slender proboscis (trunk) with one or two prehensile projections at its tip, large fan-shaped ears (largest in *Loxodonta* and a useful radiator of body heat), and huge body size. Many characteristics of this group are adaptations that serve to support the great weight of the body, which approaches the upper size limit for a terrestrial mammal. Adaptations include columnar limbs —each of the limb bones is relatively large and set in a straight vertical line— and a thick elastic pad on the sole of each foot. The heavy body is supported further by orientation of the limb bones directly under the girdles—the glenoid fossa of the scapula and acetabulum of the pelvic girdle are oriented ventrally.

The curious dentition consists of a pair of upper incisors elongated into tusks (reaching over 3 m in male *Loxodonta*) and six cheekteeth which are replaced continuously from the rear throughout life. Only one (or one and part of another) cheektooth is functional at a time. Each tooth is shed as it becomes worn.

Conspicuous inhabitants of forests, scrublands, and savannahs near water, these mammals can cause massive changes in the vegetational composition of habitats during prolonged feeding activities (Laws, 1970). Grasses and branches from trees and shrubs form the bulk of their diet.

Herds of elephants infrequently consist of as many as several hundred animals. Permanent groups are much smaller and are composed of cows, calves, and young bulls. Each group is dominated by a single matriarch. Adult males generally occur in bull herds but periodically become aggressive (a condition referred to as "musth") and invade cow herds. Temporary pair bonds are then formed with individual females. Males are considerably larger than females.

Female elephants reproduce several times during an average lifetime of perhaps 50 years. The gestation period is long (about two years) and a single calf (rarely twins) is produced.

Asiatic elephants have been employed as beasts of burden for centuries. Tusks of *Loxodonta* are prized for their ivory.

Two genera, 2 species; Africa, southeast Asia.

Recognition Characters:

- **long proboscis (trunk) present, with nostrils and finger-like projection at tip** (one projection in *Elephas*, two in *Loxodonta*).

- **pinna large, fan-like** (largest in *Loxodonta*).

- **limbs pillar-like.**

1. **size enormous (up to 4 m in height); body thick-set.**
2. tail relatively short.
3. **sole of each foot with large elastic pads.**
4. digits syndactylous.
5. nails on four to five digits of forefoot, on three to four digits of hindfoot.
6. no interparietal bone.

7. no postorbital process or bar (Fig. 123).
8. **nasal opening of skull located high on face** (Fig. 123).
9. jugal not forming part of mandibular fossa.
10. **upper incisor evergrowing, tusk-like (much larger in males)** (Fig. 123), **composed chiefly or entirely of dentine.**
11. **cheekteeth lophodont, with many transverse ridges, replaced consecutively from rear (only one functional tooth or parts of two at a time on each jaw), becoming progressively more complex posteriorly.**

Dental formula: $\frac{1\ 0\ 3\ 3}{0\ 0\ 3\ 3} = 26$ (but tusk usually absent in female *Elephas*)

Compare with: Hyracoidea.

Genera:

Elephas (1) - *E. maximus* is the Asiatic or Indian elephant.
Loxodonta (1) - *L. africana* is the African elephant.

Remarks: Carrington (1959) and Sikes (1971) provided general treatments of elephants. Evolution and paleontology were treated by Maglio (1973), Osborn (1936, 1942), and Watson (1946), and physiology was studied by Benedict (1936). Ecology and behavior were investigated by Eisenberg et al. (1971), Hendrichs and Hendrichs (1971), Kurt (1974), Laws (1974), Laws et al. (1975), McKay (1973), and Wing and Buss (1970). Spinage (1973) reviewed the history of ivory exploitation by man.

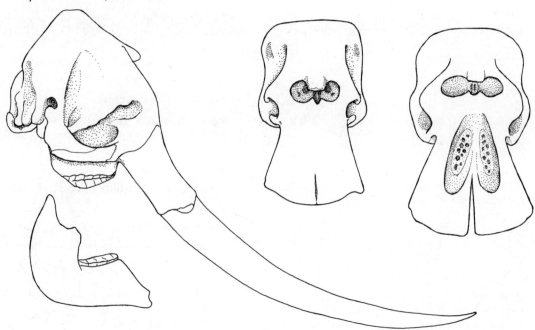

Figure 123. Skull of an elephantid (*Loxodonta*, x 1/24). Anterior views are shown of a female (center) and male (right). (After Sikes, 1973).

ORDER HYRACOIDEA

Family PROCAVIIDAE
(Hyraxes or dassies)

Because of their relatively small size, crouched stance, and short tail, hyraxes have the outward appearance of rabbits. However, their structural features reveal similarities to proboscideans (p.264) (note recognition characteristics). This is a small order—it contains fewer than a dozen species in a single extant family.

The dentition of hyraxes is unusual. The upper incisor on each side resembles a short tusk-like canine. Although there are seven permanent cheekteeth in the upper and lower jaws, they erupt sequentially and are seldom all present at the same time.

Hyraxes generally occupy forests or rocky places and are nimble climbers.

Elastic pads richly supplied with sweat glands on the soles of the feet provide remarkable traction (the sweat glands also serve as an important means of heat loss). These mammals are herbivorous. They seek shelter among rocks or in hollows of trees.

Tree hyraxes are solitary and nocturnal. Rock and brush hyraxes live in colonies containing a few to hundreds of individuals; they are mostly diurnal. Individuals of different species (or genera) often share the same rockpile. They even bask and huddle together, activities which are important for temperature regulation in these mammals. Aside from short periods of feeding, rock hyraxes spend most of their time crouching motionless on rocks and seemingly staring directly into the sun, a habit made possible by a special

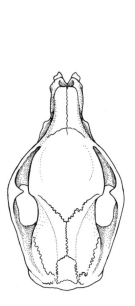
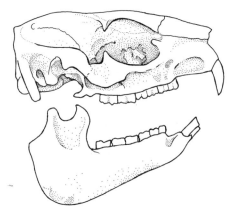
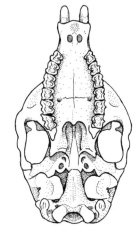

Figure 124. Skull of a procaviid (*Procavia*, x 1/2).

membrane (umbraculum) that shades the pupil of the eye (Walls, 1942). Hyraxes utter screams, whistles, and chattering sounds. These mammals seemingly breed year-round. Females usually bear one to three offspring.

Three genera, 11 species; Africa, Middle East.

Recognition Characters:

1. size medium (30-63 cm).
2. **tail very short.**
3. **soles of feet with large, elastic pads.**
4. digits syndactylous.
5. **nails on all digits except innermost toe of hindfoot, which bears a large claw.**
6. **interparietal bone well developed.** (Fig. 124).
7. **postorbital process well developed** (Fig. 124), **often forming complete postorbital bar.**
8. nasal opening of skull located at end of rostrum.
9. **jugal forming part of mandibular fossa.**
10. **upper incisor evergrowing, tusk-like** (Fig. 124), **composed chiefly or entirely of dentine.**
11. cheekteeth lophodont, relatively simple, becoming progressively more complex from front to rear.

Dental formula: $\frac{1}{2}\frac{0}{0}\frac{4}{4}\frac{3}{3} = 34$

Compare with: Proboscidea.

Genera:

Dendrohyrax (3) - Tree hyraxes.
Heterohyrax (3) - Rock hyraxes.
Procavia (5) - Brush hyraxes.

Hyrax.

UNGULATES:
ORDERS PERISSODACTYLA and ARTIODACTYLA

Characters linking these two orders stem from specializations of the limbs for cursorial locomotion. The term "ungulate" refers to the most obviously shared feature, the hoofs. Body proportions and anatomy, behavior, physiology, and food habits are all intimately tied to their cursorial habits. Most alterations in form are found in the elongate limbs and axial skeleton, including peculiarities of the bones, muscles, tendons, and ligaments. Discussions of these and other aspects of running specializations of ungulates are provided by Gambaryan (1974), Hildebrand (1974), Howell (1944), and Vaughan (1978).

Perissodactyls and artiodactyls share a common ancestral stock (the extinct order Condylarthra). Although they differ in numerous ways, the most pronounced difference between the two groups is in the digits: perissodactyls are odd-toed and mesaxonic (the axis of the foot passes through the middle, or third digit), whereas artiodactyls are even-toed and paraxonic (the axis passes between digits three and four).

All perissodactyls and most artiodactyls (ruminants) are herbivorous, but each group has evolved different specializations for digesting cellulose, a carbohydrate which forms the cell walls of plants. Since all mammals lack enzymes for digesting cellulose, ungulates employ microorganisms (bacteria, protozoa) for this purpose. Several hundred different organisms have been identified (Hungate, 1975). Through fermentation, these microorganisms provide ungulates with valuable plant proteins, vitamins, and other nutrients; additional nutrients are obtained by digesting the microorganisms themselves. In perissodactyls, the stomach is simple and microbial breakdown of cellulose takes place largely in the intestine and caecum. Ruminants, on the other hand, have a multi-chambered "stomach" containing three or four compartments, only one of which is a true stomach (Hofmann, 1973). By churning and by microbial action the food is broken down into small particles so that it can pass from the fore chambers (rumen and reticulum) to the other compartments (omasum, abomasum). Ruminants hasten this process once fermentation is initiated by periodically regurgitating the food and "chewing the cud" to break it into finer particles.

ORDER PERISSODACTYLA

Formerly a widespread and dominant group of mammals, this order now comprises relatively few species. The decline in perissodactyl diversity coincided with the proliferation of artiodactyls. Of the living perissodactyls, tapirs and rhinoceroses more closely resemble one another than either resembles horses.

The name Perissodactyla means odd-toed. The forefoot may be even-toed (tapirs have four), but the hindfoot always has an odd number (one or three). Perissodactyls also have an elongate facial region which accommodates a series of large lophodont cheekteeth (premolars and molars are very similar in size and complexity) and provides space for grinding and manipulating food.

Recognition Characters:

1. **foot posture unguligrade.**
2. **"odd-toed"—middle (third) digit of both forefoot and hindfoot larger than other digits and ± symmetrical in shape.**
3. digits usually 1-1 or 3-3 (4-3 in tapirs, but the fourth digit on forefoot is smaller than other three).
4. **femur with a third trochanter** (see Fig. 10A)**.**
5. calcaneus not articulating with fibula.
6. astragalus with pulley-like surface above, flattened below.
7. **alisphenoid canal present.**
8. nasals wide posteriorly.
9. cheekteeth lophodont.

Compare with: Artiodactyla.

Remarks: For information on classification and phylogeny of perissodactyls, see Scott (1941) and Simpson (1945). Radinsky (1966, 1969) also examined the early evolution of perissodactyls. Comparative digestive capabilities of perissodactyls and artiodactyls were examined by Janis (1976) and authors cited therein.

KEY TO FAMILIES OF PERISSODACTYLA

1a. One functional digit per foot; mane present, bushy; postorbital bar present; cheekteeth with very complex lophodont pattern .... **EQUIDAE** (p. 270)

1b. Three or four functional digits per foot; no mane; no postorbital bar; cheekteeth with relatively simple pattern of cusps and transverse ridges 2

2a (1b). "Horn(s)" present on rostrum; tail tufted at end; skin thick, rough, often with folds; occipital crest well developed; nasals large, not triangular .... **RHINOCEROTIDAE** (p.274)

2b. No "horns"; tail not tufted; skin smooth; occipital crest small or absent; nasals small, triangular .... **TAPIRIDAE** (p.272)

Family EQUIDAE
(Horses, asses, zebras)

Once widely distributed in the New World, wild populations of these mammals are now restricted to Africa and a few places in Asia (modern horses were introduced into North and South American by man). Equids are characterized by the presence of only one functional digit per foot, each of which is capped by a single symmetrical hoof. The skull is elongate. The orbit and temporal fossa are separated by a bony plate.

Equids frequent grasslands, savannahs, and deserts. Foraging mostly on grasses, foliage, and twigs, they often make seasonal movements in search of new food supplies. Their large upper and lower incisors equip them to forage on plant parts (e.g., stems) too tough for many other ungulates (Bell, 1970; Janis, 1976).

Equids are gregarious and polygamous.

The social system is variable. In mountain and plains zebras (*E. quagga* and *E. zebra*) each group contains a stallion, several females, and their offspring. Grevy's zebras (*E. grevyi*) and wild asses (*E. africanus*) occur in herds of frequently changing composition; often the males become solitary and territorial (Klingel, 1974). Zebras and asses often mingle with other species (e.g., wildebeest, buffalo, and gazelles) at common water sources or feeding places. Females are polyestrous and may breed at any time of the year; they bear one young. Species living in arid places are quite tolerant of dehydration (Schmidt-Nielsen, 1964).

Horses (*E. caballus*) have been domesticated for several thousand years. Along with donkeys (asses) they are used by people for a variety of purposes.

One genus, 7 species; Africa, desert areas of southwestern and eastern Asia.

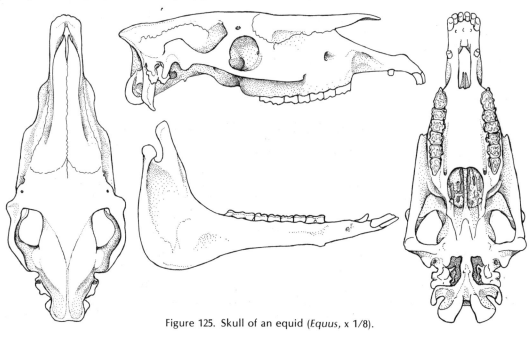

Figure 125. Skull of an equid (*Equus*, x 1/8).

Recognition Characters:

- **feet with only one distinct digit.**

- **mane present, bushy.**

- **orbit enclosed by postorbital bar** (continuous with temporal fossa in other perissodactyls) (Fig. 125).

1. **body relatively heavy, with long slender limbs.**
2. skin smooth, well haired.
3. tail long, bushy.
4. occipital crest small or absent.
5. **nasal long and narrow** (Fig. 125).
6. **cheekteeth homodont, all with similar complex lophodont pattern.** (Fig. 125).

Dental formula: $\dfrac{3}{3}\dfrac{0\text{-}1}{0\text{-}1}\dfrac{3\text{-}4}{3}\dfrac{3}{3} = 36\text{-}42$

Genus:

Equus (7) - Horses, asses, zebras. The domestic horse is *E. caballus.*

Remarks: Thorough treatments of the evolutionary history of this family were provided by Simpson (1951) and Stirton (1940). General natural history and behavior were explored by Feist and McCullogh (1976), Groves (1974), and Klingel (1967, 1968, 1974).

Family TAPIRIDAE
(Tapirs)

Living members of this family have an unusual disjunct distribution—they occur only in South America and southeast Asia. Externally, tapirs are recognizable by a short movable proboscis, a short tail, and a rounded body profile which tapers from the back toward front and rear ends. These mammals are the most primitive living perissodactyls—they possess many features in common with the ancestors of perissodactyls (e.g., a large number of relatively simple cheekteeth, short generalized limbs).

These mammals are mostly solitary, nocturnal, and retiring. They inhabit densely vegetated tropical forests, swamps, and savannahs, usually near water.

The diet consists of foliage, twigs, fruit, and green shoots of aquatic and terrestrial plants.

Tapirs apparently breed year-round. A single calf is produced. Young tapirs are dark with yellow and white spots and stripes. This color pattern changes to the more uniform dark color of adults (the Malayan tapir, *T. indicus*, is partly white) within a few months.

One genus, 4 species; tropical areas of Central and South America, and southeast Asia from Burma to Sumatra.

Recognition Characters:

- **forefoot with four digits, hindfoot with three.**

- **snout modified into movable proboscis.**

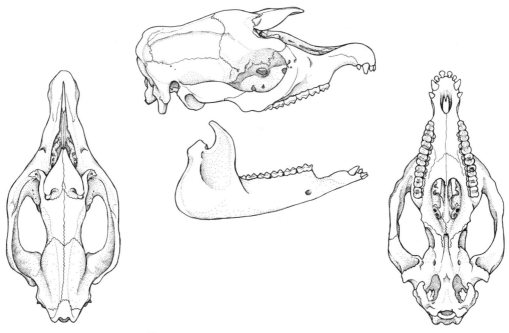

Figure 126. Skull of a tapirid (*Tapirus*, x 1/7).

Tapir.

- **nasal opening of skull very large and recessed** (Fig. 126).

1. body heavy, with short stout legs.
2. skin smooth, sparsely haired.
3. tail short.
4. occipital crest small or absent.
5. **nasal short, triangular** (Fig. 126).
6. cheekteeth not homodont (first premolars do not closely resemble other premolars and molars), simple in pattern (Fig. 126).

Dental formula: $\frac{3}{3}\frac{1}{1}\frac{4}{4}\frac{3}{3} = 44$

Compare with: Rhinocerotidae.

Genus:

Tapirus(4) - Tapirs.

Remark: Bressou (1961) and Radinsky (1963, 1965) studied the anatomy and evolution of tapirs.

Family RHINOCEROTIDAE
(Rhinoceroses)

The evolutionary history of these large ponderous ungulates parallels that of horses. Both families were formerly far more widespread and diverse than now. Both were also abundant in the New World until the late Pleistocene, when they disappeared. Rhinoceroses have continued to decline in historical time because of exploitation of the animals (horn products are used as an aphrodisiac) or their habitats by man.

Like elephants (p.264), rhinoceroses have pillar-like limbs for support of the heavy body. The skin is thick and tough. In Indian rhinoceroses, it is thrown into several folds forming plates which resemble a knight's armor. All have horns (either one or two) consisting of hair-like filaments cemented together to form a hard compact tissue that grows continuously at the base. The horns have no bony core but are buttressed by the nasal bones (also frontals if there are two horns).

Members of this family inhabit tropical forests, swamps, savannahs, plains, and scrubland, always near water. They are mostly nocturnal or crepuscular. The diet consists of a varied assortment of fruit, twigs, shoots, and foliage (most species) or strictly grasses (*Ceratotherium*). Several species of birds feed on insects and parasites that settle on the skin or are disturbed by the feet of grazing rhinos.

Bull rhinoceroses are solitary and territorial, whereas females occur chiefly in cow-offspring units consisting of fewer than a half-dozen individuals. The bulls temporarily attach themselves to female groups during mating periods. Breeding is seasonal or aseasonal. Females bear a single calf every several years.

Four genera, 5 species; tropical areas of Africa and southeast Asia from eastern India to Borneo.

Recognition Characters:

- **three digits on all feet.**

- **head concave dorsally** ($\pm$ flat in other perissodactyls) (Fig. 127).

- **one or two simple horns located near snout** (other perissodactyls are hornless).

- **temporal fossa exceptionally large** (Fig. 127).

1. body very heavy, with short stocky legs.
2. **skin thick, rough, often with folds, scantily haired.**
3. **tail short, tufted at end.**
4. **occipital crest well developed** (Fig. 127).
5. nasals large and heavy for support of horn (Fig. 127).
6. cheekteeth usually homodont, with relatively simple pattern (Fig. 127).

Dental formula: $\frac{0\text{-}2}{0\text{-}1} \frac{0}{0\text{-}1} \frac{3\text{-}4}{3\text{-}4} \frac{3}{3} = 24\text{-}34$

Compare with: Tapiridae.

Representative Genera:

Ceratotherium (1) - *C. simum* is the square-lipped or white rhinoceros.

Dicerorhinus (1) - *D. sumatrensis* is the Asian two-horned rhinoceros.

Diceros (1) - *D. bicornis* is the black rhinoceros.

Rhinoceros (2) - Indian or one-horned rhinoceroses.

Remark: Useful references on the habits of rhinoceroses include Groves (1967, 1972), Groves and Kurt (1972), Hoogerwerf (1970), Hubback (1939), Owen-Smith (1974), Schenkel and Schenkel-Hulliger (1969), Schenkel and Lang (1969), and Talbot (1960).

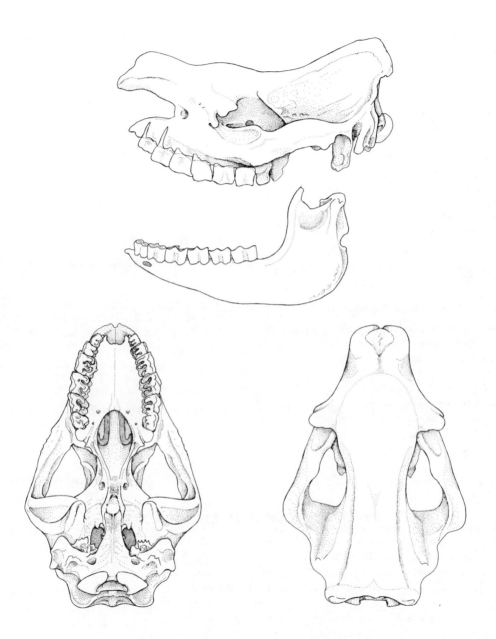

Figure 127. Skull of a rhinocerotid (*Rhinoceros*, x ⅛).

ORDER ARTIODACTYLA

This is the most diverse order of large mammals. Most are herbivorous, but others are omnivorous (e.g., pigs). They are an important source of meat for humans, both as game and as domesticated animals. Representatives of the order are most abundant and diverse in Africa, where they are especially common in savannahs and plains.

There are three suborders, one consisting of pig-like forms (Suiformes), another containing only camels (Tylopoda), and a third diverse group consisting of deer, cattle, sheep, goats, antelopes, giraffes, and their allies (Ruminantia). They differ chiefly in limb and foot structure and in cranial and dental features (see characters for suborders).

Recognition Characters:

1. **foot posture digitigrade (camels) or unguligrade.**

2. **"even-toed"—two principal digits present, nearly equal in size, not symmetrical in shape.**
3. two or four digits on all feet (three toes on hindfoot in peccaries).
4. no third trochanter on femur (see Fig. 10B).
5. calcaneus articulating with fibula.
6. astragalus with pulley-like surface above and below.
7. **no alisphenoid canal.**
8. nasals usually not wide posteriorly.
9. cheekteeth variable, either bunodont (pigs, peccaries, hippos) or selenodont.

Compare with: Perissodactyla.

Remark: Useful refernces on the phylogeny and classification of artiodactyls are Haltenorth (1963), Scott (1940), and Simpson (1945).

KEY TO FAMILIES OF ARTIODACTYLA

1a. Cannon bone not present in any feet (partial fusion of metatarsals may occur in hindfoot); postorbital bar incomplete; mastoid not exposed; canines present, sharp-edged; molars bunodont (**Suiformes**) 2

1b. Cannon bone present in all feet or hindfoot only; postorbital bar complete; mastoid exposed; canines absent, or if present, not sharp-edged; molars seleno-dont 4

2a (1a). Body very large, virtually hairless; snout broad, not elongate, mobile, or flattened at end; orbit largely separated from temporal fossa by postorbital plate; innermost pair of lower incisors large, tusk-like; lower canines larger than upper canines .... **HIPPOPOTAMIDAE** (p.283)

2b. Body of moderate proportions, usually covered with coarse hair; snout elongate, mobile, flattened at end; orbit widely continuous with temporal fossa; innermost pair of lower incisors not large or tusk-like; lower canines smaller than or ± equal in size to upper canines 3

3a (2b). Digits 4-4; paroccipital process very large; upper canines directed outward and upward .... **SUIDAE** (p.279)

3b. Digits 4-3; paroccipital process small; upper canines directed downward................................. **TAYASSUIDAE** (p.281)

4a (1b). Foot posture digitgrade; horns or antlers never present; nails present on digits; one pair of upper incisors (**Tylopoda**) .... **CAMELIDAE** (p.285)

4b. Foot posture unguligrade; horns or antlers often present; hoofs present on digits; no uppers incisors (**Ruminantia**) 5

5a (4b). Tail long, tufted at end; neck very long; "horns" each composed of a bone separated by a suture from frontal; surfaces of molars rough-textured .... **GIRAFFIDAE** (p.292)

5b. Tail short or long, not tufted; neck only moderately long; "horns" each a continuous outgrowth of frontal bone; surfaces of molars smooth 6

6a (5b). Size small—30 cm (1 ft) or less in height at shoulder; four prominent digits on feet (side toes well developed); no horns; nasal and lacrimal joined or with very small separation; upper canines present, tusk-like . . . . **TRAGULIDAE** (p.287)

6b. Size medium to large—usually greater than 30 cm in height (rarely smaller); two prominent digits on feet (side toes absent or reduced to dewclaws); horns or antlers nearly always present, at least in males; nasal and lacrimal separate or joined; upper canines present or absent, rarely tusk-like 7

7a (6b).   Horns simple, unbranched, and covered permanently with hardened sheath; no upper canines; lacrimal pit present or absent; usually only one lacrimal foramen present, inside orbit (Fig. 128A)... **BOVIDAE** (p.294)

7b.   Horns (antlers) nearly always branched, the bony core exposed or covered with soft skin ("velvet"); upper canines present or absent; lacrimal pit present, two lacrimal foramina (rarely one) present, usually at rim of or outside orbit (Fig. 128B)............................ **CERVIDAE** (p.289)

Figure 128. Single opening, a bovid (A), and double opening, a cervid (B), of the lacrimal foramen.

SUBORDER SUIFORMES

Recognition Characters:

1. foot posture unguligrade.
2. digits 4-3 or 4-4.
3. hoofs present.
4. **cannon bone lacking in all feet** (partial fusion of metatarsals in Tayassuidae).
5. **no horns or antlers.**
6. **postorbital bar never complete.**
7. **mastoid not exposed—obscured by broad contact of squamosal and occipital bones.**
8. **one to three pairs of upper incisors present.**
9. canines tusk-like, sharp-edged.
10. **molars bunodont.**
11. "stomach" with two or three chambers.

Family SUIDAE
(Pigs, hogs)

Familiar to most people because of domestic swine (derived from *Sus scrofa*, the European wild boar), members of this family are relatively unspecialized artiodactyls. They are identified externally by the long, terminally flattened snout and stout sparsely-haired body. Like tayassuids (p.281) suids have an elongate skull with a straight, sloping profile and posteriorly projecting occipitals (Fig. 129). The cheek-teeth are bunodont. The dental formula is highly variable within species because with continued wear many of the cheekteeth are shed and not replaced. The tusk-like upper canines (which are most prominent in males) are larger than the lower ones and grow outward and upward. In *Babyrousa*, these teeth pierce the upper base of the lips without ever entering the mouth cavity. Presumably these tusks are used in display.

Suids are diurnal or nocturnal and inhabit brushland, forests, and plains. Most are omnivorous (*Phacochoerus* is strictly herbivorous), subsisting on a wide variety of plants, small animals, and carrion.

These mammals are sedentary and usually gregarious. Most occur in family groups, but larger aggregations sometimes form. In *Sus scrofa*, males are solitary except at mating time. Warthogs (*Phacochoerus*) are territorial. Breeding is seasonal or aseasonal, depending upon availability of food. Prior to parturition females build nests of sticks and leaves. Whereas other artiodactyls usually deliver one young, female suids regularly bear three (sometimes more) offspring per litter (domestic swine often average 10 or more piglets per litter).

Five genera, 8 species; Europe, Asia, Africa, many islands, and many introduced populations in other areas, including North America; domesticated worldwide.

Recognition Characters:

1. size medium to large (110-200 cm).
2. **body sparsely haired or with coarse bristles.**
3. digits 4-4, but usually only two functional in locomotion (side toes small).
4. **snout elongate, mobile, flattened at end.**
5. nostrils opening anteriorly.
6. **no fusion of metacarpals or metatarsals.**
7. paroccipital process large.

8. no ventral flange on angular process of lower jaw (Fig. 129).

9. **canines usually with sharp edges; upper canines larger than lower canines, directed outward and upward** (Fig. 129).

Dental formula: $\dfrac{1\text{-}3}{3}\ \dfrac{1}{1}\ \dfrac{2\text{-}4}{2\text{-}4}\ \dfrac{3}{3}$ = 34-44 (but cheekteeth gradually lost with wear).

Compare with: Tayassuidae.

Representative Genera:

Babyrousa (1) - *B. babyrussa* is the babirusa.

Phacochoerus (1) - *P. aethiopicus* is the warthog.

Sus (4) - Wild boars. *Sus scrofa* includes the European wild boar and domestic swine.

Remarks: Frädrich (1965, 1967, 1974) investigated behavior or wild suids. Other informative sources on suids are Ewer (1958) and Mohr (1960).

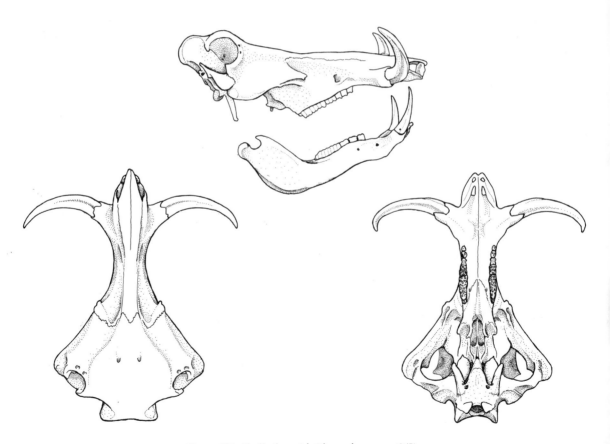

Figure 129. Skull of a suid (*Phacochoerus*, x 1/5).

Family TAYASSUIDAE
(Peccaries or javelinas)

This family of pig-like omnivores comprises three species which frequent diverse habitats, including tropical forests, deserts, and scrubland. Many features (snout, body-build, shape of skull, and bunodont cheekteeth) (Fig. 130) are similar to those of suids (p.279). However, peccaries are smaller, and the upper canines always project downward (never outward and upward).

Peccaries are highly gregarious. The collared peccary (*Tayassu tayacu*) roams in permanent bands of a few to several dozen individuals of both sexes. Despite their appearance, they are fast and agile. Tayassuids are active mostly at night. In the daytime they take shelter in thickets or holes in rocks or logs. Breeding appears to aseasonal. Females normally produce twins.

Two genera, 3 species; southwestern United States to South America.

Recognition Characters:
1. size medium (75-105 cm).
2. **body covered with stiff bristly hairs.**
3. digits 4-3, but only two functional in locomotion.
4. snout elongate, mobile, flattened at end.
5. nostrils opening anteriorly.
6. **middle two metatarsals fused proximally;** metacarpals free.
7. paroccipital process small.
8. no ventral flange on angular process of lower jaw (Fig. 130).
9. **canines with sharp cutting edges; upper canines ± same size as lower canines, directed downward** (Fig. 130).

Dental formula: $\frac{2}{3}\frac{1}{1}\frac{3}{3}\frac{3}{3}$ = 38

Compare with: Suidae.

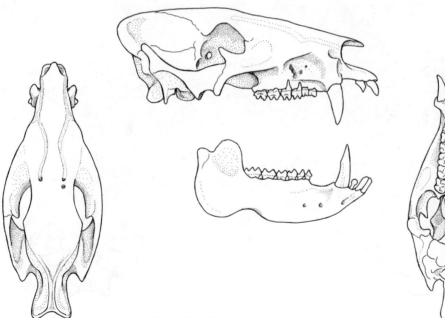

Figure 130. Skull of a tayassuid (*Tayassu*, x 1/4).

ARTIODACTYLA

Genera:

Catagonus (1) - *C. wagneri* is the recently discovered Chacoan peccary (Wetzel et al., 1975).

Tayassu (including *Dicotyles*, after Van Gelder, 1977) (2) - *T. pecari* and *T. tayacu* are the white-lipped peccary and collared peccary, respectively.

Remark: Morphology and social behavior of peccaries are described by Woodburne (1968) and Sowls (1974), respectively.

Peccary.

Family HIPPOPOTAMIDAE
(Hippopotamuses)

Hippopotamuses are like no other mammals. They are bulky and broad-snouted and have large tusk-like incisors and canines (Fig. 131). The mouth is huge and is opened widely to expose the tusks in display and combat. Apparently this large gape is made possible by refinements of the skull and cranial musculature which reduce stretching of the jaw muscles (Herring and Herring, 1974). Skin glands exude an oily secretion over the body (called a "blood sweat" because of its pinkish color) which protects the skin from desiccation. The nostrils are located on the top of the snout.

Hippopotamus is amphibious and can swim and dive well. It occurs in herds of 5-30 individuals near ponds and rivers. In contrast, *Choeropsis* is less aquatic, occurs singly or in pairs, and prefers moist forests. Both species feed predominantly on grasses, grazing by night and returning to water (*Hippopotamus*) or dense thickets (*Choeropsis*) by day. Grazing and trampling by hippos influence the distribution and structure of grasslands around watercourses (Lock, 1972). Hippopotamuses apparently breed year-round. Usually one young is produced.

Two genera, 2 species; Africa south of the Sahara.

Recognition Characters:

- **mouth very large.**

- **incisors large (especially inner pair of lower ones), tusk-like** (Fig. 131).

1. size very large (165-500 cm).
2. **body virtually hairless.**
3. digits 4-4, all functional in locomotion.
4. **snout broad, not mobile or flattened at end.**
5. **nostrils opening dorsally.**
6. no fusion of metacarpals or metatarsals.
7. paroccipital process small.
8. **angular process of lower jaw with large flange projecting ventrally**(Fig. 131).
9. **canines very large, tusk-like; upper canines much smaller than lower canines, directed downward** (Fig. 130).

Dental formula: $\dfrac{2\text{-}3}{1\text{-}3}\dfrac{1}{1}\dfrac{4}{4}\dfrac{3}{3} = 38\text{-}42$

Genera:

Choeropsis(1) - *C. liberiensis* is the pygmy hippopotamus.

Hippopotamus (1) - *H. amphibius* is the hippopotamus.

Remark: The behavior of *Hippopotamus* was studied by Verheyen (1954).

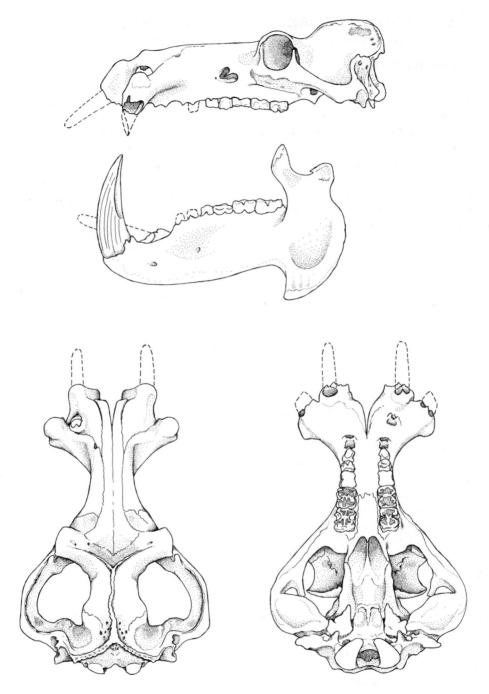

Figure 131. Skull of a hippopotamid (*Hippopotamus*, x 1/8).

SUBORDER TYLOPODA

Family CAMELIDAE
(Camels)

Although most people are familiar with the desert-dwelling camels of the Old World, few are aware that other members of this family inhabit the Andes Mountains of South America. These two geographically disjunct groups of camelids are remnants of forms that ranged widely over the world (including North America and Europe) until the Pleistocene.

Camels are ungainly (*Camelus*) or delicate (*Lama, Vicugna*) in appearance and movements. To insure effective progression in sand and on rocks, the sole of each foot is expanded into a broad pad. Although there are only two functional toes per foot, the phalanges are laterally expanded, and the foot posture is digitgrade. Each foot has a cannon bone, but the metacarpals (or metatarsals) forming the bone are separate at the distal end and bent outward.

The skull of camels (Fig. 132) is distinguished from that of ruminants by the presence of upper incisors (three pairs in young animals, one pair in adults). Upper canines (also usually absent in ruminants) are also present.

Inhabiting arid deserts and mountains, these mammals are diurnal grazers. They occur in small herds of 2-30 individuals, usually containing one male and a harem of females. Vicuña males defend year-round feeding territories and separate sleeping areas. Females are polyestrous and usually have one young. *Camelus* is remarkable in its ability to withstand extreme heat and go for long periods without water.

Llama.

Camelids have been used for centuries as beasts of burden. They also are valued for their wool, hides, meat, and other products. The llama and alpaca, which are subspecies of the guanaco (*Lama glama*), were completely domesticated in South America before the arrival of the Spanish.

Three genera, 6 species; Gobi Desert and western South America from Peru to Tierra del Fuego.

Recognition Characters:

1. **foot posture digitigrade.**
2. digits 2-2.
3. nails present (no hoofs).
4. **cannon bone in all feet, but fusion not complete at distal end.**

5. **no horns or antlers.**
6. postorbital bar complete (Fig. 132).
7. mastoid exposed.
8. one pair of upper incisors present, (three pairs in young animals)(Fig. 132).
9. canines present (Fig. 132), not sharp-edged.
10. molars selenodont (Fig. 132).
11. "stomach" three-chambered.

Dental formula: $\dfrac{1}{3}\dfrac{1}{0\text{-}1}\dfrac{2\text{-}3}{2\text{-}3}\dfrac{3}{3}$ = 30-34

Genera:

Camelus (2) - The Bactrian (two-humped) and dromedary (one-humped) camels are *C. bactrianus* and *C. dromedarius*, respectively.

Lama (1) - *L. glama* comprises the guanaco and two domesticated forms (the llama and alpaca).
Vicugna (1) - *V. vicugna* is the vicuña.

Remarks: The physiology of camels was reviewed by Schmidt-Nielsen (1964). Behavior, ecology, and management of camelids were examined by Franklin (1974), Gauthier-Pilters (1974), and Koford (1957).

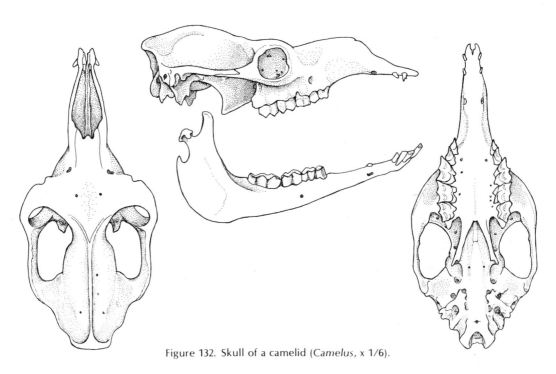

Figure 132. Skull of a camelid (*Camelus*, x 1/6).

SUBORDER RUMINANTIA

Recognition Characters:

1. foot posture unguligrade.
2. **functional digits usually 2-2, side toes reduced or absent.**
3. hoofs present.
4. **cannon bone usually present in all feet** (not present in forelimbs of some tragulids).
5. **horns or antlers usually present, at least in males** (absent in both sexes of chevrotains).
6. postorbital bar complete.
7. **mastoid exposed.**
8. **no upper incisors.**
9. canines present or absent, not sharp-edged.
10. molars selenodont.
11. "stomach" complex, usually four-chambered (three-chambered in chevrotains).

Family TRAGULIDAE
(Chevrotains or mouse deer)

These small, delicate artiodactyls possess a curious mixture of primitive and advanced ruminant characters. There are four complete digits in all limbs. A cannon bone is always present in the hindlimb but is incompletely formed in the forelimb. There are no horns or antlers. However, the upper canines are large and tusk-like (Fig. 133). The cheekteeth are selenodont.

According to Eisenberg and Lockhart (1972), mouse deer are ecological equivalents of the paca (*Agouti paca*), a Neotropical hystricomorph rodent (p.191). They are similar in size, spotted pelage, and habits—both occur in tropical forest and are nocturnal or crepuscular, solitary, and secretive, and feed largely on fruit. Otherwise, habits of chevrotains are poorly known.

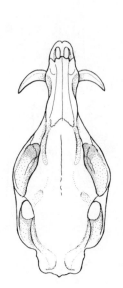
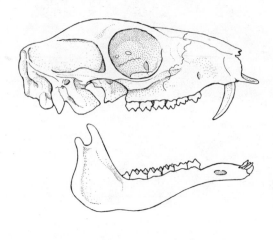
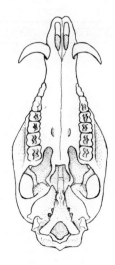

Figure 133. Skull of a tragulid (*Tragulus* × 1/2).

287

ARTIODACTYLA

Two genera, 4 species; tropical areas of western Africa, southeast Asia, India and Ceylon.

Recognition Characters:

1. size small (height at shoulder less than 30 cm).
2. **no horns or antlers.**
3. tail short.
4. neck short.
5. **digits 4-4**—side toes slender, but well developed.
6. no lacrimal depression (Fig. 133).
7. nasal and lacrimal adjoining or with little or no separation (Fig. 133).
8. one lacrimal foramen present, inside orbit.
9. **upper canines present, long and tusk-like in males** (Fig. 133).
10. surfaces of molars smooth in texture.
11. "stomach" three-chambered.

Dental formula: $\dfrac{0}{3}\dfrac{1}{1}\dfrac{3}{3}\dfrac{3}{3} = 34$

Compare with: Cervidae.

Representative Genus:

Tragulus (3) - Chevrotains or mouse deer.

Chevrotain.

Family CERVIDAE
(Deer and allies)

These lithe-bodied, graceful artiodactyls are most widely recognized by the antlers in males of most species (Fig. 134). Antlers are complexly branched horns consisting of a bony core which during growth is covered by soft skin ("velvet"). These structures are used chiefly for ritualized displays during the breeding period ("rut"). The annual cycle of antler growth is timed so that maximum size is reached just before the onset of mating activities. The velvet, which provides nourishment to the developing bony core, sloughs away at this time and exposes the antler. Dagger-like upper canines are found in genera which have small antlers (*Elaphodus*, *Muntiacus*) or which have no antlers (*Hydropotes*, *Moschus*).

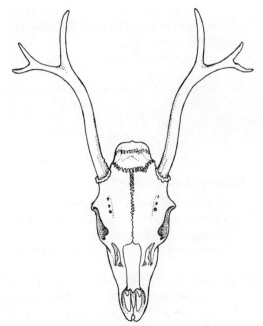

Figure 134. Dorsal view of cervid skull showing antlers.

Anterless cervids (e.g., females) may be distinguished from other similar groups (e.g., bovids, p. 294) by a combination of characters in the lacrimal bone. This bone always contains a distinct depression (which houses a scent gland), and the lacrimal foramen is double (Figs. 128B, 135). In addition, a conspicuous gap is present between the lacrimal and nasal bones. Canines are also sometimes present (these are never found in bovids).

Cervids occur in practically all terrestrial habitats from sea level to timberline. Their diet consists of grasses, lichens, twigs, shoots, bark, and aquatic plants. Some species are migratory; perhaps the best-known example is the caribou (*Rangifer*).

Most cervids are sociable, but a few (e.g., *Alces*) are solitary. In breeding season males of some species establish harems. Ritualized combat occurs as males compete for females. Males often emit a powerful bugle or bellow. The social and reproductive behavior of the more secretive species is poorly known. Female cervids usually reproduce once per year and bear one or two fawns; the Chinese water deer (*Hydropotes*) is unusual in having 4-7 offspring in a litter.

Two oddities among mammals occur in cervids. The extinct Irish elk (*Megaloceros giganteus*) possessed the world's largest known headgear—the antlers measured over three meters (10-12 feet) in spread. For details of this beast and the functional attributes of the antlers, see Gould (1974). The peculiar muntjac (*Muntiacus*) has a diploid chromosome number of only six (females) or seven (males), by far the smallest known chromosome number of any mammal (Wurster and Benirschke, 1970).

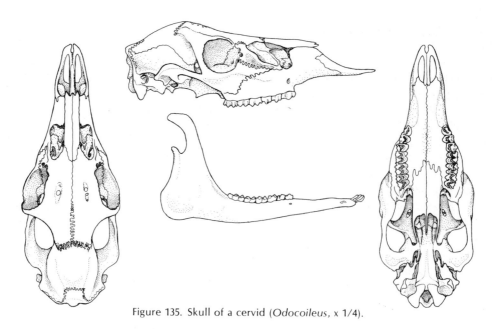

Figure 135. Skull of a cervid (*Odocoileus*, x 1/4).

Eleven genera, perhaps 37 species; worldwide except the Australian region (where they have been introduced), Antarctica, and most of Africa.

Recognition Characters:
1. size small to large (height at shoulder 30-240 cm).
2. **"horns" (antlers) found only in males** (except *Rangifer*) (Fig. 134), **usually complexly branched** (spike-like in *Elaphodus*, tufted deer), **bony core sheathed in "velvet" while growing; antler and velvet shed separately, usually every year.**
3. tail short.
4. neck short (e.g., *Alces*) to moderately long.
5. **digits 4-4—side toes (dewclaws) small and non-functional.**
6. **lacrimal depression present** (Fig. 135).
7. nasal and lacrimal separated by large oblong opening or fenestration (Fig. 135).
8. **usually two lacrimal foramina present** (only one in *Moschus*, musk deer), **at front edge of or outside orbit** (Figs. 128B, 135)**.**
9. upper canines, when present, small or large and tusk-like.
10. surfaces of molars smooth in texture.
11. "stomach" four-chambered.

Dental formula: $\dfrac{0}{3}\dfrac{0\text{-}1}{1}\dfrac{3}{3}\dfrac{3}{3} = 32\text{-}34$

Compare with: Bovidae, Tragulidae.

Representative Genera:
Alces (1) - *A. alces* is the moose.
Blastoceros (1) - *B. bezoarcticus* is the pampas deer.
Capreolus (1) - *C. capreolus* is the roe deer.
Cervus (including *Axis* and *Dama*; see **Remarks**) (12) - Well-known species are the axis deer (*C. axis*), fallow deer (*C. dama*), and elk, wapiti, or red deer (*C. elaphus*).

Mazama (4) - Brochet deer.

Moschus (1) - *M. moschiferus* is the musk deer.

Muntiacus (4) - Muntjacs.

Odocoileus (2) - *O. hemionus* and *O. virginiana* are the mule deer and white-tailed deer, respectively.

Pudu (2) - Pudus.

Rangifer (1) - *R. tarandus* is the reindeer or caribou.

Remarks: The species composition of the genus *Cervus* used here follows suggestions made by Haltenorth (1963) and Van Gelder (1977).

Literature on cervids is extensive. Chaplin (1977) and Whitehead (1972) provided general treatments of the family. Behavior of cervids was treated by de Vos et al. (1967) and Geist (1966). Selected references on individual species include: Darling (1937), McCullogh (1969), Murie (1951), and Schaller (1967) on *Cervus*; Bedard (1975), Geist (1963), and Peterson (1955) on *Alces*; Linsdale and Tomich (1953), Taber and Dasmann (1958), and Taylor (1956) on *Odocoileus*; Prior (1968) on *Capreolus*; and Kelsall (1968) on *Rangifer*. Chapman (1975) summarized general aspects of growth and shedding of antlers.

Axis deer.

Family GIRAFFIDAE
(Giraffes)

Only two species compose this family. Long limbs and neck, stubby velvety horns, and sloping body profile are diagnostic external features. A unique "third horn" often is found in front and between the other two horns; it is especially prominent in males. The bony core of the horns also is distinctive (see below and Fig.136). Giraffes have a peculiar, stiff-legged gait.

Giraffa usually is found in savannahs, always near shrubs and trees. These animals eat largely leguminous plants (particularly acacias) and can browse at heights far above potential competitors. Feeding is aided by mobile lips and an exceptionally extensible tongue. *Giraffa* generally travels in small herds of varying sex and age composition. One is the usual number of offspring.

The little-known okapi is solitary, prefers dense forests, and feeds on foliage and fruit.

Two genera, 2 species; Africa south of the Sahara.

Recognition Characters:

- **"horns" each composed of a distinct bone (horn is an outgrowth of the frontal bone in other ruminants) (Fig. 136).**

- **additional swelling or "horn" often present medial and anterior to others.**

1. size very large (height at shoulder 150-370 cm).
2. **"horns" present in both sexes, unbranched, permanently in "velvet";** velvet and bony core both non-deciduous.
3. **tail long, tufted at end.**
4. **neck very long.**

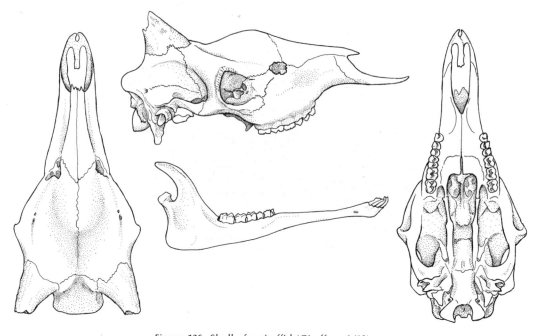

Figure 136. Skull of a giraffid (*Giraffa*, x 1/10).

5. **digits 2-2—no side toes (no dewclaws).**
6. no lacrimal depression.
7. nasal and lacrimal distinctly separated (Fig. 136).
8. one lacrimal foramen present, small, inside orbit.
9. upper canines absent.
10. **surfaces of molars rough-textured.**
11. "stomach" four-chambered.

Dental formula: $\dfrac{0}{3}\dfrac{0}{1}\dfrac{3}{3}\dfrac{3}{3} = 32$

Genera:

Giraffa (1) - *G. camelopardalis* is the giraffe.

Okapia(1) - *O johnstoni* is the okapi.

Remark: Singer and Bone (1960) discussed the taxonomy of recent and fossil giraffids. Dagg (1971), Dagg and Foster (1976), and Innis (1958) reviewed the natural history of *Giraffa*.

Giraffe.

Family BOVIDAE
(Cattle, sheep, goats, antelopes, and allies)

This family contains over one-third of all ungulates. Although native wild populations occur on all continents except Australia and South America, the center of greatest diversity of bovid species is in the savannahs and forests of Africa. The family Bovidae is an extremely difficult group to classify. Genera are grouped into subfamilies based largely on external characters (Pocock, 1910, 1918). Aside from the recent inclusion of the pronghorn (*Antilocapra*) in the Bovidae (O'Gara and Matson, 1975), the subfamilies provided in the list of genera below follow Ansell (1971).

Bovids are sometimes difficult to distinguish from members of other similar families (e.g., Cervidae, p.289). Male and horned female bovids are easily recognized by their simple, unbranched headgear (Fig. 137). Identification of hornless individuals is more difficult. However, bovids generally lack either a lacrimal pit or a gap between lacrimal and nasal bones. Bovids with both the pit and gap have only a single lacrimal foramen.

All species of bovids have horns which often occur in both sexes. Horns differ from antlers in having a permanent bony core encased in a hardened sheath. In only one species (*Antilocapra americana*) is the sheath regularly shed.

Most members of this family inhabit plains, savannahs, deserts, tundra, and scrubland. Others frequent mountainous areas (e.g., goats, sheep) or forest (e.g., duikers). Although most species are grazers, some browse on the foliage of forbs, scrubs, and trees. Generally bovids breed at only one time of year (ordinarily in the fall). The usual number of young is one.

The social behavior of bovid species is highly variable. Most are gregarious, associating year-round or seasonally in small to large herds of various sex and age compositions. Males often establish harem groups during the breeding period or are otherwise solitary or live in bachelor herds. Forest-dwelling forms are solitary. Social species characteristically have well-developed scent glands which are used to mark territorial boundaries.

Some forms of bovids (e.g., cattle, sheep, goats) have been domesticated by man. Many others are hunted for sport, meat, and hides.

Forty genera, approximately 110 species; worldwide except for the Australian region, Antarctica, and Central and South America (introduced everywhere).

Recognition Characters:

1. size small to large (height at shoulder 25-200 cm).
2. **horns always present in males** (except some domestic forms), **variable in females, unbranched** (additional prong in *Antilocapra*), **with hardened sheath; sheath and bony core non-deciduous** (except in *Antilocapra*) (see Figs. 137 and 138).
3. tail long or short, not tufted.
4. neck moderately long.
5. **digits usually 4-4, but side toes (dewclaws) small and nonfunctional (occasionally absent).**
6. lacrimal depression present or absent.
7. nasal and lacrimal separated or united (Figs. 137, 138).
8. **usually one lacrimal foramen present** (two in *Antilocapra*), **usually inside orbit** (see Fig. 128B).

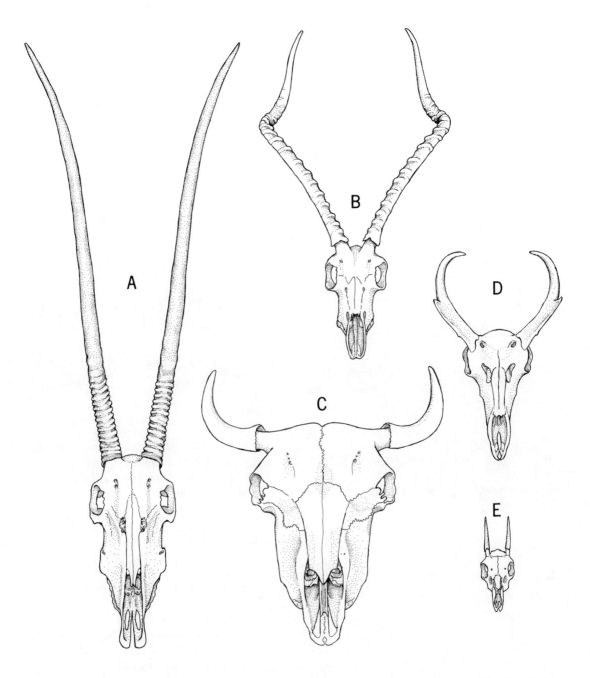

Figure 137. Skulls of representative bovids showing differences in shape of horns and in size and proportion of skulls. A, *Oryx*; B, *Kobus*; C. *Bison*; D, *Antilocapra*; E, *Raphiceros* (all x 1/8).

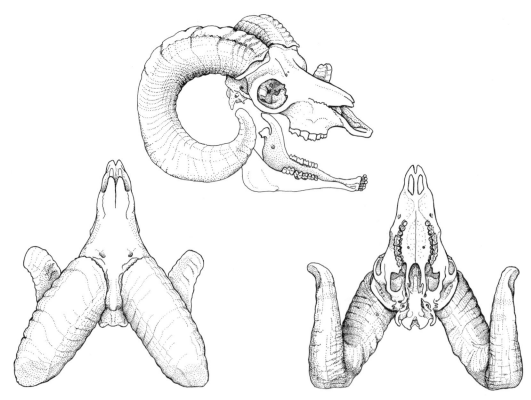

Figure 138.   Skull of a bovid (*Capra*, x ⅛).

9.   upper canines absent.
10. surfaces of molars smooth in texture.
11. "stomach" four-chambered.

Dental formula: $\dfrac{0\;0\;\;3\;\;3}{3\;1\;2\text{-}3\;\;3} = 30\text{-}32$

Compare with: Cervidae.

Representative Genera:

Aepycerotinae
  Aepyceros (1) - *a. melampus* is the impala.

Alcelaphinae
  Alcelaphus (including *Damaliscus*) (2) - Hartebeests.
  Connochaetes (5) - Gnus or wilde-beests, topi, blesbok. *C. taurinus*, the blue wildebeest, is a common species in African savannahs.

Antilocaprinae
  Antilocapra (1) - *A. americana.* is the pronghorn.

Antilopinae
  Antidorcas (1) - *A. marsupialis* is the springbuck.
  Antilope (1) - *A. cervicapra* is the blackbuck.
  Gazella (12) - Gazelles.
  Litocranius (1) - *L. walleri* is the gerenuk.
  Madoqua (4) - Dik-diks.
  Oreotragus (1) - *O. oreotragus* is the klipspringer.

Bovinae

Bison (1) - *B. bison* is the bison.

Bos (5) - Cattle; the domestic species is *B. taurus.*

Bubalis (including *Synceros*) (4) - Buffaloes. The African buffalo is *B. caffer.* The water buffalo (*B. bubalis*) is widely domesticated in Asia.

Tragelaphus (including *Taurotragus*) (8) - Bushbuck, kudus, elands, nyalas, and allies.

Caprinae

Capra (including *Ammotragus* and *Ovis*) (5) - Sheep, goats. Familiar species are Barbary sheep (*C. lervia*), mouflan (*C. aries*), bighorn sheep (*C. canadensis*), and ibex (*C. ibex*).

Hemitragus (3) - Tahrs.

Oreamnos (1) - *O. americanus* is the mountain goat.

Ovibos (1) - *O. moschatus* is the musk ox.

Rupicapra (1) - *R. rupicapra* is the chamois.

Saiga (1) - *S. tatarica* is the saiga antelope.

Cephalophinae

Cephalophus (13) - Duikers.

Hippotraginae

Hippotragus (2) - *H. niger* and *H. equinus* are the sable and roan antelopes, respectively.

Oryx (3) - Oryx.

Peleinae

Pelea (1) - *P. capreolus* is the rhebuck.

Reduncinae

Kobus (including *Adenota*) (5) - waterbuck, kob, puku, and lechwes.

Redunca (3) - Reedbucks.

Remarks: Taxonomic assignment of species to genera and subfamilies follows Ansell (1971) as modified by O'Gara and Matson (1975) and Van Gelder (1977). For references on characteristics of the family and subfamilies see Haltenorth (1963), Pocock (1910, 1918), and Simpson (1945).

The literature on natural history of bovids is enormous and widely scattered. Excellent reviews of the behavior and ecology of African bovids were provided by Bere (1970), Estes (1974), Jarman (1974), Leuthold (1977), and Sinclair (1977). See also references therein. References on the biology of other bovids include McHugh (1958) and Roe (1951) on bison, and Geist (1971) and Schaller (1977) on sheep and goats. Many papers in Geist and Walther (1974) discussed behavior and management of bovids.

ORDER RHINOGRADENTIA
(Rhinogrades or snouters)

This marvelously adapted group of about 150 species is known only from the obscure South Sea archipelago of Hi-yi-yi. Snouters have peculiar modifications of the skull and snout enabling them to use the nose for a variety of purposes, including locomotion and feeding. For example, each of the several species of flower-faced snouters lures insects to a snout specially equipped with flaps of skin which resemble a flower. As Stumpke (1967) stated, "this group of animals has particular significance because among them are found principles of structure, modes of behavior, and ecological types that are unknown elsewhere, not just among mammals but among vertebrates in general." Stumpke recognized two suborders—the Monorrhina (uni-snouters) and Polyrrhina (multi-snouters)—containing a total of 14 families.

Diagnoses of the order and families are not possible because Stumpke provided descriptions for only a few representative species and because he gave no general descriptions of major taxonomic groups. For further details, see Stumpke (1967). Moreover, the authenticity of certain of the species is open to question because Stumpke used curious taxonomic procedures. For example, one genus (*Dulcidauca*, sugartails) is an anagram of another (*Dulcicauda*, honeytails). Some have suggested that the snouters represent figments of an inventive imagination. In any case, the questions surrounding rhinogrades will probably never be resolved. The entire archipelago (including Stumpke) was inadvertently destroyed during nuclear tests there two decades ago.

± more or less.

aerial - pertaining to flying. Bats are the only truly aerial mammals.

ambulatory - pertaining to a walking habit, as in bears and raccoons.

arboreal - pertaining to living in trees, as in many primates, squirrels, and sloths.

bone - hard supportive tissue consisting of cells distributed in a matrix of fibrous protein (collagen) and salt (chiefly calcium and phosphate).

calcar - a cartilaginous rod that projects from the ankle in many bats and serves to support the tail membrane. A similar structure protrudes laterally from the wrist or elbow of some rodents and supports the gliding membrane.

canal - perforation, or foramen, that tends to be elongated into a tube. Examples are alisphenoid canal, infraorbital canal.

cartilage - relatively soft supportive tissue consisting of rounded cells in a matrix of polysaccharides and fibrous protein (collagen).

claw - keratinized projection at the tips of the digits; long, curved, and sharply pointed.

cloaca - "dumping ground" or chamber into which the reproductive, urinary, and digestive products enter just before leaving the body.

crepuscular - active at twilight, i.e., at dusk or at dawn.

cursorial - pertaining to a running habit, as in artiodactyls and perissodactyls.

cusp - projection, or bump, on occlusal surface of a tooth.

cuspidate - having prominent cusps.

deflected - bent outward or laterally.

dewclaws (or **dewhoofs**) - clawed or hoofed remnants of side toes in many carnivores and artiodactyls, located just above the main functional digits.

digastric muscle - the primary muscle functioning to open the jaws, i.e., depress the mandible. It originates on the mastoid and paroccipital processes and inserts on the lower border of the mandible. It is prominent in many herbivores.

digits - toes.

e.g. - for example.

fenestrated - having a network of irregular perforations or holes.

foramen (pl. **foramina**) - a hole, opening, or perforation through bone. An example is the foramen magnum.

fossa (pl. **fossae**) - a depression, usually forming a site of muscular attachment or bone articulation. Examples are glenoid fossa, mandibular fossa, masseteric fossa, temporal fossa.

fossorial - pertaining to an underground mode of life, as in moles and gophers.

globular - globe-like, spherical.

guard hair - the prominent, coarse hair in the pelage of mammals. Spines, bristles, and mane-hairs are examples.

heterodont - a dentition in which there are teeth of different forms (e.g., incisors, canines, etc.).

heterothermic - having a variable body temperature.

Holarctic Region - zoogeographic region which collectively comprises the Palearctic and Nearctic regions.

homodont - dentition in which the teeth closely resemble one another (e.g., the teeth of porpoises).

hoof (pl. **hoofs** or **hooves**) - keratinized projection at the tips of digits that completely encase the tip of the phalanx.

i.e. - that is.

inflected - bent inward or medially.

insertion - the site of attachment of a muscle (usually on a bone) on the more movable of the two elements, or bones, that are joined by the muscle.

interfemoral membrane - membrane between tail and hindlimbs in bats.

ischial callosities - a pair of naked, thickly keratinized skin patches on the rump of certain primates.

masseter muscle - a muscle often consisting of several bands that originates on and adjacent to the zygomatic arch and inserts mostly in the masseteric fossa of the lower jaw.

nail - keratinized projection at the tips of the digits; usually short, flat, and blunt.

Nearctic Region - zoogeographic region containing temperate and arctic regions of the New World (North America south to central Mexico).

Neotropical Region - zoogeographic region containing the tropics of the New World (central Mexico south to South America and the West Indies).

occlusal - referring to crown, or biting surface of teeth where contact is made as jaws are closed, i.e., when upper and lower teeth occlude.

origin - the site of attachment of a muscle (usually on a bone) on the less movable of the two elements, or bones, that are joined by the muscle.

Palearctic Region - zoogeographic region containing temperate and arctic regions of the Old World (Europe, Africa north of the Sahara, and Asia except for southern tropical portions).

pelage - hair, fur.

pentadactyl - five toed.

perforate - pierced by an opening or openings.

pinna (pl. **pinnae**) - the fleshy skin flap that surrounds the external ear opening.

prismatic - prism-like, as in the cheekteeth microtine rodents which have sharply angular ridges on the occlusal surface.

procumbent - horizontally protruding condition of the incisors in some mammals, notably many marsupials, insectivores, and primates.

rhinarium - naked nose pad.

saltatorial - pertaining to hopping, as in kangaroos.

scansorial - pertaining to mammals that climb by use of claws, such as squirrels and cats.

scutes - flat bony plates of dermal tissue covered by epidermis forming the outer shell of armadillos.

sesamoid - a bone formed in a tendon. Examples are the patella and baculum (os penis).

syndactylous - a condition in which two or more digits are bound together in a common tube of skin. The underlying bones remain distinct.

talon (id) - a posterior "tail" or expansion on an upper (lower) cheektooth which produces a square outline to the tooth and expands the crushing surface.

temporal muscle - the muscle that originates on the posterodorsal and lateral portions of the braincase and inserts chiefly on the coronoid process of the lower jaw. It is especially large in carnivores.

tragus - a projection of skin that arises at the anteroventral margin of the pinna. Found in most bats and in springhares (Rodentia: Pedetidae).

tuberculo-sectorial - a tritubercular tooth with sharp cutting edges (cusps).

underfur - soft, often woolly insulative hairs in the pelage of mammals. It provides the bulk of the hair covering in most species.

vibrissae - long whiskers specialized as tactile receptors, commonly located in the facial region.

LITERATURE CITED

Allen, G.M. 1939. Bats. Cambridge, Mass.: Harvard Univ. Press, 368 pp.

Alpers, A. 1961. Dolphins, the myth and the mammal. Boston: Houghton Mifflin Co., 268 pp.

Andersen, H.T. 1969. The biology of marine mammals. New York: Academic Press, 511 pp.

Anderson, E. 1970. Quaternary evolution of the genus *Martes* (Carnivora, Mustelidae). Acta Zool. Fennica, 130:1-132.

Anderson, S. 1967. Primates. Pp. 151-177 *in* Recent mammals of the world (S. Anderson and J.K. Jones, Jr., eds.). New York: Ronald Press, 453 pp.

Anderson, S., and J.K. Jones, Jr. 1967. Recent mammals of the world. New York: Ronald Press, 453 pp.

Ansell, W.F.H. 1971. Order Artiodactyla. Part 15 *in* The mammals of Africa. An identification manual (J. Meester and H.W. Setzer, eds.). Washington, D.C.: Smithsonian Inst. Press.

Arata, A.A. 1967. Muroid, gliroid, and dipodoid rodents. Pp. 226-253 *in* Recent mammals of the world (S. Anderson and J.K. Jones, Jr., eds.). New York: Ronald Press, 453 pp.

Archer, M. 1976a. The dasyurid dentition and its relationships to didelphids, thylacinids, borhyaenids (Marsupicarnivora) and peramelids (Peramelina, Marsupialia). Aust. J. Zool., Suppl. Ser., 39:1-34.

Archer, M. 1976b. The basicranial region of marsupicarnivores (Marsupialia), interrelationships of carnivorous marsupials, and affinities of the insectivorous peramelids. Zool. J. Linn. Soc. London, 59: 217-322.

Archer, M., and J.A.W. Kirsch. 1977. The case for the Thylacomyidae and Myrmecobiidae, Gill, 1872, or why are marsupials so extended? Proc. Linn. Soc. N.So. Wales, 102:18-25.

Asibey, E.O.A. 1974. The grasscutter, *Thryonomys swinderianus* Temminck, in Ghana. Symp. Zool. Soc. London, 34:161-170.

Augee, M.L. (ed.). 1978. Monotreme biology. Australian Zool., 20:1-257.

Ayensu, E.S. 1974. Plant and bat interactions in West Africa. Ann. Missouri Bot. Garden, 61:702-727.

Baker, R.J., J.K. Jones, Jr., and D.C. Carter (eds.). 1976. Biology of bats of the New World family Phyllostomatidae. Part 1. Spec. Publ. Mus., Texas Tech Univ., 10:1-218.

Baker, R.J., J.K. Jones, Jr., and D.C. Carter (eds.). 1977. Part 2. Ibid. Spec. Publ. Mus. Texas Tech Univ., 13:1-364.

Barash, D.P. 1974. The evolution of marmot societies: a general theory. Science, 185:415-420.

Barnett, S.A. 1958. Social behaviour in wild rats. Proc. Zool. Soc. London, 130:107-152.

Beck, A. 1973. The ecology of stray dogs. A study of free-ranging urban animals. Baltimore: York Press, 98 pp.

Bédard, J. (ed.). 1975. Moose ecology. Le Naturaliste Canadien, 101:1-741.

Beebe, W. 1926. The three-toed sloth. Zoologica, 7:1-67.

Bekoff, M. (ed.). 1978. Coyotes. Biology, behavior, and management. New York: Academic Press, 384 pp.

Bell, R.H.V. 1970. The use of the herb layer by grazing ungulates in the Serengeti. Pp. 111-125 *in* Animal populations in relation to their food supply (A. Watson, ed.). Oxford: Blackwell Scientific Publ., 477 pp.

Benedict, F.G. 1936. The physiology of the elephant. Carnegie Inst. Washington, 302 pp.

Bere, R. 1970. Antelopes. New York: Arco Publ. Co., 96 pp.

Bergin, T.J. (ed.). 1978. The koala. Sydney: Zool. Parks Brd., New South Wales, 239 pp.

Bermant, G., and D.G. Lindburg. 1975. Primate utilization and conservation. New York: John Wiley & Sons, 196 pp.

Bertram, G.L.C. 1940. The biology of the Weddell and crabeater seals, with a study of the comparative behavior of the Pinnipedia. Spec. Rept., Brit. Mus. (Nat. Hist.), 1:1-139.

Berzin, A.A. 1972. The sperm whale. Jerusalem: Israel Program for Scientific Translations, 394 pp.

Best, P.B. 1979. Social organization in sperm whales, *Physeter macrocephalus*. Pp. 227-289 *in* Behavior of marine animals. Vol. 3: Cetaceans (H.E. Winn and B.L. Ollo, eds.). New York: Plenum Press, 438 pp.

Black, C.C. 1963. A review of the North American Tertiary Sciuridae. Bull. Mus. Comp. Zool., 130:109-248.

Black, C.C. 1972. Holarctic evolution and dispersal of squirrels (Rodentia: Sciuridae). Pp. 305-322 *in* Evolutionary Biology, Vol. 6 (Dobzhansky, T., M.K. Hecht, and W.C. Steere, eds.). New York: Appleton-Century-Crofts, 445 pp.

Black, H. 1974. A north temperate bat community: structure and prey populations. J. Mamm., 55:138-157.

Blatt, C.M., C.R. Taylor, and M.B. Habal. 1972. Thermal cooling in dogs: the lateral nasal gland, a source of water for evaporative cooling. Science, 177:804-806.

Bloedel, P. 1955. Hunting methods of fish-eating bats, particularly *Noctilio leporinus*. J. Mamm., 36:390-399.

Bourne, G.H. (ed.). 1969-1972. The Chimpanzee, Vols. 1-5. Baltimore: University Park Press.

Bradbury, J.W. 1977a. Social organization and communication. Pp. 1-72 in Biology of bats, Vol. 3 (W.A. Wimsatt, ed.). New York: Academic Press, 651 pp.

Bradbury, J.W. 1977b. Lek behavior in the hammer-headed bat. Z. Tierpsychol., 45:225-255.

Bradbury, J.W., and L. Emmons. 1974. Social organization in some Trinidad bats. I. Emballonuridae. Z. Tierpsychol., 36:137-183.

Braithwaite, R.W., and A.K. Lee. 1979. A mammalian example of semelparity. Amer. Nat., 113:151-155.

Bressou, C. 1961. La myologie du tapir (*Tapirus indicus* L.). Mammalia, 25:358-400.

Britton, S.W. 1941. Form and function in the sloth. Quart. Rev. Biol., 16:13-34, 190-207.

Brooks, J.W. 1954. A contribution to the life history and ecology of the Pacific walrus. Spec. Rept., Alaska Coop. Wildl. Unit, 1:1-103.

Brosset, A. 1966. La biologie des Chiroptéres. Paris: Masson et Cie, 240 pp.

Brosset, A. 1976. Social organization in the African bat, *Myotis boccagei*. Z. Tierpsychol., 42:50-56.

Brown, J.H., and R.C. Lasiewski. 1972. Metabolic rate of weasels: the cost of being long and thin. Ecology, 53:939-943.

Brown, P. 1976. Vocal communication in the pallid bat, *Antrozous pallidus*. Z. Tierpsychol., 41:34-54.

Bryant, M.D. 1945. Phylogeny of Nearctic Sciuridae. Amer. Midland Nat., 33:257-390.

Buchmann, O.L.K., and E.R. Guiler. 1977. Behaviour and ecology of the Tasmanian devil, *Sarcophilus harrisii*. Pp. 155-168 in The biology of marsupials (B. Stonehouse and D. Gilmore, eds.). Baltimore: University Park Press, 486 pp.

Bueler, L.E. 1973. Wild dogs of the world. New York: Stein and Day, 274 pp.

Burrell, H. 1927. The platypus. Sydney: Angus and Robertson Ltd., 227 pp.

Calhoun, J.B. 1963. The ecology and sociology of the Norway rat. U.S. Public Health Serv. Publ., 1008:1-288.

Camp, C.L., and A.F. Borell. 1937. Skeletal and muscular differences in the hind limbs of *Lepus*, *Sylvilagus*, and *Ochotona*. J. Mamm., 18:315-326.

Campbell, C.B.G. 1974. On the phyletic relationships of the tree shrews. Mammal Rev., 4:125-143.

Carpenter, C.R. 1934. A field study of the behavior and social relations of howling monkeys. Comp. Psychol. Monogr., 10(2):1-168.

Carpenter, C.R. 1940. A field study in Siam of the behavior and social relations of the gibbon (*Hylobates lar*). Comp. Psychol. Monogr., 16:1-212.

Carrington, R. 1959. Elephants. A short account of their natural history, evolution, and influence on mankind. New York: Basic Books, 272 pp.

Cartmill, M. 1972. Arboreal adaptations and the origin of the order primates. Pp. 97-122 *in* The functional and evolutionary biology of primates (R.H. Tuttle, ed.). Chicago: Aldine-Atherton, 487 pp.

Cartmill, M. 1974. Rethinking primate origins. Science, 184:436-443.

Chaplin, R.E. 1977. Deer. Poole, England: Blandford Press, 218 pp.

Chapman, D.I. 1975. Antlers — bones of contention. Mammal Rev., 5:121-172.

Charles-Dominique, P. 1977. Ecology and behavior of nocturnal primates. New York: Columbia Univ. Press, 277 pp.

Chivers, D.J. 1974. The siamang in Malaya. Contrib. Primatol., 4:1-335.

Clark, W.E. LeGros. 1971. The antecedents of man. An introduction to the evolution of primates. Chicago: Quadrangle Books, 394 pp.

Clark, W.E. Le Gros, and C.F. Sonntag. 1926. A monograph of *Orycteropus afer*. 3. The skull, the skeleton of the trunk and limbs. General summary. Proc. Zool. Soc. London, 1926:445-485.

Clemens, W.A. 1977. Phylogeny of marsupials. Pp. 51-68 *in* The biology of marsupials (B. Stonehouse and D. Gilmore, eds.). Baltimore: University Park Press, 486 pp.

Clutton-Brock, J., G.B. Corbet, and M. Hills. 1976. A review of the family Canidae, with a classification by numerical techniques. Bull. Brit. Mus. (Nat. Hist.), Zool., 29:117-199.

Clutton-Brock, T.H. 1977. Primate ecology: studies of feeding and ranging behaviour in lemurs, monkeys, and apes. New York: Academic Press, 631 pp.

Corbet, G.B. 1971. Subfamily Potamogalinae. Part 1.2 *in* The mammals of Africa. An identification manual (J. Meester and H.W. Setzer, eds.). Washington, D.C.: Smithsonian Inst. Press.

Corbet, G.B., and J. Hanks. 1968. A revision of the elephant-shrew family (Macroscelididae). Bull. Brit. Mus. (Nat. Hist.), 16:45-111.

Couturier, M.A.J. 1954. L'ours brun. Grenoble, France: Dr. Marcel Couturier, 904 pp.

Crook, J.H. 1970. The socio-ecology of primates. Pp. 103-166 *in* Social behaviour in birds and mammals. London: Academic Press, 492 pp.

Crompton, A.W., and F.A. Jenkins, Jr. 1973. Mammals from reptiles: a review of mammalian origins. Ann. Rev. Earth Planet. Sci., 1:131-155.

Crowcroft, P. 1957. The life of shrews. London: Reinhardt, 166 pp.

Dagg, A.I. 1971. *Giraffa camelopardalis*. Mamm. Species, 5:1-8.

Dagg, A.I., and J.B. Foster. 1976. The giraffe, its biology, behavior, and ecology. New York: Van Nostrand Reinhold Co., 210 pp.

Darling, F.F. 1937. A herd of red deer. A study in animal behavior. Oxford: Oxford Univ. Press, 215 pp.

Davis, D.D. 1964. The giant panda: a morphological study of evolutionary mechanisms. Fieldiana: Zool. Mem., Chicago Mus. Nat. Hist., 3:1-399.

Dawson, M.R. 1967. Fossil history of the families of Recent mammals. Pp. 12-53 *in* Recent mammals of the world (S. Anderson and J.K. Jones, Jr., eds.). New York: Ronald Press, 453 pp.

Devore, I. (ed.). 1965. Primate behavior. Field studies of monkeys and apes. New York: Holt, Rinehart and Winston, 654 pp.

de Vos, A., P. Brokx, and V. Geist. 1967. A review of the social behavior of the North American cervids during the rutting period. Amer. Midland Nat., 77:390-417.

Dohl, T.P., K.S. Norris, and I. Kang. 1974. A porpoise hybrid: *Tursiops* x *Steno*. J. Mamm., 55:217-221.

Dominis, J., and M. Edey. 1968. The cats of Africa. New York: Time-Life Books, Inc., 192 pp.

Dwyer, P.D. 1970. Social organization in the bat *Myotis adversus*. Science, 168:106-108.

Eaton, R.L. 1973. The cheetah. The biology and behavior of an endangered species. New York: Van Nostrand Reinhold Co., 178 pp.

Eaton, R.L. (ed.). 1973. The world's cats. Vol. 1. Winston, Ore.: World Wildlife Safari, 349 pp.

Eaton, R.L. (ed.). 1974. Ibid. Vol. 2. Seattle, Wash.: Feline Res. Grp., 260 pp.

Eaton, R.L. (ed.). 1976-77. Ibid. Vol. 3. Seattle, Wash.: Carnivore Res. Inst.

Eibl-Eibesfeldt, I. 1958. Das Verhalten der Nagetiere. Handb. Zool., 8(10):1-188.

Eisenberg, J.F. 1963. The behavior of heteromyid rodents. Univ. California Publ. Zool., 69:1-100.

Eisenberg, J.F. 1967. A comparative study in rodent ethology with emphasis on evolution of social behavior. I. Proc. U.S. Natl. Mus., 122:1-51.

Eisenberg, J.F., and E. Gould. 1970. The tenrecs: a study in mammalian behavior and evolution. Smithsonian Contrib. Zool., 27:1-137.

Eisenberg, J.F., and M. Lockhart. 1972. An ecological reconnaissance of Wilpattu National Park, Ceylon. Smithsonian Contrib. Zool., 101:1-118.

Eisenberg, J.F., G.M. McKay, and M.R. Jainudeen. 1971. Reproductive behavior of the Asiatic elephant *(Elaphus maximus maximus* L.). Behaviour, 38:193-225.

Eisner, T., and J.A. Davis. 1967. Mongoose throwing and smashing millipedes. Science, 155:577-579.

Ellerman, J.R. 1940. The families and genera of living rodents. Vol. 1. London: Brit. Mus. (Nat. Hist.), 689 pp.

Ellerman, J.R. 1941. Ibid. Vol. 2, 690 pp.

Ellerman, J.R. 1949. Ibid. Vol. 3, 210 pp.

Elliott, D.G. 1913. A review of the primates. Monogr. Amer. Mus. Nat. Hist., 1:3 Vols.

Eloff, G. 1958. The functional and structural degeneration of the eye in the African rodent moles *Cryptomys bigalkei* and *Bathyergus maritimus*. S. Afr. J. Sci., 54.

Elton, C. 1942. Voles, mice, and lemmings. Oxford: Oxford Univ. Press, 496 pp.

Errington, P.L. 1963. Muskrat populations. Ames, Ia.: Iowa State Univ. Press, 665 pp.

Estes, R.D. 1974. Social organization of the African Bovidae. Pp. 166-205 *in* The behaviour of ungulates and its relation to management (V. Geist and F. Walther, eds.). Internat. Union Conserv. Nature Publ., new series, 24, Vol. 1:1-511.

Estes, R.D., and J. Goddard. 1967. Prey selection and hunting behaviour of the African wild dog. J. Wildlife Mgmt., 31:52-70.

Evans, F.G. 1942. The osteology and relationships of elephant shrews (Macroscelididae). Bull. Amer. Mus. Nat. Hist., 80:85-125.

Ewer, R.F. 1958. Adaptive features of the head of African Suidae. Proc. Zool. Soc. London, 131:135-155.

Ewer, R.F. 1963. Behaviour of the meerkat, *Suricata suricatta* (Schreber). Z. Tier-psychol., 20:570-607.

Ewer, R.F. 1967. The behaviour of the African giant rat *(Cricetomys gambianus* Waterhouse), Z. Tierpsychol., 24:6-79.

Ewer, R.F. 1973. The carnivores. Ithaca, N.Y.: Cornell Univ. Press, 494 pp.

Feist, J.D., and D.R. McCullogh. 1976. Behavior patterns and communication in feral horses. Z. Tierpsychol., 41:337-371.

Fiedler, W. 1956. Übersicht über das System der Primates. Primatologia, 1:1-266.

Fiennes, R., and A. Fiennes. 1968. The natural history of the dog. London: Weidenfeld & Nicolson, 187 pp.

Findley, J.S. 1967. Insectivores and dermopterans. Pp. 87-108 *in* Recent mammals of the world (S. Anderson and J.K. Jones, Jr., eds.). New York: Ronald Press, 453 pp.

Fisher, E.M. 1942. The osteology and myology of the sea otter. Stanford, Ca.: Stanford Univ. Press, 66 pp.

Folk, G.E., Jr., A. Larson, and M.A. Folk. 1976. Physiology of hibernating bears. Pp. 373-380 *in* Bears — their biology and management (Pelton, M.R., J.W. Lentfer, and G.E. Pol, eds.). Internat. Union Conserv. Nature Publ., new series, 40, 467 pp.

Fox, M.W. 1971. Behaviour of wolves, dogs, and related canids. New York: Harper and Row, 220 pp.

Fox, M.W. (ed.). 1975. The wild canids. New York: Van Nostrand Reinhold, 508 pp.

Fox, M.W. 1978. The dog: its domestication and behavior. New York: Garland, 296 pp.

Frädrich, H. 1965. Zur Biologie und Ethologie des Warzenschweines *(Phacochoerus aethiopicus,* Pallus), unter Berucksichtigung des Verhaltens anderer Suiden. Z. Tierpsychol., 22:328-393.

Frädrich, H. 1967. Das Verhalten der Schweine (Suidae, Tayassuidae) und Flusspferde (Hippopotamidae). Handb. Zool., 10(26):1-44.

Frädrich, H. 1974. A comparison of behaviour in the Suidae. Pp. 133-143 *in* The behaviour of ungulates and its relation to management (V. Geist and F. Walther, eds.). Internat. Union Conserv. Nature Publ., new series, 24, Vol. 1:1-511.

Franklin, W.L. 1974. The social behavior of the vicuña. Pp. 477-487 *in* The behaviour of ungulates and its relation to manage-ment (V. Geist and F. Walther, eds.). Internat. Union Conserv. Nature Publ., new series, 24, Vol. 1:1-511.

Fraser, C.F. 1966. Comments on the Del-phinoidea. Pp. 7-31 *in* Whales, dolphins, and porpoises (K.S. Norris, ed.). Berke-ley, Ca.: Univ. California Press, 789 pp.

Friedman, H. 1955. The honey-guides. Bull. U.S. Natl. Mus., 208:1-292.

Frith, H.J., and J.H. Calaby. 1969. Kangaroos. Melbourne: F.W. Cheshire, 209 pp.

Gambaryan, P.P. 1974. How mammals run. Anatomical adaptations. New York: John Wiley & Sons, 367 pp.

Gardner, A.L. 1973. The systematics of the genus Didelphis (Marsupialia: Didel-phidae) in North and Middle America. Spec. Publ. Mus., Texas Tech Univ., 4:1-81.

Gaskin, D.E. 1972. Whales, dolphins, and seals, with special reference to the New Zealand region. New York: St. Martins Press, 200 pp.

Gaskin, D.E. 1976. The evolution, zoogeography and ecology of Cetacea. Ann. Rev. Oceanogr. Marine Biol., 14:247-346.

Gauthier-Pilters, H. 1974. The behaviour and ecology of camels in the Sahara, with special reference to nomadism and water management. Pp. 542-551 in The behaviour of ungulates and its relation to management (V. Geist and F. Walther, eds.). Internat. Union Conserv. Nature Publ., new series, 24, Vol. 2:512-940.

Geist, V. 1963. On the behaviour of the North American moose in British Columbia. Behaviour, 20:377-416.

Geist, V. 1966. Ethological observations on some North American cervids. Zool. Beiträge, 12:219-250.

Geist, V. 1971. Mountain sheep: A study in behavior and evolution. Chicago: Univ. Chicago Press, 383 pp.

Geist, V., and F. Walther (eds.). 1974. The behaviour of ungulates and its relation to management. Internat. Union Conserv. Nature, new series, 24, 2 Vols., 940 pp.

George, W. 1974. Notes on the ecology of gundis (F. Ctenodactylidae) Symp. Zool. Soc. London, 34:143-160.

George, W., and B.J. Weir. 1972. Record chromosome number in a mammal? Nature, New Biol., 236:205-206.

Godfrey, G., and P. Crowcroft. 1960. The life of the mole (Talpa europaea Linnaeus). London: Museum Press, 152 pp.

Goethe, F. 1964. Das Verhalten der Musteliden. Handb. Zool., 10:1-80.

Goldman, E.A. 1950. Raccoons of North and Middle America. No. Amer. Fauna, 60:1-153.

Golani, I. 1969. The golden jackal. Tel Aviv: The Movement Notation Soc., 124 pp.

Gould, E., and J.F. Eisenberg. 1966. Notes on the biology of the Tenrecidae. J. Mamm., 47:660-686.

Gould, E., N.C. Negus, and A. Novick. 1964. Evidence for echolocation in shrews. J. Exp. Zool., 156:19-38.

Gould, S.J. 1974. The origin and function of "bizarre" structures: antler size and skull size in the "Irish elk," Megaloceros giganteus. Evolution, 28:191-220.

Gray, A.P. 1972. Mammalian hybrids. A checklist with bibliography. Edinburgh: Commun. Commonwealth Bureau Animal Breeding and Genet., 10:1-262.

Gregory, W.K., and M. Hellman. 1939. On the evolution and major classification of the civets (Viverridae) and allied fossil and recent Carnivora: a phylogenetic study of the skull and dentition. Proc. Amer. Philos. Soc., 81:309-392.

Griffin, D.R. 1958. Listening in the dark. New Haven, Conn. Yale Univ. Press, 413 pp.

Griffiths, M. 1968. Echidnas. Oxford: Pergamon Press, 282 pp.

Griffiths, M. 1978. The biology of monotremes. New York: Academic Press, 368 pp.

Groves, C.P. 1967. On the rhinoceroses of southeast Asia. Säugetierk. Mitt., 15: 221-237.

Groves, C.P. 1972. Ceratotherium simum. Mamm. Species, 8:1-6.

Groves, C.P. 1974. Horses, asses, and zebras in the wild. Hollywood, Fla.: R. Curtis Books, 192 pp.

Groves, C.P., and F. Kurt. 1972. *Dicerorhinus sumatrensis*. Mamm. Species, 21:1-6.

Guggisberg, C.A.W. 1975. Wild cats of the world. New York: Taplinger Publ. Co., 328 pp.

Hall, E.R. 1951. American weasels. Univ. Kansas Publ., Mus. Nat. Hist., 4:1-466.

Hall, K.R.L., and G.B. Schaller. 1964. Tool-using behaviour of the California sea otter. J. Mamm., 45:287-298.

Haltenorth, T. 1958. Klassifikation der Saügetiere. Handb. Zool., 8(16):1-40.

Haltenorth, T. 1963. Klassifikation der Saügetiere: Artiodactyla. Handb. Zool., 8(32):1-167.

Hamilton, J.E. 1934. The southern sea lion, *Otaria byronia* (de Blainville). Discovery Repts., 8:269-318.

Hamilton, J.E. 1939. A second report on the southern sea lion, *Otaria byronia* (de Blainville). Discovery Repts., 19:121-164.

Hanney, P.W. 1975. Rodents. Their lives and habits. New York: Taplinger Publ. Co., 224 pp.

Harris, C.J. 1968. Otters. A study of the recent Lutrinae. London: Weidenfeld & Nicholson, 397 pp.

Harrison, R.J. (ed.). 1972. The functional anatomy of marine mammals. Vol. 1. New York: Academic Press, 451 pp.

Harrison, R.J. (ed.). 1974. Ibid. Vol. 2. New York: Academic Press, 366 pp.

Harrison, R.J. (ed.). 1977. Ibid. Vol. 3. New York: Academic Press, 428 pp.

Harrison, R.J. et al. (eds.). 1968. Behavior and physiology of pinnipeds. New York: Appleton-Century-Crofts, 441 pp.

Harrison, R.J., and J.E. King. 1965. Marine mammals. London: Hutchinson Univ. Library, 192 pp.

Hartman, C.G. 1952. Possums. Austin, Tex.: Univ. Texas Press, 174 pp.

Hatt, R.T. 1932. The vertebral columns of ricochetal rodents. Bull. Amer. Mus. Nat. Hist., 63:599-738.

Hayman, D.L. 1977. Chromosome number — constancy and variation. Pp. 27-48 in The biology of marsupials (B. Stonehouse and D. Gilmore, eds.). Baltimore: University Park Press, 486 pp.

Heinsohn, G.E. 1966. Ecology and reproduction of the Tasmanian bandicoots (*Perameles gunni* and *Isoodon obesulus*). Univ. California Publ. Zool., 80:1-96

Hendrichs, H., and U. Hendrichs. 1971. Dikdik und Elephanten. Munich: R. Piper, 173 pp.

Herald, E.S., et al. 1969. Blind river dolphin: first side-swimming cetacean. Science, 166:1408-1410.

Herrero, S. (ed.). 1972. Bears — their biology and management. Internat. Union Conserv. Nature Publ., new series, 23, 371 pp.

Herring, S.W., and S.E. Herring. 1974. The superficial masseter and gape in mammals. Amer. Nat., 108:561-576.

Hershkovitz, P. 1955. On the cheek pouches of the tropical American paca, *Agouti paca* (Linnaeus, 1766). Saugetierk. Mitt., 3:67-70.

Hershkovitz, P. 1962. Evolution of Neotropical cricetine rodents. Fieldiana: Zool., Chicago Mus. Nat. Hist., 46:1-524.

Hershkovitz, P. 1966. Catalog of living whales. Bull. U.S. Natl. Mus., 246:1-259.

Hershkovitz, P. 1978. Living New World monkeys (Platyrrhini). Vol. 1. Chicago: Univ. Chicago Press, 1117 pp.

Herter, K. 1938. Die Biologie der europaeischen Igel. Monogr. Wildsauget., 5: 1-222.

Hewer, H.R. 1974. British seals. London: W. Collins Sons & Co. Ltd., 256 pp.

Hildebrand, M. 1964. Comparative morphology of the body skeleton in recent Canidae. Univ. California Publ. Zool., 52:399-470.

Hildebrand, M. 1974. Analysis of vertebrate structure. New York: John Wiley & Sons, 710 pp.

Hill, W.C.O. 1953. Primates. comparative anatomy and taxonomy. 1. Strepsirhini. Edinburgh: Edinburgh Univ. Press, 798 pp.

Hill, W.C.O. 1955. Ibid. 2. Haplorhini. Tarsioidea. Edinburgh: Edinburgh Univ. Press, 347 pp.

Hill, W.C.O. 1957. Ibid. Comparative anatomy and taxonomy. 3. Pithecoidea. Platyrrhini (Families Hapalidae and Callimiconidae). Edinburgh: Edinburgh Univ. Press, 354 pp.

Hill, W.C.O. 1959. The anatomy of *Callimico goeldii* (Thomas). Trans. Amer. Philos. Soc., 49:1-116.

Hill, W.C.O. 1960. Primates. Comparative anatomy and taxonomy. 4. Cebidae, Part A. New York: Wiley-Interscience, 523 pp.

Hill, W.C.O. 1962. Ibid. 5. Cebidae, Part B. New York: Wiley-Interscience, 537 pp.

Hill, W.C.O. 1966. Ibid. 6. Catarrhini. Cercopithecoidea. Cercopithecinae. Edinburgh: Edinburgh Univ. Press, 757 pp.

Hill, C.W.O. 1970. Ibid. 8. Cynopithecinae. *Papio, Mandrillus, Theropithecus.* Edinburgh: Edinburgh Univ. Press, 680 pp.

Hill, C.W.O. 1972. Evolutionary biology of primates. New York: Academic Press, 233 pp.

Hill, C.W.O. 1974. Primates. Comparative anatomy and taxonomy. 7. Cercopithecinae. *Cercocebus, Macaca, Cynopithecus.* Edinburgh: Edinburgh Univ. Press, 934 pp.

Hill, J.E. 1974. A new family genus and species of bat (Mammalia: Chiroptera) from Thailand. Bull. Brit. Mus. (Nat. Hist.), 27:303-336.

Hinton, H.E., and A.M.S. Dunn. 1967. Mongooses. Their natural history and behaviour. Berkeley, Ca.: Univ. California Press, 144 pp.

Hoffstetter, R. 1972. Relationships, origins, and history of the ceboid monkeys and the caviomorph rodents, a modern interpretation. Pp. 323-347 *in* Evolutionary biology (T. Dobzhansky, M.K. Hecht, and W.C. Steere, eds.), Vol. 6. New York: Appleton-Century-Crofts, 445 pp.

Hofmann, R.R. 1973. The ruminant stomach. E. Afr. Monogr. Biol., 2:1-354.

Hoogerwerf, A. 1970. Udjong Kulon: Land of the last Javan rhinoceros. Leiden: E.J. Brill, 512 pp.

Hooper, E.T., and G.G. Musser. 1964. The glans penis in Neotropical cricetines (Family Muridae) with comments on classification of muroid rodents. Misc. Publ. Mus. Zool., Univ. Michigan, 123:1-57.

Hornocker, M.G. 1970. An analysis of mountain lion predation upon mule deer and elk in the Idaho Primitive Area. Wildl. Monogr., 21:1-39.

Horst, R. 1969. Observations on the structure and function of the kidney of the vampire bat *(Desmodus rotundus murinus)*. Pp. 73-83 *in* Physiological systems in semiarid environments. Albuquerque: Univ. New Mexico Press (C.C. Hoff and M.L. Riedesel, eds.)., 293 pp.

Howell, A.B. 1930. Aquatic mammals. Baltimore: Charles C. Thomas, 338 pp.

Howell, A.B. 1944. Speed in animals. Chicago: Univ. Chicago Press, 270 pp.

Howell, A.H. 1938. Revision of the North American ground squirrels, with a classification of the North American Sciuridae. No. Amer. Fauna, 56:1-256.

H.S.H. Prince Rainier III of Monaco, and G.H. Bourne. 1977. Primate conservation. New York: Academic Press, 658 pp.

Hubback, T.R. 1939. The Asiatic two-horned rhinoceros. J. Mamm., 20:1-20.

Huggett, A. St. G., and W.F. Widdas. 1951. The relationship between mammalian foetal weight and conception age. J. Physiol., 207:783-788.

Hungate, R.E. 1975. The rumen microbial ecosystem. Ann. Rev. Ecol. Syst., 6:39-66.

Hunsaker, D. (ed.). 1977a. The biology of marsupials. New York: Academic Press, 537 pp.

Husar, S.L. 1976. Behavioral character displacement: evidence of food partitioning in insectivorous bats. J. Mamm., 57:331-338.

Husar, S.L. 1977. *Trichechus inunguis*. Mamm. Species, 72:1-4.

Husar, S.L. 1978a. *Dugong dugon*. Ibid., 88: 1-7.

Husar, S.L. 1978b. *Trichechus senegalensis*. Ibid., 89:1-3.

Husar, S.L. 1978c. *Trichechus manatus*. Ibid., 93:1-5.

Innis, A.C. 1958. The behaviour of the giraffe, *Giraffa camelopardalis*, in the eastern Transvaal. Proc. Zool. Soc. London, 131: 245-278.

Jacobi, A. 1938. Der Seeotter. Monogr. Wildsäuget., 6:1-93.

Janis, C. 1976. The evolutionary strategy of the Equidae and the origins of rumen and cecal digestion. Evolution, 30:757-774.

Jarvis, J.U.M., and J.B. Sale. 1971. Burrowing and burrow patterns in East African mole-rats *Tachyoryctes*, *Heliophobius* and *Heterocephalus*. J. Zool., 163:451-479.

Jarman, P.J. 1974. The social organization of antelope in relation to their ecology. Behaviour, 48:215-267.

Jay, P.C. (ed.). 1968. Primates. Studies in adaptation and variability. New York: Holt, Rinehart and Winston, 529 pp.

Jenkins, F.A. (ed.). 1974. Primate locomotion. New York: Academic Press, 390 pp.

Jenkins, S.H., and P.E. Busher. 1979. *Castor canadensis*. Mamm. Species, 120:1-8.

Jolly, A. 1966. Lemur behavior. Chicago: Univ. Chicago Press, 187 pp.

Jolly, A. 1972. The evolution of primate behavior. New York: The MacMillan Co., 397 pp.

Kaiser, H.E. 1974. Morphology of the Sirenia. A macroscopic and x-ray atlas of the osteology of recent species. Basel, Switz.: S. Karger, 76 pp.

Kaufmann, J.H. 1962. Ecology and social behaviour of the coati, *Nasua narica,* on Barro Colorado Island, Panama. Univ. California Publ. Zool., 60:95-222.

Kaufmann, J.H. 1974. The ecology and evolution of social organization in the kangaroo family (Macropodidae). Amer. Zool., 14:51-62.

Kean, R.I. 1961. The evolution of marsupial reproduction. Tech. Paper Forest Res. Inst., New Zealand Forest Serv., 35:1-40.

Keast, A. 1977. Historical biogeography of the marsupials. Pp. 69-95 *in* The biology of marsupials (B. Stonehouse and D. Gilmore, eds.). Baltimore: University Park Press, 486 pp.

Keith, L.B. 1963. Wildlife's ten-year cycle. Madison, Wisc.: Univ. Wisconsin Press, 201 pp.

Kellogg, R. 1928. The history of whales — their adaptation to life in the water. Quart. Rev. Biol., 3:29-76, 176-208.

Kellogg, W.N. 1961. Porpoises and sonar. Chicago: Univ. Chicago Press, 177 pp.

Kelsall, J.P. 1968. The migratory barren-ground caribou of Canada. Ottawa: Queen's Printer, 340 pp.

Kenagy, G.J. 1972. Saltbush leaves: excision of hypersaline tissue by a kangaroo rat. Science, 178:1094-1096.

Kenagy, G.J. 1973. Adaptations for leaf eating in the Great Basin kangaroo rat, *Dipodomys microps.* Oecologia, 12: 383-412.

Kenyon, K.W. 1969. The sea otter in the eastern Pacific Ocean. No. Amer. Fauna, 68:1-352.

Kihlstrom, J.E. 1972. Period of gestation and body weight in some placental mammals. Comp. Biochem. Physiol., 43A:673-679.

King, J.A. 1955. Social behavior, social organization, and population dynamics in a black-tailed prairiedog town in the Black Hills of South Dakota. Cont. Lab. Vert. Biol., Univ. Michigan, 67:1-123.

King, J.A. (ed.). 1968. Biology of *Peromyscus* (Rodentia). Spec. Publ., Amer. Soc. Mamm., 2:1-593.

King, J.E. 1956. The monk seals *(Monachus).* Bull. Brit. Mus. (Nat. Hist.), 3:201-256.

King, J.E. 1964. Seals of the world. London: Brit. Mus. (Nat. Hist.), 154 pp.

Kingdon, J. 1971. East African mammals. An atlas of evolution in Africa. New York: Academic Press, Vol. 1:1-446.

Kingdon, J. 1974a. Ibid. New York: Academic Press, Vol. 2A:1-341.

Kingdon, J. 1974b. Ibid. New York: Academic Press, Vol. 2B:342-704.

Kingdon, J. 1977. Ibid. New York: Academic Press, Vol. 3A:1-476.

Kirsch, J.A.W. 1968. Prodromus of the comparative serology of marsupials. Nature, 217:418-420.

Kirsch, J.A.W. 1977. The comparative serology of Marsupialia, and a classification of marsupials. Aust. J. Zool., Suppl. Ser., 52:1-152.

Kirsch, J.A.W. 1977. The classification of marsupials with special reference to karyotypes and serum proteins. Pp. 1-50 *in* The biology of marsupials (D. Hunsaker, ed.). New York: Academic Press, 537 pp.

Kirsch, J.A.W., and J.H. Calaby. 1977. The species of marsupials: an annotated list. Pp. 9-26 in The biology of marsupials (B. Stonehouse and D. Gilmore, eds.). Baltimore: University Park Press, 486 pp.

Kleiman, D.G. 1966. Scent-marking in the Canidae. Symp. Zool. Soc. London, 18: 143-165.

Kleiman, D.G. 1967. Some aspects of social behaviour in the Canidae. Proc. Zool. Soc. London, 18:167-177.

Kleiman, D.G. (ed.). 1977. The biology and conservation of the Callitrichidae. Washington, D.C.: Smithsonian Inst. Press, 354 pp.

Kleiman, D.G., and J.F. Eisenberg. 1973. Comparisons of canid and felid social systems from an evolutionary perspective. Anim. Behav., 21:637-659.

Kleinenberg, S.E., A.V. Yablokov, B.M. Bel'kovich, and M. N. Tarasevich. 1969. Beluga (Delphinapterus leucas). Investigation of the species. Jerusalem: Israel Progrom for Scientific Translations, 376 pp.

Klingel, H. 1967. Soziale Organisation und Verhalten freilebender Steppenzebras. Z. Tierpsychol., 24:580-624.

Klingel, H. 1968. Soziale Organisation und Verhaltensweisen von Hartmann-und Bergzebras (Equus zebra hartmannae und E.z. zebra). Z. Tierpsychol., 25:76-88.

Klingel, H. 1974. A comparison of the social behaviour of the Equidae. Pp. 124-132 in The behaviour of ungulates and its relation to management (V. Geist and F. Walther, eds.). Internat. Union Conserv. Nature Publ., new series, 24, Vol. 1:1-511.

Koford, C.B. 1957. The vicuña and the puna. Ecol. Monogr., 27:153-219.

Kolb, A. 1977. Wie erkennen sich Mutter und Junges des Mausohrs, Myotis myotis, bei der Ruckkehr vom Jagdflüg wieder? Z. Tierpsychol., 44:423-431.

Koopman, K.F., and J.K. Jones, Jr., 1970. Classification of bats. Pp.. 22-28 in About bats (B.H. Slaughter and D.W. Walton, eds.). Dallas: So. Methodist Univ. Press, 339 pp.

Krott, P. 1959. Der Vielfrass (Gulo gulo L. 1758). Monogr. Wildsäuget., 13:1-159.

Krutzsch, P.H. 1954. North American jumping mice (genus Zapus). Univ. Kansas Publ., Mus. Nat. Hist., 7:349-472.

Kruuk, H. 1972. The spotted hyaena. Chicago: Univ. Chicago Press, 335 pp.

Kruuk, H. 1975. Hyaena. Oxford: Oxford Univ. Press, 80 pp.

Kruuk, H., and W.A. Sands. 1972. The aardwolf (Proteles cristatus Sparrman 1783) as predator of termites. E. Afr. Wildl. J., 10:211-227.

Kuhme, W. 1965. Freilandstudien zur Socialogie des Hyänenhundes Lycaon pictus lupinus Thomas 1902. Z. Tierpsychol., 22:495-541.

Kulu, D.D. 1972. Evolution and cytogenetics. Pp. 503-527 in Mammals of the sea. Biology and medicine (S.H. Ridgeway, ed.). Springfield, Ill.: Charles C. Thomas, 812 pp.

Kunz, T.H. 1973. Resource utilization: temporal and spatial components of bat activity in central Iowa. J. Mamm., 54: 14-32.

Kurt, F. 1974. Remarks on the social structure and ecology of the Ceylon elephant in the Yala National Park. Pp. 618-634 in The behaviour of ungulates and its relation to management (V. Geist and F. Walther, eds.). Internat. Union Conserv. Nature Publ., new series, 24, Vol. 2:512-940.

Landry, S.O. 1957. The interrelationships of the New and Old World hystricomorph rodents. Univ. California Publ. Zool., 56:1-118.

Landry, S.O. 1970. Rodents as omnivores. Quart. Rev. Biol., 45:351-372.

Lavocat, R. 1974. What is an hystricomorph? Symp. Zool. Soc. London, 34:7-20.

Laws, R.M. 1970. Elephants as agents of habitat and landscape change in East Africa. Oikos, 21:1-15.

Laws, R.M. 1974. Behaviour, dynamics and management of elephant populations. Pp. 513-529 in The behaviour of ungulates and its relation to management (V. Geist and F. Walther, eds.). Internat. Union Conserv. Nature Publ., new series, 24, Vol. 2:512-940.

Laws, R.M., I.S.C. Parker, and R.C.B. Johnstone. 1975. Elephants and their habitats. The ecology of elephants in North Bunyoro, Uganda. London: Oxford Univ. Press, 376 pp.

LeBoeuf, B.J., and K.T. Briggs. 1977. The cost of living in a seal harem. Mammalia, 41:168-195.

Lee, A.K., A.J. Bradley, and R.W. Braithwaite. 1977. Corticosteroid levels and male mortality in Antechinus stuarti. Pp. 209-220 in The biology of marsupials (B. Stonehouse and D. Gilmore, eds.). Baltimore: University Park Press, 486 pp.

Leuthold, W. 1977. African ungulates. A comparative review of ethology and behavioral ecology. New York: Springer-Verlag, 307 pp.

Leyhausen, P. 1956. Das Verhalten der Katzen. Handb. Zool., 8:1-34.

Lillegraven, J.A. 1974. Biogeographical considerations of the marsupial-placental dichotomy. Ann. Rev. Ecol. Syst., 5:263-283.

Lillegraven, J.A. 1976. Biological considerations of the marsupial-placental dichotomy. Evolution, 29:707-722.

Linsdale, J.M., and L.P. Tevis, Jr. 1951. The dusky-footed woodrat. Berkeley, Ca.: Univ. California Press, 664 pp.

Linsdale, J.M., and P.Q. Tomich. 1953. A herd of mule deer. Berkeley, Ca.: Univ. California Press, 567 pp.

Llanos, A.C., and J.A. Crespo. 1952. Ecologia de la vizcacha ("Lagostomus maximus" Blainv.) en el nordeste de la provincia de Entre Rios. Rev. Invest. Agricola, Buenos Aires, 6:289-378.

Lock, J.M. 1972. The effects of hippopotamus grazing on grasslands. J. Ecol., 60:445-467.

Lotze, J.H., and S. Anderson. 1979. Procyon lotor. Mamm. Species, 119:1-8.

Lorenz, R. 1972. Management and reproduction of the Goeldi's monkey Callimico goeldii (Thomas, 1904), Callimiconidae, Primates. Pp. 92-109 in Saving the lion marmoset (D.D. Bridgewater, ed.). Proc. Wild Animal Propagation Trust Golden Lion Marmoset Conf.

Luckett, W.P. (ed.). 1974. Reproductive biology of primates. Contrib. Primatol., 3:1-288.

Lyon, M.W. 1913. Tree shrews: an account of the mammalian family Tupaiidae. Proc. U.S. Natl. Mus., 45:1-188.

MacClintock, D. 1970. Squirrels of North America. New York: Van Nostrand Reinhold Co., 184 pp.

MacMillen, R.E. 1972. Water economy of nocturnal desert rodents. Symp. Zool. Soc. London, 31:147-174.

Maglio, V.J. 1973. Origin and evolution of the Elephantidae. Trans. Amer. Philos. Soc., 63:1-149.

Mansfield, A.W. 1958. The biology of the Atlantic walrus *Odobenus rosmarus* in the eastern Canadian Arctic. Bull. Fish. Res. Brd. Canada, 653:1-146.

Marlow, B.J. 1967. Australian seals. Australian Nat. Hist., 15:209-293.

Marlow, B.J. 1975. The comparative behavior of the Australian sea lions *Neophoca cinerea* and *Phocarctos hookerii* (Pinnipedia: Otariidae). Mammalia, 39:159-230.

McCullogh, D.R. 1969. The Tule elk. Univ. California Publ. Zool., 88:1-209.

McDowell S.B. 1958. The Greater Antillean insectivores. Bull. Amer. Mus. Nat. Hist., 115:115-214.

McHugh, T. 1958. Social behaviour of the American buffalo. Zoologica, 43:1-40.

McKay, G.M. 1973. Behavior and ecology of the Asiatic elephant in southeastern Ceylon. Smithsonian Contrib. Zool., 125:1-113.

McLaren, I.A. 1960. Are the Pinnipedia biphyletic? Syst. Zool., 9:18-28.

McLaren, I.A. 1958. The biology of the ringed seal (*Phoca hispida*) in the eastern Canadian Arctic. Bull. Fish. Res. Brd. Canada, 118:1-97.

McLaughlin, C.A. 1967. Aplodontoid, sciuroid, geomyoid, castoroid, and anomaluroid rodents. Pp. 210-225 *in* Recent mammals of the world (S. Anderson and J.K. Jones, Jr., eds.). New York: Ronald Press, 453 pp.

McNab, B.K. 1966. The metabolism of fossorial rodents: a study of convergence. Ecology, 47:712-733.

McNab, B.K. 1978. The comparative energetics of Neotropical marsupials. J. Comp. Physiol., 62A:813-820.

McNab, B.K. 1979. Climatic adaptation in the energetics of heteromyid rodents. Comp. Biochem, Physiol., 62A: 813-820.

Mech, L.D. 1970. The wolf: the ecology and behavior of an endangered species. Garden City, N.Y.: The Natural History Press, 384 pp.

Mellanby, K. 1971. The mole. London: William Collins Sons & Co., 159 pp.

Melton, D.A. 1976. The biology of aardvark (Tubulidentata — Orycteropodidae). Mammal Rev., 6:75-88.

Miller, G.S., Jr. 1907. The families and genera of bats. Proc. U.S. Natl. Mus., 57: 1-281.

Miller, G.S., Jr. 1923. The telescoping of the cetacean skull. Smithsonian Misc. Coll., 76:1-72.

Misonne, X. 1969. African and Indo-Australian Muridae. Evolutionary trends. Ann. Sci. Zool., Mus. Royal L'Afrique Central, 172:1-219.

Mitchell, E.D. 1967. Controversy over diphyly in pinnipeds. Syst. Zool., 16:350-351.

Mitchell, E.D. 1975. Parallelism and convergence in the evolution of Otariidae and Phocidae. Pp. 12-26 *in* Biology of the seal K. Ronald, and A.W. Mansfield, eds.). Rapp. P.-v. Réun. Conserv. int. Explor. Mer, 169:1-557.

Mitchell, E.D. 1975. Review of biology and fisheries for smaller cetaceans. J. Fish. Res. Brd. Canada, 32:875-1240.

Mitchell, E.D., and R.H. Tedford. 1973. The Enaliarctinae. A new group of extinct aquatic Carnivora and a consideration of the origin of the Otariidae. Bull. Amer. Mus. Nat. Hist., 151:201-284.

Moehres, F.P. 1953. Über die Ultraschallorientierung der Hufeisennasen (Chiroptera—Rhinolophidae). Z. Vergl. Physiol., 34:547-588.

Mohr, E. 1941. Schwanzverlust und Schwanzregeneration bei Nagetieren. Zool. Anzeig., 135:49-65.

Mohr, E. 1957. Sirenen oder Seekuhe. Die neue Brehm-Bucherei. Wittenberg Lutherstadt: A. Ziemsen Verlag, 61 pp.

Mohr, E. 1960. Wilde Schweine. Die neue Brehm-Bucherei. Wittenberg Lutherstadt: A. Ziemsen Verlag.

Moore, J.C. 1959. Relationships among squirrels of the Sciurinae. Bull. Amer. Mus. Nat. Hist., 118:153-206.

Moore, J.C. 1961. Geographic variation in some reproductive characteristics of diurnal squirrels. Bull. Amer. Mus. Nat. Hist., 122:1-32.

Moore, J.C., and G.H.H. Tate. 1965. A study of the diurnal squirrels, Sciurinae, of the Indian and Indochinese subregions. Fieldiana: Zool., Chicago Nat. Hist. Mus. 48:1-351.

Moors, P.J. 1977. Studies of the metabolism, food consumption and assimilation efficiency of a small carnivore, the weasel (Mustela nivalis). Oecologia, 27:185-202.

Morris, D. 1962. The behavior of the green acouchi (Myoprocta pratti) with special reference to scatter hoarding. Proc. Zool. Soc. London, 139:701-732.

Morris, R., and D. Morris. 1966. Men and apes. London: Hutchinson and Co., 271 pp.

Moynihan, M. 1976. The New World primates. Princeton, N.J.: Princeton Univ. Press, 262 pp.

Murie, A. 1944. The wolves of Mt. McKinley. U.S. Natl. Park Serv. Fauna Series, 5:1-238.

Murie, O.J. 1951. The elk of North America. Harrisburg, Pa.: The Stackpole Co., 376 pp.

Myers, P. 1978. Sexual dimorphism in size of vespertilionid bats. Amer. Nat., 112:701-711.

Napier, J.R., and P.H. Napier, 1967. A handbook of living primates. New York: Academic Press, 456 pp.

Napier, J.R., and P.H. Napier (eds.). 1970. Old World monkeys. Evolution, systematics, and behavior. New York: Academic Press, 660 pp.

Neal, E.G. 1977. Badgers. Poole, England: Blandford Press, 321 pp.

Norris, K.S. (ed.). 1966. Whales, dolphins, and porpoises. Berkeley, Ca.: Univ. California Press, 789 pp.

Nungesser, W.C., and E.W. Pfeiffer. 1965. Water balance and maximum concentrating capacity in the primitive rodent, Aplodontia rufa. Comp. Biochem. Physiol., 14:289-297.

O'Gara, B.W., and G. Matson. 1975. Growth and casting of horns by pronghorns and exfoliation of horns by bovids. J. Mamm., 56:829-846.

Osborn, H.F. 1936, 1942. Proboscidea. A monograph of the discovery, evolution, migration and extinction of the mastodonts and elephants of the world. New York: Amer. Mus. Nat. Hist., 2 Vols.

Osgood, W.H. 1921. A monographic study of the American marsupial, Caenolestes. Zool. Ser., Field Mus. Nat. Hist., 10:1-156.

Owen-Smith, N. 1974. The social system of the white rhinoceros. Pp. 341-355 *in* The behaviour of ungulates and its relation to management (V. Geist and F. Walther, eds.). Internat. Union Conserv. Nature Publ., new series, 24, Vol. 1:1-511.

Packard, R.L. 1967. Octodontoid, bathyergoid, and ctenodactyloid rodents. Pp. 273-290 *in* Recent mammals of the world. (S. Anderson and J. K. Jones, Jr., eds.) New York: Ronald Press, 453 pp.

Patterson, J.T. 1913. Polyembryonic development in Tatusia novemcincta. J. Morph., 24:559-683.

Pearson, O.P. 1948. Life history of mountain viscachas in Peru. J. Mamm., 29:345-374.

Pearson, O.P. 1949. Reproduction of a South American rodent, the mountain viscacha. Amer. J. Anat., 84:143-174.

Pearson, O.P. 1960. Biology of the subterranean rodents, *Ctenomys*, in Peru. Mem. del Museo de Hist. "Javier Prado", 9:1-56.

Pelton, M.R., J.W. Lentfer, and G.E. Polk (eds.). 1976. Bears — their biology and management. Internat. Union Conserv. Nature Publ., new series, 40, 467 pp.

Peterson, R.L. 1955. North American moose. Toronto: Univ. Toronto Press, 280 pp.

Peterson, R.S. 1968. Social behavior of pinnipeds with particular reference to the northern fur seal. Pp. 3-53 *in* The behavior and physiology of pinnipeds (R.J. Harrison et al., eds.). New York: Appleton-Century-Crofts, 441 pp.

Peterson, R.S., and G.A. Bartholomew. 1967. The natural history and behavior of the California sea lion. Spec. Publ., Amer. Soc. Mamm., 1:1-79.

Petter, J.J. 1977. The aye-aye. Pp. 37-57 *in* Primate conservation (H.S.H. Prince Rainier III of Monaco and G.H. Bourne, eds.). New York: Academic Press, 658 pp.

Pilleri, G. (ed.). 1969-1978. Investigations on Cetacea. Vols. 1-9. Berne, Switz.: Benteli Ag.

Pocock, R.I. 1910. On the specialized cutaneous glands of ruminant Artiodactyla. Proc. Zool. Soc. London, 1910: 840-986.

Pocock, R.I. 1914. On the feet and other external features of the Canidae and Ursidae. Ibid., 1914: 913-941.

Pocock, R.I. 1915a. On the feet and glands and other external characteristics of the Viverrinae, with the description of a new genus. Ibid., 1915:131-149.

Pocock, R.I. 1915b. On the feet and glands and other external characters of the paradoxurine genera *Paradoxurus, Arctictis, Arctogalidia,* and *Nandinia*. Ibid., 1915:387-412.

Pocock, R.I. 1916. On the external characters of the mongooses (Mungotidae). Ibid., 1916:349-374.

Pocock, R.I. 1917. The classification of existing Felidae. Ann. Mag. Nat. Hist., series 8, 20:329-350.

Pocock, R.I. 1918. On some external characters of ruminant Artiodactyla. Parts 1-6. Ann. Mag. Nat. Hist., series 9, 1:426-435, 2:125-144, 214-225, 367-374, 440-448, 449-459.

Pocock, R.I. 1921a. The external characters and classification of the Procyonidae. Proc. Zool. Soc. London, 1921:389-422.

Pocock, R.I. 1921b. On the external characters and classification of the Mustelidae. Ibid., 1921:803-807.

Pocock, R.I. 1923. The classification of the Sciuridae. Ibid., 1923:209-246.

Pocock, R.I. 1924. The external characters of the South American edentates. Ibid., 1924:983-1031.

Pocock, R.I. 1925. On the external characters of the lagomorph rodents. Ibid., 1925: 669-700.

Pocock, R.I. 1951. Catalogue of the genus *Felis*. Norwich, England: Jarrold & Sons, 187 pp.

Prakash, I., and P.K. Ghosh. 1975. Rodents in desert environments. The Hague: Dr. W. Junk b.v., Publ., 624 pp.

Prior, R. 1968. The roe deer of Cranborne Chase. London: Oxford Univ. Press, 222 pp.

Pucek, Z. 1970. Seasonal and age change in shrews as an adaptive process. Symp. Zool. Soc. London, 26:189-207.

Quimby, D.C. 1951. The life history and ecology of the jumping mouse, *Zapus*. Ecol. Monogr., 21:61-95.

Radinsky, L.B. 1963. Origin and early evolution of North American Tapiroidea. Bull. Peabody Mus., Yale Univ., 17:1-106.

Radinsky, L.B. 1965. Evolution of the tapiroid skeleton from *Heptodon* to *Tapirus*. Bull. Mus. Comp. Zool., 134:69-106.

Radinsky, L.B. 1966. The adaptive radiation of the phenacodontid condylarths and the origin of the Perissodactyla. Evolution, 20:408-417.

Radinsky, L.B. 1969. The early evolution of the Perissodactyla. Evolution, 23:308-328.

Ralls, K. 1976. Mammals in which females are larger than males. Quart. Rev. Biol. 51:245-276.

Rasa, O.A.E. 1977. Ethology and sociology of the dwarf mongoose *(Helogale undulata rufula)*. Z. Tierpsychol., 43:337-406.

Rathbun, G.B. In press. Ecology and social structure of elephant-shrews. Z. Tierpsychol., Adv. Ethol. Suppl.

Ray, G.C., and W.A. Watkins. 1975. Social function of underwater sounds in the walrus *Odobenus rosmarus*. Pp. 524-526 *in* Biology of the seal (K. Ronald and A.W. Mansfield, eds.). Rapp. P.-v Réun. Conserv. int. Explor. Mer, 169:1-557.

Reinhart, R.H. 1959. A review of the Sirenia and Desmostylia. Univ. California Publ. Geol. Sci., 36:1-145.

Repenning, C.A. 1967. Subfamilies and genera of the Soricidae. Geol. Surv. Prof. Paper, 565:1-74.

Repenning, C.A., and R.H. Tedford. 1977. Otarioid seals of the Neogene. Geol. Surv. Prof. Paper, 992:1-93.

Rice, D.W. 1967. Cetaceans. Pp. 291-324 *in* Recent mammals of the world (S. Anderson and J.K. Jones, Jr., eds.). New York: Ronald Press, 453 pp.

Rice, D.W. 1977. A list of the marine mammals of the world. NOAA Tech. Rept., NMFS SSRF-711: 1-15.

Rice, D.W., and A.A. Wolman. 1971. The life history and ecology of the gray whale *(Eschrichtius robustus)*. Spec. Publ., Amer. Soc. Mamm., 3:1-142.

Ride, W.D.L. 1964. A review of Australian fossil marsupials. J. Royal Soc. West. Australia, 47:97-131.

Ride, W.D.L. 1970. A guide to the native mammals of Australia. Melbourne: Oxford Univ. Press, 249 pp.

Ridgeway, S.H. (ed.). 1972. Mammals of the sea. Biology and medicine. Springfield, Ill.: Charles C. Thomas, 812 pp.

Roe, F.G. 1951. The North American buffalo. A critical study of the species in its wild state. Toronto: Univ. Toronto Press, 957 pp.

Romer, A.S. 1966. Vertebrate paleontology. Chicago: Univ. Chicago Press, 468 pp.

Ronald, K., and A.W. Mansfield (eds.). 1975. Biology of the seal. Rapp. P.-v Réun. Conserv. int. Explor. Mer, 169:1-557.

Rood, J.P. 1970. Ecology and social behavior of the desert cavy (Microcavia australis). Amer. Midland Nat., 83:415-454.

Rosenblum, L.A., and R.W. Cooper. 1968. The squirrel monkey. New York: Academic Press, 451 pp.

Rosevear, D.R. 1969. The rodents of West Africa. London: Brit. Mus. (Nat. Hist.), 604 pp.

Rosevear, D.R. 1974. The carnivores of West Africa. London: Brit. Mus. (Nat. Hist.), 548 pp.

Rowlands, I.W. (ed.). 1966. Comparative biology of marsupials. Symp. Zool. Soc. London, 15:1-559.

Rowlands, I.W., and B.J. Weir (eds.). 1974. The biology of hystricomorph rodents. Ibid., 34:1-482.

Rudnai, J.A. 1973. The social life of the lion. A study of the behavior of wild lions (Panthera leo massaica [Newman]) in Nairobi National Park, Kenya. Wallingford, Pa.: Washington Square East Publ., 122 pp.

Russell, E.M. 1974. The biology of kangaroos (Marsupialia — Macropodidae). Mammal Rev., 4:1-59.

Russel, R.J. 1968. Evolution and classification of the pocket gophers of the subfamily Geomyinae. Univ. Kansas Publ., Mus. Nat. Hist., 16:473-579.

Sanborn, C.C. 1937. American bats of the subfamily Emballonurinae. Zool. Ser., Field Mus. Nat. Hist., 20:321-354.

Sarich, V.M. 1973. The giant panda is a bear. Nature, 245:218-220.

Schaller, G.B. 1963. The mountain gorilla. Chicago: Univ. Chicago Press, 431 pp.

Schaller, G.B. 1967. The deer and the tiger. A study of wildlife in India. Chicago: Univ. Chicago Press, 370 pp.

Schaller, G.B. 1972. The Serengeti lion. A study of predator-prey relations. Chicago: Univ. Chicago Press, 480 pp.

Schaller, G.B. 1977. Mountain monarchs. Wild sheep and goats of the Himalaya. Chicago: Univ. Chicago Press, 425 pp.

Scheffer, V.B. 1958. Seals, sea lions, and walruses. Stanford, Ca.: Stanford Univ. Press, 179 pp.

Schenkel, R., and E.M. Lang. 1969. Das Verhalten der Nashorner. Handb. Zool., 10:1-56.

Schenkel, R., and L. Schenkel-Hulliger. 1969. Ecology and behaviour of the black rhinoceros (Diceros bicornis L.). A field study. Hamburg: Verlag P. Parey, 101 pp.

Schevill, W.E., W.A. Watkins, and G.C. Ray. 1966. Analysis of underwater *Odobenus* calls with remarks on the development and function of the pharyngeal pouches. Zoologica, 51:103-106.

Schliemann, H., and B. Maas. 1978. *Myzopoda aurita.* Mamm. Species, 116:1-2.

Schmidt-Nielsen, K. 1964. Desert animals. Physiological problems of heat and water. Oxford: Oxford Univ. Press, 277 pp.

Schmidt-Nielsen, K. 1975. Animal physiology. London: Cambridge Univ. Press, 699 pp.

Schmidt-Nielsen, K., W.L. Bretz, and C.R. Taylor. 1970. Panting in dogs: unidirectional air flow over evaporative surfaces. Science, 169:1102-1104.

Schmidt-Nielsen, K., F.R. Hainsworth, and D.E. Murrish. 1970. Counter-current heat exchange in the respiratory passages: effects on water and heat balance. Resp. Physiol., 9:263-276.

Schultz, A.H. 1969. The life of primates. New York: Universe Books, 281 pp.

Scott, J.P. 1968. Evolution and domestication of the dog. Pp. 243-275 in Evolutionary biology, Vol. 2 (T. Dobzhansky, M.K. Hecht, and W.C. Steere, eds.). New York: Appleton-Century-Crofts, 452 pp.

Scott, J.P., and J.L. Fuller. 1965. Genetics and social behavior of the dog. Chicago: Univ. Chicago Press, 468 pp.

Scott, W.B. 1940. Artiodactyla. Pp. 363-746 in The mammalian fauna of the White River Oligocene (W.B. Scott and G.L. Jepsen, eds.). Trans. Amer. Philos. Soc., 28:1-980.

Scott, W.B. 1941. Perissodactyla. Pp. 747-980 in The mammalian fauna of the White River Oligocene (W.B. Scott and G.L. Jepsen, eds.). Ibid., 28:1-980.

Setchell, B.P. 1977. Reproduction in male marsupials. Pp. 411-457 in The biology of marsupials (B. Stonehouse and D. Gilmore, eds.). Baltimore: University Park Press, 486 pp.

Sharman, G.B. 1970. The reproductive physiology of marsupials. Science, 167: 1221-1228.

Shotwell, J.A. 1958. Evolution and biogeography of aplodontid and mylagaulid rodents. Evolution, 12:451-484.

Shufeldt, R.W. 1911. The skeleton in the flying lemurs, Galeopteridae. Philippine J. Sci., 6:139-211.

Sikes, S.K. 1971. The natural history of the African elephant. New York: American Elsevier Publ. Co., 397 pp.

Simmons, J.A., M.B. Fenton, and M.J. O'Farrell. 1979. Echolocation and pursuit of prey by bats. Science, 203:16-21.

Simpson, G.G. 1932. Fossil Sirenia of Florida and the evolution of the Sirenia. Bull. Amer. Mus. Nat. Hist., 59:419-503.

Simpson, G.G. 1941. Large Pleistocene felines of North America. Amer. Mus. Novitates, 1118:1-6.

Simpson, G.G. 1945. The principles of classification and a classification of mammals. Bull. Amer. Mus. Nat. Hist., 85:1-350.

Simpson, G.G. 1951. Horses. New York: Oxford Univ. Press, 247 pp.

Simpson, G.G. 1974. Chairman's introduction: taxonomy. Pp. 1-5 in The biology of hystricomorph rodents (I.W. Rowlands and B.J. Weir, eds.). Symp. Zool. Soc. London, 34:1-482.

Sinclair, A.R.E. 1977. The African buffalo. A study of resource limitation of populations. Chicago: Univ. Chicago Press, 355 pp.

Singer, R., and E.L. Boné. 1960. Modern giraffes and the fossil giraffids of Africa. Ann. So. Afr. Mus., 45:375-548.

Sivertsen, E. 1941. On the biology of the harp seal, *Phoca groenlandica* Erxl. Hvalradets Skrifter, 26:1-166.

Slaughter, B.H., and D.W. Walton (eds.). 1970. About bats. Dallas, Tex.: So. Methodist Univ. Press, 399 pp.

Slijper, E.J. 1936. Die Cetaceen, vergleichend-anatomisch und systematisch. Capita Zool., 7:1-590.

Slijper, E.J. 1962. Whales. London: Hutchinson & Co. Ltd., 475 pp.

Slijper, E.J. 1976. Whales and dolphins. Ann Arbor: Univ. Michigan Press, 170 pp.

Small, G.L. 1971. The blue whale. New York: Columbia Univ. Press, 248 pp.

Smith, J.D. 1972. Systematics of the chiropteran family Mormoopidae. Misc. Publ. Mus. Nat. Hist., Univ. Kansas, 56:1-132.

Smith, J.D. 1976. Chiropteran evolution. Pp. 49-69 *in* Biology of bats of the family Phyllostomatidae, Part 1 (R.J. Baker et al., eds.). Spec. Publ. Mus., Texas Tech Univ., 10:1-218.

Smythe, N. 1978. The natural history of the Central American agouti *(Dasyprocta punctata).* Smithsonian Contrib. Zool., 257:1-52.

Smythe, D.R., and C.M. Philpott. 1968. A field study of the rabbit bandicoot, *Macrotis lagotis,* Marsupialia,

from central Western Australia. Trans. Roy. Soc. So. Australia, 92:3-14.

Sonntag, C.F. 1921. A contribution to the anatomy of the three-toed sloth *(Bradypus tridactylus).* Proc. Zool. Soc. London, 1921:157-177.

Sonntag, C.F. 1925. A monograph of *Orycteropus afer.* I. Anatomy except the nervous system, skin, and skeleton. Proc. Zool. Soc. London, 1925:331-437.

Sonntag, C.F., and H.H. Woollard. 1925. A monograph of *Orycteropus afer.* 2. Nervous system, skin, and skeleton. Ibid., 1925:1185-1235.

Sowls, L.K. 1974. Social behaviour of the collared peccary *Dicotyles tajacu* (L.). Pp. 144-165 *in* The behaviour of ungulates and its relation to management (V. Geist and F. Walther, eds.). Internat. Union Conserv. Nature Publ., new series, 24, Vol. 1:1-511.

Spinage, C.A. 1973. A review of ivory exploitation and elephant population trends in Africa. E. Afr. Wildl. J., 11:281-289.

Stains, H.J. 1967. Carnivores and pinnipeds. Pp. 325-354 *in* Recent mammals of the world (S. Anderson and J.K. Jones, Jr., eds.). New York: Ronald Press, 453 pp.

Starrett, A. 1967. Hystricoid, erethizontoid, cavioid, and chinchilloid rodents. Pp. 254-290 *in* Recent mammals of the world (S. Anderson and J.K. Jones, Jr., eds.). New York: Ronald Press, 453 pp.

Stirton, R.A. 1940. The phylogeny of the North American Equidae. Bull. Dept. Geol. Sci., Univ. California, 25:165-197.

Stodart, E. 1977. Breeding and behaviour of Australian bandicoots. Pp. 179-191 in The biology of marsupials (B. Stonehouse and D. Gilmore, eds.). Baltimore: University Park Press, 486 pp.

Stonehouse, B., and D. Gilmore (eds.). 1977. The biology of marsupials. Baltimore: University Park Press, 486 pp.

Stumpke, H. 1967. The snouters. Form and life of the rhinogrades. New York: The Natural History Press, 92 pp.

Taber, F.W. 1945. Contribution on the life history and ecology of the nine-banded armadillo. J. Mamm., 16:211-226.

Taber, R.D., and R.F. Dasmann. 1958. The black-tailed deer of the chaparral. Its life history and management in the north coast range of California. Game Bull., California Dept. Fish Game, 8:1-163.

Talbot, L.M. 1960. A look at threatened species. Oryx, 5:153-294.

Tate, G.H.H. 1933. A systematic revision of the marsupial genus Marmosa. Bull. Amer. Mus. Nat. Hist., 66:1-250.

Tate, G.H.H. 1948a. Results of the Archbold expeditions. No. 59. Studies on the anatomy and phylogeny of the Macropodidae (Marsupialia). Bull. Amer. Mus. Nat. Hist., 91:233-352.

Tate, G.H.H. 1948b. Results of the Archbold expeditions. No. 60. Studies in the Peramelidae (Marsupialia). Ibid., 92:313-346.

Tate, G.H.H. 1951. The wombats (Marsupialia, Phascolomyidae). Amer. Mus. Novitates, 1525:1-18.

Tattersall, I., and R.W. Sussman (eds.). 1975. Lemur biology. New York: Plenum Press, 365 pp.

Taylor, W.P. 1918. Revision of the rodent genus Aplodontia. Univ. California Publ. Zool., 17:435-504.

Taylor, W.P. (ed.). 1956. The deer of North America. Harrisburg, Pa.: The Stackpole Co., 668 pp.

Tedford, R.H. 1976. Relationship of pinnipeds to other carnivores (Mammalia). Syst. Zool., 25:363-374.

Thomas, S.P., and R.A. Suthers. 1972. The physiology and energetics of bat flight. J. Exp. Biol., 57:317-335.

Thorington, R.W., Jr., and P.G. Haltne (eds.). 1976. Neotropical primates: field studies and conservation. Washington, D.C.: Natl. Acad. Sci., 135 pp.

Troughton, E. 1957. Furred mammals of Australia. Sixth edition, Sydney: Angus and Robertson, 376 pp.

Turner, D.C. 1975. The vampire bat. Baltimore, Md.: Johns Hopkins Univ. Press, 145 pp.

Twigg, G.I. 1978. The role of rodents in plague dissemination: a worldwide review. Mammal Rev., 8:77-110.

Tyndale-Biscoe, D.H. 1973. Life of marsupials. New York: American Elsevier, 254 pp.

Van Deusen, H.M., and J.K. Jones, Jr. 1967. Marsupials. Pp. 61-86 in Recent mammals of the world (S. Anderson and J.K. Jones, Jr., eds.). New York: Ronald Press, 453 pp.

Van Gelder, R.G. 1977. Mammalian hybrids and generic limits. Amer. Mus. Novitates, 2635:1-25.

Van Gelder, R.G. 1978. A review of canid classification. Amer. Mus. Novitates, 2646:1-10.

van Lawick-Goodall, J. 1968. The behaviour of free-living chimpanzees in the Gombe Stream area. Anim. Behav. Monogr., 1:161-311.

Vas-Ferriera, R. 1975. Behavior of the southern sea lion, *Otaria flavescens* (Shaw) in the Uruguayan Islands. Pp. 219-227 *in* Biology of the seal (K. Ronald and A.W. Mansfield, eds.). Rapp. P. -v Réun. Conserv. int. Explor. Mer, 169:1-557.

Vaughan, T.A. 1966. Morphology and flight characteristics of molossid bats. J. Mamm., 47:249-260.

Vaughan, T.A. 1970a. The skeletal system. Pp. 97-138 *in* The biology of bats (W.A. Wimsatt, ed.). New York: Academic Press, 406 pp.

Vaughan, T.A. 1970b. The muscular system. Pp. 139-194 *in* The biology of bats (W.A. Wimsatt, ed.). New York: Academic Press, 406 pp.

Vaughan, T.A. 1970c. Flight patterns and aerodynamics. Pp. 195-216 *in* The biology of bats (W.A. Wimsatt, ed.). New York: Academic Press, 406 pp.

Vaughan, T.A. 1978. Mammalogy. Second ed. Philadelphia: W.B. Saunders Co., 522 pp.

Verheyen, R. 1954. Exploration du Parc National Albert. Monographie ethologique de l'hippopotame *(Hippopotamus amphibius* Linné). Brussels: Inst. Parcs Nat. Congo Belge, 91 pp.

Virchow, H. 1935. Der Gebiss von *Orycteropus aethiopicus*. Z. Morph. Anthro., 34:413-435.

Walker, E.P., et al. 1975. Mammals of the world. Third ed. (J.L. Paradiso, ed.). Baltimore: The Johns Hopkins Univ. Press, 1500 pp.

Walls, G.L. 1942. The vertebrate eye and its adaptive radiation. Bull. Cranbrook Inst. Sci., 19:1-785.

Waring, H., R.J. Moir, and C.H. Tyndale-Biscoe. 1966. Comparative physiology of marsupials. Adv. Comp. Physiol. Biochem., 2:237-376.

Watson, D.M.S. 1946. The evolution of the Proboscidea. Biol. Rev., 21:15-29.

Weir, B.J. 1971. The reproductive organs of the female plains viscacha, *Lagostomus aguti*. J. Reprod. Fert., 25:365-373.

Weir, B.J. 1974a. Reproductive characteristics of hystricomorph rodents. Symp. Zool. Soc. London, 34:265-301.

Weir, B.J. 1974b. Notes on the origin of the domestic guinea-pig. Symp. Zool. Soc. London, 34:437-446.

Wemmer, C.M. 1977. Comparative ethology of the large-spotted genet *(Genetta tigrina)* and some related viverrids. Smithsonian Contrib. Zool., 239:1-93.

Wetzel, R.M., R.E. Dubos, R.L. Martin, and P. Myers. 1975. *Catagonus*, an extinct peccary, alive in Paraguay. Science, 189:379-381.

Whitaker, J.O., Jr. 1963. A study of the meadow jumping mouse, *Zapus hudsonius* (Zimmerman), in central New York. Ecol. Monogr., 33:215-254.

Whitehead, G.K. 1972. Deer of the world. New York: Viking Press, 194 pp.

Wilson, D.E. 1978. *Thyroptera discifera*. Mamm. Species, 104:1-3.

Wilson, D.E., and J.S. Findley. 1977. *Thyroptera tricolor.* Mamm. Species, 71:1-3.

Wimsatt, W.A. (ed.). 1970a. Biology of bats. Vol. 1. New York: Academic Press, 406 pp.

Wimsatt, W.A. (ed.). 1970b. Ibid. Vol. 2, 477 pp.

Wimsatt, W.A. (ed.). 1977. Ibid. Vol. 3, 651 pp.

Wimsatt, W.A., and B. Villa-R. 1970. Locomotor adaptations in the disc-winged bat *Thyroptera tricolor.* Amer. J. Anat., 129:89-120.

Wing, D.L., and I.O. Buss. 1970. Elephants and forests. Wildl. Monogr., 19:1-92.

Winge, H. 1941. The interrelationships of the mammalian genera. Vol. 2. Copenhagen: C.A. Reitzels Forlag, 376 pp.

Winn, H.E., and B.L. Ollo (eds.). 1979. Behavior of marine animals. Vol.3: Cetaceans. New York: Plenum Press, 438 pp.

Wood, A.E. 1935. Evolution and relationship of the heteromyid rodents with new forms from the Tertiary of western North America. Ann. Carnegie Mus., 24:73-262.

Wood, A.E. 1955. A revised classification of the rodents. J. Mamm., 36:165-187.

Wood, A.E. 1957. What, if anything, is a rabbit? Evolution, 11:417-425.

Wood, A.E. 1959a. Are there rodent suborders? Syst. Zool., 7:169-173.

Wood, A.E. 1959b. Eocene Radiation and the phylogeny of the rodents. Evolution, 13:354-361.

Wood, A.E. 1965. Grades and clades among rodents. Ibid., 19:115-130.

Wood, A.E. 1974. The evolution of Old World and New World hystricomorph rodents. Symp. Zool. Soc. London, 34: 21-60.

Wood, A.E. 1975. The problem of hystricognathus rodents. Univ. Michigan Papers Paleontol., 12:75-80.

Woods, C.A., and E.B. Howland. 1979. Adaptive radiation of capromyid rodents: anatomy of the masticatory apparatus. J. Mamm., 60:95-116.

Woodburne, M.O. 1968. The cranial myology and osteology of *Dicotyles tajacu,* the collared peccary, and its bearing on classification. Mem. So. California Acad. Sci., 7:1-48.

Woodburne, M.O., and R.H. Tedford. 1975. The first Tertiary monotreme from Australia. Amer. Mus. Novitates, 2588: 1-11.

Woolley, P. 1966. Reproduction in Antechinus spp. and other dasyurid marsupials. Proc. Zool. Soc. London, 15:281-294.

Woolley, P., and S.J. Webb. 1977. The penis of dasyurid marsupials. Pp. 307-323 *in* The biology of marsupials (B. Stonehouse and D. Gilmore, eds.). Baltimore: University Park Press, 486 pp.

Wurster, D.H., and K. Benirschke. 1970. Indian muntjac, *Muntiacus muntjak:* a deer with a low diploid number. Science, 168:1364.

Yalden, D.W., and P.A. Morris. 1975. The lives of bats. New York: Quadrangle Books, 247 pp.

Yerkes, R.M., and A.W. Yerkes. 1929. The great apes. A study of anthropoid life. New Haven, Conn.: Yale Univ. Press, 652 pp.

Young, S.P. 1958. The bobcat of North America. Harrisburg, Pa.: The Stackpole Co., 193 pp.

Young, S.P., and E.A. Goldman. 1946. The puma — mysterious American cat. Harrisburg, Pa.: The Stackpole Co., 358 pp.

Young, S.P., and E.A. Goldman. 1964. The wolves of North America. New York: Dover Publs., 2 vols., 636 pp.

Young, S.P., and H.H.T. Jackson. 1951. The clever coyote. Harrisburg, Pa.: The Stackpole Co., 411 pp.

INDEX TO FAMILIES